CONCEPTS

A ProtoTheist Quest
for Science-Minded Skeptics

of Catholic, and other Christian,
Jewish* & Muslim* Backgrounds

by Paul Dehn Carleton

*Appendixes

CARLETON HOUSE
  P U B L I S H E R
295 Cherokee Road
Pontiac, Michigan 48341
carletonhouse@comcast.net
CarletonHousePublisher.com

Manufactured in the United States of America
10 9 8 7 6 5 4 3 2 1

Library of Congress Control Number: 2003097135
Library of Congress Cataloging-in-Publication Data
Carleton, Paul Dehn
Concepts: a prototheist quest for science-minded skeptics
/ Paul Dehn Carleton
      p.   cm.
Includes bibliographical references and index.
1. Science of Religion 2. Evolution's Trajectory
ISBN 0-9745583-0-3 hardcover

To Life![1]

*And to Mariette, Mary, Michael,
David, John, Frank and Camille*

Lasciate ogni speranza, voi ch'entrate!

Dante Alighieri, *LoInferno*[2]

CONTENTS

Chapter One

Some Preliminaries

Contemplating the arduous adventure that lies ahead
if we're to reach the far Mountain . . .

In struggling through this book we'll be spending much time together, so like any new relationship, we should start out with some small talk to get acquainted. Unfortunately I'll be doing all the talking. You can't even talk back except to yourself and friends, in your margin notes and via the Internet. Or by chucking the book and shutting me up for good (which hopefully you won't be infuriated into doing). So forget the small talk—let's just wade in. And at the risk of sounding like I'm launching a diatribe, let's jettison some negative issues at the outset to clear the air for a more productive positive approach.

First off, the book of course is written from my own perspective as an ex-Catholic—that's my background—but I surmise most of it applies to skeptics of other Christian, Jewish and Muslim backgrounds, as its sub-subtitle states. The book's *not* addressed to devout Catholics and other true believers. On the contrary, it's intended for those whose beliefs have been eroded by their open-mindedness to today's world. In an ironic twist, skeptical Catholics' open-mindedness inadvertently may be impelled by the Church itself in its attempts to impose close-minded dominance. The more the Catholic Church tries to impose absolute authority, the more their intransigence exposes the absurdity of their positions until eventually 'believers' are impelled to question their beliefs, to think for themselves—which is a blessing in disguise. In short, this book's not meant for the devout religious—it might cast them adrift—but for those already adrift to offer them a 'lifeline'.

Though in general the book speaks to all skeptics, as written, it's addressed to nominal Catholics who've been bothered by a whole load of issues: By the Church's pretenses, such as annulment to avoid divorce (thus making the children feel like bastards). By its callous close-mindedness, such as its ban on contraception in spite of overpopulation and underprivileged children. By its disconnectedness from today's world, such as its authoritarianism in a democratizing and egalitarian society. By its anachronisms, such as its centuries of resistance, until very recently, to Galileo's evidence that Earth isn't the center of the universe. By its disdainful cover-up of clerical sexual abuse. And such issues as women priests, euthanasia, cloning ... on and on. The book speaks especially to those who've turned from Catholic and other Christian denominations but have yet to find a replacement that gives meaning to their lives and guidance as parents.

Moreover I suspect there are many enlightened people who still accept God and the Church but only by default. They see more and more discrepancies and anachronisms in the age-old dogmas the Church has fashioned over the centuries. But they have yet to find alternative answers compatible with today's knowledge. So by default they reluctantly accept God and the Church, but may feel a twinge of hypocrisy. My attempt in researching this book was to discover an alternative—a comprehensive contemporary recourse—setting aside as a fruitless distraction any lingering resentment toward the Church. What we'll do is scrutinize my own research and proposals (fully referenced in notes) so you can use my spadework to reach your own conclusions.

Furthermore I suspect these proposals may also be applicable to other religions, particularly to Judaism and to Islam which also are plagued by intransigent conservatives. But not being conversant with them I've drawn on sources who are, in order to pursue those suppositions in Appendices. Anyway most chapters don't have much of a specific denominational viewpoint—except this one and Chapters Three and Twelve—so these ideas likely address a wider audience.

A few quick clarifications: In the book's title 'concept' is used in the same sense as 'paradigm'—how we consciously explain and make sense of what we perceive with our un/aided senses or in our mind.[1] Perhaps the most common example is whether one conceives of the Earth as flat or round. The old concept of a flat Earth still works pretty well for our everyday living, unless we want to fly around it or understand how satellites work. Secondly in the subtitle the prefixed term '*proto*theist' concerns both the origin and the primordial taproot of theism—What is it in human nature that predisposes belief in gods and God?—which we'll start exploring in the next chapter. In other words theism is belief in gods or God, *a*theism is non-belief in gods or God and what I'm calling '*proto*theism' is a search for the basis of the belief in gods or God. Prototheism is *not* a religion but is a *science* of religion. It's not a religion any more than today's scientific study of the Sun is a religion even though many ancient religions worshipped a Sun-god.

So why me? Who am I to say "The emperor has no clothes!"? What are my credentials to take on such an audacious and far-reaching challenge? Not a professional theologian, scholar or scientist, but neither a naïve, complacent bystander. Indeed this provides a fresh perspective. I was raised and educated Catholic, and for many years tried to practice it, to adhere to all the Church's teachings, not just those that suited (until some proved patently absurd). But I'm not naturally a conformist. I've always had a penchant for innovative (some might say maverick) solutions—a layman's perspective with an inquisitive, somewhat iconoclastic mind.[2]

So I read and pondered, especially after retiring with more leisure. This book started as a study guide and notes for my own questions, explorations, insights and conclusions—a personal research project. I used the discipline of writing down and putting thoughts in a logical order to critique their veracity or at least their plausibility. But then suspecting there are many other disillusioned, estranged and ex-Catholics, I thought to leave a trail some might wish to pursue. This book tries to convey what I've learned and concluded presuming that it may prove useful to others— and not just with Catholic backgrounds—who're abandoning obsolete concepts and searching for better, more relevant answers. You're probably one of them, since you're reading it. You too must have an inquiring mind and be reading periodicals, books and the Internet on science and nature topics and watching germane TV programs. You're at least somewhat acquainted with many of the topics we'll cover, if not some of the twists and spin I put on them or the conclusions I draw. These proposals are alternatives to the Church's teachings and worldview (or other-world view). I've learned a lot and enjoyed the years it's taken to research and write the book—hopefully you'll derive as much from reading it. Use my spadework, summarized in the text and notes, to facilitate your own research and to draw your own conclusions.

Be advised though, there could be a few rough spots if some of these concepts are new to you. If you're like me it takes a while to digest new concepts. Sometimes I'll reread a passage in a book, think about it, and then go make a mug of coffee, ponder some more, and maybe sleep on it ... Finally what made no sense, makes sense, even seems obvious—Aha! It's like 'rewiring' my brain, reprogramming it which may take days, weeks, even months of gestation. In the interim I may wallow in confusion, fogginess, even anxiety until the dawn breaks. I console myself that it's a natural phase in the learning process, a transition between not knowing and knowing, between holding onto an old paradigm and letting go to grasp the new one. Finally what at first seemed counter-intuitive becomes intuitive, better yet, not just intellectual but visceral. So even though this book may be challenging, I suggest you approach it as an exciting adventure.

Look at it this way: The various concepts described herein are like pieces of a jigsaw puzzle. But we don't have all the pieces and some we do have don't belong or else are somehow wrong. And of course we don't know what the picture looks like—that's what we're trying to discover. So throughout the book we'll be examining concepts as I understand them and placing them where I think they fit into a partial preliminary picture, into a framework or 'map'. I've fit the pieces together as I think best but you're encouraged to put them together into your own 'map' that best suits your Life, your quest.

Maps are neat. When venturing into a strange territory, it's nice to have a map of it. Even though the 'map' offered through this book doesn't have all the details, at least it gives a broad overview of this new 'territory,' our modern world as I see it. Hopefully it makes it less daunting to leave the old familiar but obsolescent worldview the Church taught us and explore contemporary worldviews. It's analogous to the way maps changed as knowledge of the world broadened half-a-millennium ago. Picking up on the concept/paradigm example above, when mankind thought the world was flat their maps of the known world were basically wrong but adequate for their journeys, even for voyaging around the Mediterranean. And even today, as said, changing the paradigm from a flat Earth to round makes little difference for short trips. But as explorers in the fifteenth to eighteenth centuries ventured ever farther around the Earth they pieced together ever better maps. Hopefully the framework proposed herein, this 'map', encourages you to explore contemporary worldviews and helps you piece together your own 'map' for your life's 'voyage' through today's world.

To facilitate your quest I've used a device that may seem hokey: likening this study to a mountaineering expedition. At the head of each chapter there's a pseudo-epigraph describing a leg of the 'expedition' as an allegory for the material covered in that chapter. Perhaps this'll encourage viewing our travail as an adventure, suggested in the photo on the book's title page and dust jacket. But if you feel the epigraphs are silly or melodramatic, just skip over them.

The intent of this book is not so much to provide the 'answers'—nobody has all the answers. Rather the intent is to provide a perspective, a framework, through which to view the ever emerging information our scientific culture generates. The whole scientific enterprise is a 'work in progress'. And science often is less a matter of proof than of plausibility—Is a scientific explanation consistent with the evidence and does it lead to a search for additional evidence and better theories? Hopefully this book enables grasping, not final 'answers' but, plausible tentative insights useful in drawing our 'maps' and choosing the paths we'd like to pursue throughout our lives.

If you're uncomfortable with ambiguity—tentative explanations that don't go far enough and leave you hanging, or worse, put you into free-fall—just stay with it awhile. Wallow around in your discomfort to see what feelings come up and from where. It might lead to important insights. (Some people can't abide unexplained events so call them miracles.) Soon you should become comfortable enough with this 'map' to explore further those topics that still bother or intrigue you. This 'map' is like any map of a strange city or country in that it provides an orientation so you don't feel lost. Use it to reconnoiter places of interest and then explore them further. (I've tried to keep the text fairly straightforward and mostly have put references,[3] details, asides, ruminations and anecdotes in the notes.)

Another point: As said, this book is specifically addressed to skeptical Christians. Still it might be read by a few Christians of unwavering faith. (Though I'm curious, I won't be so gauche as to ask why you're reading it if you don't fit the subtitle's target audience.) Instead I'd ask any such faithful Christian readers to withhold judgment and consider what I'm trying to say. Even though you can't agree with my premises and conclusions, at least the book will be useful in bringing these issues to the fore. You can then think them through to your own conclusions. Having a sometimes pedestrian mind, perhaps some aspects of my thesis are wrong. But to figure out which, you should 'chew' the whole of it before you decide which pieces to 'spit out'. You may end up ingesting some. Moreover you might want to ponder how they could revitalize your own faith—perhaps a neo-Christianity?

Finally again, it's not my purpose to dwell on the Church's past failings and abuses, or to denigrate the contributions that Christianity has made to civilization. Any resentment should be put aside; it's not productive to dwell on the negative. Rather, think back to the beginning of Christianity and consider mustering the same kind of courage those stalwart early Christians had. Those early Christians saw that the religions of their day were no longer appropriate. They heroically brought a message of love and tolerance into a cruel and superstitious world. They had the foresight and the courage to abandon old and adopt new beliefs and values that were more appropriate to their world and to their lives at that time.

And they asserted their innovative convictions among a mostly complacent or apathetic populace in spite of intransigent conservatives.

But much has changed in the sixteen centuries since Constantine
converted the Roman world to Christianity. Nonetheless that early Christian worldview has basically persisted unchanged into these enlightened
centuries. That worldview is now clearly obsolescent. So then shouldn't
we emulate the early Christians' courage and tenacity, and search out our
own best understanding for today's world?

Maybe we don't know yet if we have the courage of our convictions.
And anyway we need to be sure what those convictions are. Let's press on.

Part I

Gods Concepts

Chapter Two

Gods

To climb the Mountain we have to trek to it, which takes us through a dense rain forest where literally we can't see the forest for the trees. The undergrowth dwells in ambiguous shadows cast by the canopy high overhead. Eyes lurk in those shadows, sounds come from everywhere and the heavy air has a musty fragrance. We dare not step off the narrow trail lest we lose our way in the tangle of vines and decaying fallen branches. We urbanites are torn between fear and fascination.

Asked if I believe in God, in turn I'll ask, Which god? Hopefully this ploy provides the opportunity to elaborate.

For example we don't believe in the fire-god. Yet probably not too many generations ago, our early ancestors did believe in a fire-god. Back then they explained fire as a god dancing on wood or whatever, dispersing its heat and light. Our forebears likely explained natural phenomena as gods and related to them the same way they related to the other members of their troop. They learned each member's idiosyncrasies—what pleased and what irritated them—and dealt with each member accordingly. Similarly they learned what pleased the fire-god: nice dry wood but not too much, air but not too much. And what irritated the fire-god: water might miff the fire-god to vanish in a puff of smoke, or if they came too close the fire-god would burn them, or if they drove the fire-god into a rage it'd destroy everything it could reach.[1] So we no longer believe in a fire-god; that is, we don't believe that the phenomenon we call fire is a god. We've displaced the theistic belief with a scientific explanation—but we can still be mesmerized by a fire.

We don't believe in a wind-god either—we now know that the phenomenon we call wind has a scientific explanation (air pressure differences). And we don't believe in all the many other gods—in rocks, in streams, in trees, in snakes, in goats ... everywhere—who 'controlled' our ancestors' world. Even though our ancestors didn't understand nature, they believed the gods understood and controlled it. And so in order for our ancestors to deal with nature, they cajoled and propitiated the gods with prayer, sacrifice, alms and penance as they would a parent or some other authority figure. (To get a feel for those times, listen to Virgil's *Aeneid*.[2]) So whether we mean many gods who together variously control the world or one omnipotent omniscient God—"Our Father Who art in Heaven ..."—no longer do I believe in any god. But of course I believe there's a phenomenon that's called God. What is it?

Let me be concise. By saying I don't believe in the fire-god, doesn't mean I don't believe in fire, in the phenomenon we call fire—that'd be absurd. I don't believe in a Sun-god either but I believe in the Sun. And saying I don't believe in God doesn't mean I don't believe in the phenomenon that's called God. The challenge in this book is to find out just what that phenomenon we call God really is. Then after you've assimilated my explanation, you can better frame your own.

Quest for Knowledge

Believing that fire is a god, it seems to me, closes out any attempt to learn the true nature of fire. The same goes for all the other gods or God. If one truly believes in a fire-god, one dare not even question what fire is for fear of offending that god: "It's a mystery that cannot be penetrated by mere man." But just three centuries ago as alchemy waned men did try to understand fire, first unsuccessfully with the phlogiston theory and then successfully in 1772–7 with Lavoisier's oxygenation theory (more later). Thus began the science of chemistry. Having the courage to question phenomena, even if at first we fail, can free us from the tyranny of superstition and from vulnerability to those who claim to possess 'revealed truth'.

Of course as phenomena are demythologized at one level, the belief in gods can simply be abstracted to the next higher level, say from fire-god to Sun-god, then from Sun-god to a dematerialized, ethereal entity.[3] So belief hasn't fundamentally changed, it's just abstracted on up the hierarchy and consolidated into fewer entities—the many gods become one God.[4] But if it doesn't make sense to invoke gods to explain natural phenomena, does it make sense to invoke a god to explain the phenomenon of 'God'? As the evidence supporting non-mythical explanations of natural phenomena mounts, the evidence supporting a belief in God recedes until all that's left is blind faith. If there's no God, what's this phenomenon that's called 'faith' and where's it originate?

Coupled with belief in gods 'out there' in nature was belief in the spirits of deceased ancestors and tribal elders. Back then knowledge was largely empirical based on observations and experience passed on down from generation to generation. Children were taught by their parents and other adults, and internalized those lessons. The strong bond that formed between parent and child continued into adulthood and beyond. Elders were valued as repositories of knowledge, and the older and wiser they got the more they were valued, indeed venerated. When they died their knowledge lived on in vivid memories as though they were still around somehow—their advice and admonitions 'heard' as if their spirit 'spoke' to their descendants, what Freud would call a descendant's superego. During their lifetimes ancestors were in charge and even after their deaths their 'spirits' were still in charge even though they lived-on only in the imaginations of their descendants.

Perhaps what it comes down to today is that believers still look to a parent figure who's in charge, namely God, rather than face the unknown, the existential angst. And since these believers are not in charge, they're not answerable, not able to respond, not 'response-able.' Admittedly there's a great deal in our lives that we can't be in charge of. Even though today we can know far more than our early ancestors ever could, there's still much we don't know. But relying on a mystical explanation is no explanation at all, it explains nothing. Is it to avoid the discomfort of facing the unknown, a classic case of denial?

Afterlife

It seems we're especially vulnerable to mystical explanations if we believe in life-after-death. Death is necessary for evolution to work (as'll be explained in Chapter Seven). But rather than face the unknown terror of death, we'd deny the reality of death.[5] We wouldn't expect to really 'die,' to end it all, but just to move, in spirit at least—hopefully to a utopia, namely Heaven 'if we've been good'. We'd believe it doesn't all end at death but that we pass on to an afterlife. We'd live our lives always with a wary eye on how it'll affect our afterlife.[6] It'd be as though we believe in life-after-death more than in life-before-death! The hitch is that for guidance on how to live such a life we'd have to rely on those who claim to possess revealed truth about that afterlife—we'd turn to mystical explanations. Rather than accept ultimate responsibility for our own life including death, we'd abandon decision making to our religious leaders. Yet to be truly responsible we should avoid resorting to mystical explanations and learn to tolerate the anxiety of our ultimate death. Getting beyond the existential angst can free us to contemplate the 'fruitful void'.

There are a couple other problems with belief in an afterlife. A person who goes around always focused on some other world would normally be seen as delusional, unless they're religious then they're seen as devout. Isn't that crazy? Also a religion based on an afterlife implicitly encourages separation, even alienation, from our here-and-now world, like a kind of 'Earth tourist'—"My Kingdom is not of this world." "I'm only a stranger here, Heaven is my home." And so on. Regarding the here-and-now as only a try-out, an 'audition' for the hereafter could be seen as an excuse for not accepting responsibility for this 'transitory' world-stage which can have far reaching consequences.[7]

Life's a marvelous gift. Even as boring or difficult as it sometimes gets it's still a treasure we grieve to lose—specially our own or a loved one's. We should try to savor every moment of life here-and-now and never delude ourselves that it's just an audition for an afterlife.

While we don't want to live our life based on obviously obsolete concepts such as life-after-death, still we'd like to have *some* valid concepts to live our life by. But we can't be sure whether what currently seem to be the most plausible concepts will ultimately prove to be the truly valid concepts. Unfortunately 'ultimate' may come long after we're dead and gone. So we have to live with the best concepts that we can currently muster rather than with patently obsolete concepts. It seems the only alternative is to give up and have no beliefs at all.

Projection

In trying to understand natural phenomena there are two aspects, the physical and the psychic, the objective and the subjective. So far I've only alluded to the physical aspect, for example what fire actually is, its combustive nature. The other aspect has to do with how we 'project' our expectations and personality out onto the phenomenon, for example what we imagine we see in the fire.

To understand the process of 'projection' we need to consider how our mind attempts to grasps reality, the process of inferring what's outside ourselves, 'out there'. Our senses receive inputs from outside our body, say light-rays from exterior objects gathered into our eyes. These light-rays are focused onto the retinas at the backs of our eyes where they're converted into signals, sensations, which are transmitted to our brain for processing. All this jumble of sensations is systematically compared in our brain with previously experienced images or ideas to find a likeness. The more meager the sensations coming into our brain, the more our brain must fill-in to guess what's being seen, that is, the fewer the clues, the more we must use our imagination. And our mind's guess is influenced by what we expect to see, the *gestalt* our mind's trying to form. If we expect to see a face in the flames or cloud, we'll probably see a face of some sort. The less we're consciously aware of these expectations, the more we're convinced of what we think we see. This process is called 'projection' because it's analogous to the way a movie or slide film is projected onto a blank screen. We unconsciously 'project' our expectation onto a nearly blank 'screen', then see on the 'screen' what we expect to see. Note however that we don't project a light beam out onto a scene as does a film projector, rather we project our expectations.

So if we're convinced there's a fire-god, we'll probably see her in the flames. And if we're convinced there's a wind-god we'll see him in the clouds and hear him too. "... all the gods are *within us.*"[8] The personality of a particular god is a blend of appropriate aspects of our own personality and of what we've been taught about that god. For example fire can be warming and protecting or burning and destroying. So if we've been taught that the fire is our friend by wise and nurturing parents, we'll 'project' our love onto the fire-god. But if we've been taught that fire is our enemy by thoughtless, uncaring parents, we might 'project' our fear and anger onto the fire-god.[9] In practice it's probably a mix of both. (The process of seeing and 'projecting' will be covered in greater detail in Chapter Nine.)

If as children we're taught these kinds of 'explanations' of our world, we internalize them so that we 'project' these expectations, these concepts out onto what we perceive and thus get feedback that reinforces those concepts.[10] These 'explanations' may be wrong, just myths. But until proven wrong or superseded by better 'explanations' they can appear to make sense out of a seemingly senseless world thereby providing a 'handle' to deal with that world.

Revelation

Perhaps the real power of myth though is when we don't see it as an explanation but believe that it's really true. This happens when the concepts are taught not just as legends, stories and fairy tales, not just as the best explanation available to date. Rather they are taught as 'revelations', that is, some venerated elder unconsciously projected his attitudes and longings out onto a 'burning' bush or cloud or whatever, then took them back-in as revelation. He truly believed the 'revelation' because of course it resonated with his unconscious.[11] Unfortunately as so often happens, in his enthusiasm, rather than just apply his insight to himself, he may project it onto others and try to get them to accept it too (or his disciples fanatically do).[12] But he wouldn't be successful—there'd be no 'market' for his 'invention'—

if his 'revelation' didn't resonate with the others' latent needs and nascent intuitions. (We'll pursue what these might be in Chapters Nine and Ten.)

And so it's passed on down the generations as 'revealed truth'. Thus these concepts take on power reinforced by the culture, "the word of God" to be believed "under pain of sin and eternal damnation." Unfortunately this power can be misused to control people for political purposes, personal gain, aggrandizement or whatever. It's particularly effective when the perpetrator truly believe in what they're doing, rationalizing their own behavior—their shadow side.

There may have been an additional, more insidious factor. Until less than three millennia ago, man may have experienced his thoughts as the voice of a god speaking to him. What today most of us know as our internal dialog or subvocalization, early man may have believed was a god speaking to him privately inside his head. (In Chapter Nine on the evolution of consciousness we'll explore how thoughts arise out of our unconscious.[13]) Giving a voice to one's projection 'out there' certainly would reinforce the belief that it is indeed a revelation from a god.

But a profound 'revelation' doesn't have to be interpreted as communion with gods or God, or with an ancestor or saint. It can be understood simply as a natural internal ineffable, numinous experience that can come about unexpectedly and spontaneously, or be induced through meditation, ritual or otherwise as we'll explore in Chapter Ten. You'll see there can still be 'magic and mystery' without mythology.

Mythology

With early man's vulnerability and their meager understanding of nature, it's understandable that the 'gods' mentality was man's way of dealing with their world then. Even though they weren't in charge, they thought at least these parent figures were. For early man mythology proved useful in coping with a terrifying world.[14] They didn't have the knowledge science has gained for us. Today we no longer have that excuse for clinging to myths. We certainly don't have all the answers but we have enough to know that the 'gods' mentality is not the answer. Today the 'gods' mentality (theism) is no longer necessary. It's not just unproductive, it's detrimental in that it can block our pursuit of a real understanding, not so much any more of external phenomena but certainly of internal phenomena, namely of understanding our Self.

This is a key point. Today belief in God seems so endemic that it doesn't even occur to some people not to believe in God. And if one's mind is locked into an absolute belief in God then their mind is blocked, blinded to the possibility of an alternative explanation. Their eyes are closed tight with no thought even of opening them. Yet ... sometimes ... it's amazing what one can see by just looking.

Whither?

So why does this theist mentality persist? Certainly it's comforting to believe that a parent figure is in charge of this vast Universe—God the Father in Heaven. But I suspect a more important reason is that a viable alternative hasn't yet been proposed which, of course, is what I'm attempting to do with this book. The purpose of my writing is to concisely sketch as much of what's known—as is appropriate and feasible at this time—and then point to a possible explanation or to paths for exploration. In other words I propose we look deep into our human nature to find the roots of our belief in God, not 'out there' but 'in here'. This search for the roots of theism I believe is appropriately called '*proto*theism.'[15] Hence my use of 'prototheist' in the book's subtitle. It's a science *of* religion, not science *and* religion.[16]

Being more specific, we need to take a good look at how our mind/brain works in order to get some idea of why we look outside our Self rather than within. Such an investigation necessitates going back in time: To look at how our mind works we need to look at how our mind/brain evolved. And before looking at our mind/brain evolution we need to look at our species' evolution, after we've looked at the whole train of evolution leading up to us from the beginning of Life, especially at how Life probably originated. But of course we must first look at how our Earth began. This may seem like an overwhelming task, but instead why not think of it as an exciting adventure, like climbing a mountain (as in the epigraphs). A mountain expedition must be divided into challenging but attainable segments and each leg must be approached as an adventure. And just as on a mountain expedition, we need to give our body and mind time to acclimatize to the height—the rarified air and the broad vistas— you'll need time to gestate these ideas. In other words you may want to read this book in small doses.

Perhaps now is the time to address the feelings of disorientation and vertigo one can experience when letting loose of long held beliefs. Like a person scaling a mountain face, it must be exhilarating as they swing from one handhold to the next higher one. But the next handhold had better be there and not crumble as you grasp it! Well, don't let go of your old beliefs until you're pretty sure you've something substantial to grab hold of. In this book I've tried to provide the best handholds I can. But you may still experience discomfort, angst, maybe even mild panic as you go through a transition from your old, crumbling beliefs to tentative new ones. You may even vacillate between them. That's ok, give yourself time, don't rush, and be gentle with yourself. Just imagine how people must have felt four centuries ago when they began to realize that the Earth wasn't the center of the universe. It not only took a profound conceptual leap, a major paradigm shift. There was the terror of realizing that the Earth wasn't the solid ground beneath their feet but was only one of many 'balls' somehow 'floating' in space. Now that truly *was* vertigo! Change can be very upsetting—go easy.

But what if . . . . there *actually is* life after death and a God!! . . . . . Now you've *really* pissed Him off !

Or have you? Well, try this: If we've tried to live a good and ethical life based on our best knowledge and thinking, and not just because of fear of an afterlife or a reward for good behavior,[17] then how could a just 'Father in Heaven' be pissed off? As a father myself I want my children to be responsible, self-sufficient, intelligent adults. I gave them what I was able to then and can let them go now, knowing they can never fully appreciate what I tried to do. I didn't appreciate nor always agree with my father, nor did he his; so why should mine? Nor do I need their adoration. So why should "Our Father in Heaven ..." be any less? Only a father with a neurotic need for awe and control would want his children to slavishly follow his commands, would want them to not grow into responsible adults free to make their own judgments, to make their own mistakes and learn from them.[18] Then why would a loving God be any less of a Father?

Chapter Three

Christianity's Beginnings

As we emerge form the dense forest, in the distance across meadows we can discern an ancient settlement nestled against the high formidable cliffs, the Wall that obstructs our way to the Mountain. As we near the settlement and enter the narrow cobbled streets we encounter a perplexing mixture of the old—donkeys, carts, icons and exotic artifacts—among the modern like motor bikes, cell phones, Coca-Cola signs and satellite dishes on tile roofs. We'll linger a short while to peruse this dichotomy but soon we must press on.

In order to understand why the gods/God mentality, theism, has persisted, we need to examine how Christianity* became the dominant religion of Europe and the Americas—the Western World. In this chapter I've endeavored to be as factual and dispassionate as I'm able. I've drawn on contemporary scholars who are informed by recent discoveries and who've analyzed texts and sources such as the Dead Sea Scrolls, the Nag Hammadi codices and archaeological digs. Moreover I've tried to filter out whatever obvious bias these scholars might have in an attempt to distill the truth from Scripture's hagiography.[1]

Pagans

Imagine what the world was like two thousand years ago. Their 'world' was centered around the Mediterranean (middle-land) and that world was flat, solid, immobile and unchanging.[2] There was no concept of continents—what were called Asia and Africa were just provinces in what are now respectively west Turkey and North Africa. Barbaric tribes were thought to inhabit the distant lands far beyond the shores of the Mediterranean Sea and the reach of civilization. The various peoples who inhab-

---

*Readers with a Judaic or Islamic heritage may prefer to read an Appendix instead of, or in addition to, this chapter.

ited the Mediterranean basin had in recent centuries been subjugated by the Romans, either as subjects or slaves, and were being assimilated into the Greco-Roman culture. Rome itself had been a quasi-pluralistic repub- lic but after the assassination of Julius Caesar it came to be ruled by a se- ries of emperors for the next several centuries.

But the real rulers of that world were the many invisible, immortal gods who seemed to favor anarchy rather than even a republic. True, there were stronger gods and weaker gods but none was completely in charge and each was 'doing their own thing'—debauching, wenching, tricking, and forming and breaking alliances with other gods or rulers or heroes. Each person, family, craft, town and country had their patron god or gods (like patron saints). The Romans generally honored them all in order to avoid stirring up jealousy and animosity among some gods for fear of bringing their wrath down on everyone. After all, the invisible gods were like powerful visible humans whom people had to deal with through flat- tery, gifts and obeisance not unlike today's corporate politicking. But the gods were "... powers of immense superiority." The common denomina- tor in all pagan cults was the precept 'give to the giver'; "... the gods were concerned with honour and the due offering of gifts." And at any moment some gods might just be present even though just out of sight.[3]

Now try to put yourself in their shoes (or sandals). You're the same person you are now but back in their time and world. Imagine your day in that world. Dawn came when the Sun-god (called Apollo or Helios or Sol depending on your cult) vaulted up out of the land beyond the Tigris- Euphrates and steadily drove across the heavens just overhead above the clouds in the abode of Zeus/Jupiter and his thunderbolts. You might start your day with an oblation to your household gods protecting your door- way. You might place a small portion of your morning meal before a shrine in your atrium, not forgetting to thank Demeter/Ceres for the harvest. If you were undertaking some venture that day you might consult an oracle[4] or astrologer or magician for guidance from the gods.

And so on throughout the day until the Sun plunged into the ocean beyond the Gates of Hercules (Gibraltar) leaving your world again in dark- ness. Thankfully at times the darkness was relieved by images of the gods in the firmament as it passed overhead (the Zodiac star constellations) and by the inconstant Moon (Luna or Selene). But the night was haunted by other gods (Hades, Pluto ...) from the underworld dwelling in the shadows, in caves and in hot mud vents (like our Yellowstone's). Oc- casionally when angered the gods Vulcan would erupt in volcanoes or Poseidon cause earthquakes shaking your trust in the *terra firma* beneath your feet.[5]

Jews

A people dwelling near the eastern shore of the Mediterranean and 'enjoying' an enforced uneasy peace under Roman rule were the Hebrews with their own unique, ancient cult.[6] Nominally they worshipped only one God but they too had many 'sub-gods' they called angels and devils who could affect their lives.[7] Their myths promised them their own land "... flowing with milk and honey" (the Promised Land) if they upheld a contract made with their God (the Covenant) and that their God would give them a leader (a Messiah) who, as told of their revered King David, would drive out their enemies and lead them once again to greatness for a thousand years. "The Messiah could not appear at any time, but only at the End of the Days, at a time of testing and great tribulations for Israel."[8]

However there was not unanimity among them on just how the Covenant should be kept. The priest caste (Sadducees) controlled the Temple where every Jew was obligated annually to sacrifice—particularly burdensome for the poor. Their lawyers (Pharisees) believed in a meticulous interpretation of the Scriptures. The purists (Essenes) were totally disgusted with what was going on in Jerusalem (*JeruSalem* means 'City of Peace') and left town to live an ascetic life in the desert mostly near the Dead Sea awaiting the Messiah. And of course there were worldly Jews like Herod the Great[9] and his sons who collaborated with the Romans. There were many other Jews who had dispersed out of their 'homeland'; for instance so many Jews in Alexandria Egypt no longer spoke Hebrew that their Scriptures were translated into Greek (the Septuagint).[10]

Jesus

Around 6BC[11] into this world a precocious Hebrew boy was born in tiny Nazareth (not Bethlehem nor of a virgin to fulfill the prophecy,[12] nor some argue not even anytime near December 25[13]) probably the oldest of five brothers and at least two sisters. Since Nazareth was near the rebuilding Roman city of Sepphoris, Jesus undoubtedly was exposed to the Greco-Roman culture. Moreover Nazareth was near a trade route[14] so he may have learned of other religions like Mithraism of Persia and Buddhism (Siddhartha Gautama, called the Buddha, predated Jesus by five-hundred years). Whether he spent his childhood in Egypt (Alexandria?) is problematic. It seems likely that as a youth Jesus grew into a rebel; apparently he didn't marry as customary for young Jewish men and he mixed with an unsavory crowd to his family's chagrin.[15]

Dissatisfied with his life Jesus trekked south eighty miles across the desert to observe another malcontent who had been raised as an Essene but had gone out on his own to preach repentance before what he believed was the impending apocalypse. Followers listened to John's teachings, then demonstrated their change of heart by allowing John to symbolically wash away their past life-style by dipping them in the Jordan River. Jesus was thus dipped (baptized) experiencing an epiphany.[16] He began preaching with his mentor. John suspected that Jesus just might be the Messiah and after a period of contemplation Jesus himself began to wonder. In Hebrew the Messiah, the Anointed One, is in Greek the Christ (from the Greek word *christos*,[17] oil used in anointing, as Samuel did David). Jesus then went back on up to Galilee (Bethany?) with some of John's other followers who became Jesus' disciples (apostles). Because of John's castigation of the Sadducees and their Temple abuses, he became a marked man to be watched as did his principal followers including Jesus.

Evidently Jesus became an outstanding, charismatic figure. Magicians were common in those days so Jesus' 'miracles' were suspect by the less gullible. But discounting the hype that developed as Jesus' fame grew (some two-thirds of the reported miracles are now thought to be of later origin) he can at least be credited for the placebo effect some healers can elicit in their patients.[18] Moreover some of the other 'miracles' can be viewed not as unnatural phenomena, but as shrewd insights into human nature such as the story of the loaves and fishes.[19] Indeed in my opinion, claiming that Jesus was God to explain his accomplishments does grave injustice to his human abilities and slights his hard work ('Oh sure, easy for him, he was God's son').

Some time later, Jesus reportedly went with his disciples to celebrate the Feast of the Passover at the Temple in Jerusalem as was customary. He provoked a crisis by staging[20] in the Temple precincts a confrontation with the men there who exchanged secular coinage for the prescribed Temple coinage and who sold unadulterated animals for the prescribed sacrifice. The Sadducees and Pharisees were both enraged and the Romans wanted to avoid an uprising—accordingly they had Jesus crucified.

Back then crucifixion was a cruel but not unusual punishment. It was the standard Roman practice for dealing with non-Roman troublemakers. For example when Spartacus' slaves' rebellion finally was crushed in 71BC the Romans lined their roads with six thousand crucified captive fugitive slaves as a warning to others. And during the Jewish War 66–70AD the Romans crucified as many as five hundred a day.[21] So Jesus suffered the most horrible and ignominious of deaths and that should have been the end of it—but of course it wasn't. Today the cross has a completely different symbolism than it had in Roman times. In an ingenious reframing of this tragic though common event, the cross and crucifix[22] were to become over the next two millennia the principal symbols of Christianity.

But why did Jesus follow such a suicidal course? He must have seen where it could lead. The simplest explanation is that Jesus had come to believe that he truly was the expected Messiah.[23] One theory is that his crucifixion was Jesus' daring scheme that almost worked.[24] Determining what actually happened to Jesus' corpse is plagued by little fact and much controversy.[25] Given the Roman's grisly practices it's conceivable "... his body was eaten by dogs at the foot of the Cross."[26]

Christ

Afterwards Jesus' followers didn't know what to make of it and were in fear for their own lives. Most went into hiding. Some thought they'd seen[27] Jesus (perhaps as now some imagine they've seen Elvis Presley). Understandably they continued retelling and embellishing many reassuring stories about Jesus. Regardless of what or who Jesus actually was, his followers eventually converted him into the Christ. They invented Jesus Christ largely in their own images of what he should be.[28] And because his teachings were largely through parables, their meanings were intentionally obscure and thus susceptible to whatever spin their hearers were disposed to put on them.

Some examples (from Shorto:115–9, with my italics): Those who heard "the kingdom of God is *within* you" looked inside themselves to find Christ which grew into Gnosticism (from the Greek *gnosis*=knowledge). Those devout Jews who heard "the *kingdom* of God ..." looked for the apocalypse and Jesus' prompt, triumphant return as the Messiah to cleanse the corruption and hypocrisy from Judaism, drive out the Romans[29] and lead the Jews to a new millennium. Jesus' brother James headed this group in Jerusalem (but was killed just before the Romans' destruction of the city and the Temple in 70AD[30]). Paul of Roman Tarsus never met Jesus but had a numinous experience he attributed to Christ.[31] He understood "the kingdom of God is like yeast ... *mixed* in with ... flour until *all* of it was leavened" to mean to spread the Word to the whole Roman world along with Peter and other disciples. As we know Paul eventually prevailed.[32] With his Greek philosophical background he was able to cast Christ as the Son of God and Peter as Christ's designated heir which gave them authenticity and authority, the credentials needed for their mission.

Christians

When Jesus didn't reappear in the lifetimes of his disciples as foretold, in fact after several generations, the concept of life-after-death provided an alternative explanation: namely that rather than Jesus coming back to them, they'd go to Him. Was this what Jesus meant by "the kingdom of God"? What had been the Hebrews' 'promised land' if they kept the Covenant, several generations after Jesus died became the Christians' 'heavenly kingdom' if they kept His Word.

To some extent in Jesus' time Egyptians, Jews, Greeks and Romans all held some belief in an underworld, Hades or Gehenna,[33] a dismal place where most people went after death except heroes who lived on among the immortal gods in Elysium.[34] Christians developed the belief that man's miserable life here and hereafter was punishment for Adam and Eve's original sin in the Garden of Eden (paradise) passed on down to their descendants.[35] Because theirs was a sin against God only the Son of God could redeem paradise for mankind which they believed Christ did by His suffering on the cross. Thus one could be saved from hell and enjoy Heaven if they accepted Jesus Christ as their Lord and Savior. Whereas early in Roman paganism, only the gods were immortal and dwelt in the heavens above the clouds (along with the few mortals they deified) or in Hades below the Earth, in time many other 'salvation religions' became prevalent throughout the Empire—an egalitarian but pernicious trend as we'll see.

If death was not to be feared but welcomed as your ticket to Heaven provided you'd kept the faith, then Christians could come out of hiding. They could practice and preach their faith openly and in defiance of the 'false' pagan gods. Not only did the Christians ridicule the pagan gods, they wouldn't offer sacrifice to them calling down the gods' wrath on everybody. So the Christians were persecuted and martyred not because the Romans didn't tolerate or respect the Christian religion but because the Christians wouldn't tolerate and honor the Romans' religion. In the eyes of the pagan Romans the Christians were *atheists!*[36] They didn't believe in and honor the gods and so had to be sacrificed to appease the gods. And pagans could feel righteous about it.[37]

Those Christians whose belief was strong enough to stand before a Roman official and 'confess' their faith in Christ as God and their defiance of the other gods were condemned to be slaughtered in a local Roman amphitheater as the 'main attraction' to placate the gods and set an example for others who might also contemplate defying the gods. Of course these Christians believed martyrdom guaranteed them direct entrance to

Heaven. While those who had *confessed* their faith awaited their day in some local arena or in Rome's Colosseum, they became *confessors* for other Christians (prisons were pretty open then for the unchained) because they could put in a good word for other Christians as soon as the martyrs got to Heaven.[38]

Facilitated by the Romans' network of roads and ships, Christianity spread throughout the Empire appealing especially to those marginalized by Roman society—women, the poor and slaves—willing to bear indignities if their reward was in Heaven. After three centuries—though only a very small percent of the population[39]—Christians could be found in virtually every city, meeting in their more affluent members' homes, sharing meals and praying together. Under elected bishops and clergy they supported one another, welcoming and sheltering visiting Christians in a diffuse subculture. Adversity drew them together, such as recurring persecutions, but when the adversity subsided their suppressed internal differences and disputes resurfaced.

A major and recurring topic of dispute was Christ's relation to God. If Christ was truly God—the eternal God of all creation high in the heavens above the clouds—why would He deign to relate to man? But if He wasn't God, what was His authority? By the end of the third century there were many other disputes. In addition to Gnostics, there were Donatists, Manichaeans, Marcions, Meletian, Montanists, and Novatians, with Arians yet to come.[40] All these sects were declared to be heretical by the predominant sect, the 'orthodox' Christians who were the best organized and included half of all those calling themselves Christians.[41] They claimed their authority was passed down from Peter and Paul. A number of 'dramatic narratives'[42] had by then been recorded attributed to various apostles to give the stories authenticity.[43] Those stories and beliefs that the self-appointed 'orthodox' (*ortho*=correct, *dox*=opinion) disagreed with, they attempted to purge, branding those narrators heretics and destroying all such writings they could find.[44]

Constantine

In the early part of the fourth century the Christians' fortunes changed dramatically thanks to Emperor Constantine the Great. A legend grew about Constantine's 'miraculous' conversion to Christianity on seeing a 'cross' on the Sun with the words *In Hoc [Signo] Vincens*, (In This [Sign] Conquer; Catholic crosses frequently bear the initials IHS). But that's not quite what I read into it. Constantine's father, Emperor Constantius, was a devotee of the Sun-god but like most pagans he paid due honor to all the gods. In 306AD when Constantius died in Britain with his son at his side, he declared Constantine emperor.

Constantine bided his time until 312AD, then marched for Italy to secure his title of emperor. As his army approached Rome, he looked to the Sun to favor his campaign (remember they thought the Sun passed overhead just above the clouds). They saw some unusual phenomena[45] which—probably influenced by a chaplain, the banished Spanish bishop Ossius (or Hosius)—Constantine became convinced was a cross or the *Chi-Rho* symbol ☧. That night he dreamed of a young man he believed was Apollo (the Sun-god) or Christ or himself. The next morning, again with Ossius' influence, he had his troops paint crosses on their shields (it was customary to adopt a patron god). When Constantine marched on Rome his rival Maxentius, rather than stay behind the city's twenty foot high walls, foolishly lead his larger force out of the city which Constantine saw as divine intervention. Constantine's troops drove them back across the Tiber River over their own makeshift Milvian Bridge and Maxentius drowned with many others. Constantine attributed his good fortune to the Sun-god and/or Christ, and so continued to curry both gods' favor and to forsake the other gods as he campaigned down Italy and eventually to the eastern Mediterranean. By 324AD he dominated the whole Roman Empire.[46]

Initially Constantine only gave Christians freedom from oppression with the Edict of Milan in 313AD. But as time went on he increasingly favored Christianity as a way of bringing harmony to the overextended and fragmenting Roman Empire. (Certainly there were other influences such as his Christian advisors and womenfolk.) However he soon discovered that Christianity too had its factions and rivalries which initially he tried to mediate. But soon both his personality and his goal of unifying the Roman world impelled him to take on leadership of Christianity.[47]

I'll explain: It seems to me that aside from his "overweening ambition"[48] Constantine came to see Christianity as the solution to control of the Empire. Back when Rome was a republic prior to Augustus (say before 31BC) its form of government acknowledged diverse political views (a quasi-democracy at least for male patricians) along with diverse gods (polytheism). But for the next three-and-half centuries under an absolute emperor, the Roman Empire's *hier*archical government was inconsistent with its *an*archical polytheism[49]—an authoritarian government with a divisive 'democratic' religion. In other words Constantine was trying to run a vast empire with an orderly central government but with a chaotic system of beliefs in a pantheon of anarchistic gods. And as said, every town, trade, army unit and so on had their own patron god ('my god vs your god'). The multitude of Greco-Roman gods in the heavens on down into Hades were inherently disorderly, whereas the Christian heaven and hell had a tight organization with a Trinity Godhead under which came angels, saints/martyrs, on down to outcast rebellious angels/devils.

Meanwhile, here on Earth, whereas earlier Christians had looked to charismatic holy men and women (confessors/martyrs, dubbed religious 'overachievers'[50]) for guidance (Gnostics, anchorites and so on), by Constantine's time orthodox Christianity was busily consolidating its organization through a *hier*archy of bishops. The Roman bishops constructed a tenuous 'unbroken' succession down from Peter and claimed Jesus had made Peter His chief apostle and heir. It's my contention Constantine realized that the orthodox Christians had the organized belief system the Empire needed.[51] He insinuated himself into the Christian hierarchy as "a friend of God," "Christ's companion" and a leading 'bishop' at the Council of Nicaea in 325AD, and ultimately as the implicit head of the Roman Christian (catholic) church thus amalgamating church and state. Constantine insisted on Christ's authority by His being consubstantial with the Father (*homoousios*). Consequently Jesus Christ's heir, His descendent representative, (Constantine?) spoke with the authority of God.[52] Roman emperors had routinely portrayed themselves as gods but Constantine clinched it.

Thus I believe Constantine didn't just *adopt* Christianity, he *adapted* Christianity to suit what he considered to be the Empire's needs. This can be consistently inferred from Constantine's actions throughout his twenty-five year career although I haven't found it explicitly stated by him, but I wouldn't expect to either. If Constantine did deliberately set out to accomplish such objectives he certainly wouldn't have wanted them put into writing and may not have even told anyone. He even may not have consciously realized it himself or thought it through but oftentimes unconscious strategies work best. Certainly such an interpretation is consistent with his behavior.[53]

Some religious historians explain Rome's precipitous conversion to Christianity as 'God's plan'.[54] But instead of turning to a mystical supernatural explanation, it seems to me much simpler to just see political expediency as the principal reason.* The times were ripe with the decadence

---

*Not only does it seem likely that political expediency was the principal reason for Christianity's proliferation, but there's now compelling evidence that both Judaism before and Islam after owe their establishments to political expediency, as described in their Appendixes. However it also seems that none of these forms of monotheism could have taken root if there wasn't some exploitable basic prototheistic disposition in human nature.

of the pagan gods and the Roman upper class, along with the strain of governing the vast smoldering Empire. Orthodox Roman Christianity was the means and Constantine was the man.[55]

Of course Constantine couldn't have done it without collaborators. No doubt bishops and other church officials saw their work as carrying Christ's mission forward—but it was also a good career move. Constantine supported Christian churches at the expense of pagan temples[56] and exempted Christian clergy from taxes. In fact many pagans 'converted' to Christianity[57] and became clergy because of the benefits, the perks.[58] Thus bishops had a vested interest in the success of orthodox hierarchical Christianity (they were the hierarchy) over grass roots Christianity such as Gnosticism with its direct access to God without benefit of clergy. They helped establish "... an organization whose foundational figure [Jesus] was himself suspicious of organizations." "The great irony of Christianity ... is that the man [Jesus] who preached an unbrokered relationship with God was himself made into the ultimate broker."[59]

By the time Constantine died in 337 he had set in motion at least three pragmatic benefits from converting the Roman Empire to Christianity. As described above, the orthodox Christians' nominal monotheism[60] was more consistent with the Roman hierarchy than had been their sanctioned polytheism. Secondly, rather than try to control with soldiers, by then mostly non-Roman mercenaries and slaves, it was much easier and cheaper to have the populace control themselves in compliance with Christian beliefs—provided those Christian beliefs bore Constantine's influence. Thirdly Christianity engendered cooperation among the populace through Christians' selfless deeds, such as in times of plague staying to nurse the stricken rather than fleeing.[61]

A Thousand Years

Under Constantine's leadership, what the early Christians accomplished was outstanding. In a 'flat-earth' world dominated by multiple rulers, both human and supernatural, Christianity replaced the then obsolete beliefs and sought to bring order based, not on the sword, but on love of neighbor. True, like most human organizations over the centuries theirs was vulnerable to petty egos, corruption, hypocrisy, schism and ossification. But what they did then was revolutionary, even though today it's obsolescent.[62]

In the century beginning with Constantine, and certainly in the next few centuries say by 600AD, Christianity became firmly established as a dominant concept in the northern Mediterranean world (southern too before Islam). Constantine would have been disappointed though, that Christianity didn't revitalize the Empire, at least in the west. The Vandals, Lombards, Germanic tribes, Goths, Visigoths and Franks, and later the Arabs, swept over various portions of the Western Empire crippling or destroying the Roman civilization. Ironically the barbarians' success was due in part to the Roman Christians' estrangement from their world, their other-worldliness.[63] A further irony is that the barbarians were Christianized—the barbarians conquered the Roman Christians' lands but the Christians conquered the barbarians' 'souls'. The 'Dark Ages' ensued[64]—dominated by a powerful, autocratic, aristocratic, wealthy, rigid and superstitious Roman Church—while Western Europe struggled over the centuries to climb out of the dark.

For over a thousand years the Church's mentality prevailed.[65] From the point-of-view of the clergy during those long years, they had the awesome responsibility of maintaining a stable order at all levels of society in a stagnant world obsessed with preparing for the next world. The clergy's power was the threat of an afterlife to be spent in purgatory or hell, unless the Church granted indulgence therefrom.[66] Beginning in the fifteenth century—with Gutenberg and the ensuing Protestant Reformation, with Copernicus, Bruno, Kepler and Galileo, and especially with Bacon's inductive reasoning as an alternative to the deductive reasoning used by Aristotle down to Aquinas[67]—the Church began to lose its authoritarian grip on men's minds.[68] But I leave it to others to trace that intriguing history.[69]

Reframing

However before we move on let's pause and briefly look back at Christianity's beginnings recast into Chapter Two's 'gods' perspective. Pagans dealt with their world by projecting personalities onto natural phenomena as did their pre-civilized ancestors. The civilized pagans had developed standardized practices, protocols and customs for such projections which they embedded in their cultures. Since there were gods everywhere in each part of nature—trees, sky, sea, rocks, brooks—it was easy for a pagan to project an appropriate part of their own personality out onto that particular target as if it were a god. In addition they made statues of their gods, 'graven images', as ready targets for their projections. Because they were unconsciously projecting a part of their own selves onto the 'gods', it could be a very emotional, moving, visceral experience, an epiphany, numinous.

The Jews, say after Moses' 'burning bush' at least until the second destruction of their Temple in 70AD, had generally abstracted their projections away from objects and out into the sky, the firmament, the heavens, ascending with the smoke from their burnt offering up to God. I suspect that Jesus, apparently from whatever he projected out of himself onto his 'Father in Heaven' (his father apparently died while Jesus was a youth), he took back in and reingested as his image of the dutiful Son, accepting the mantle of the Jewish Messiah. In turn, from whatever Paul projected of himself out onto 'Christ in Heaven', he took back in and reingested as his image of Christ's 'least' apostle, accepting his mission to the Gentiles.

Similarly the earliest Christians projected their longings onto the soon-to-return Messiah/Christ. But as that expectation receded into the hereafter, their religion shifted from epiphany—an immediate divine experience—to anticipation of divine experiences in the hereafter. The tension developed by this unmet need could be exploited by clergy who interposed themselves as mediators. Their religion became less numinous and more cerebral—it went from spirituality to morality. But humans are human and unmet needs will surface some other way[70] as we'll explore in the final three chapters.

The world of pagans and early Christians was difficult at best. It was worst for those marginalized or exploited by society such as women and slaves, the poor and the disabled who were some of the first to be attracted to Christianity. So it's understandable that they would hope for something better, if not here, in the hereafter. But with today's resources should we still be looking to an afterlife for those needs?

Moreover, given their distorted understanding of nature, it seems to me it's no wonder they looked to parent figures, gods or God, to deal with their world. Such an attitude would impede their learning about nature and keep them captive in ignorance, just as believing in a fire-god kept man from understanding what fire really was. But let's give them credit for doing the best they could to make a better world with what they knew then of nature, man and gods. Then given what we know now of natural phenomena we face a challenge: Shouldn't we emulate their perspicacity, courage and fortitude, and step up to the challenge of making the best world that we can given our current knowledge of nature, man and 'gods'? Rather than criticize their theological descendants—today's resolute Christians—for still clinging to outmoded concepts, instead let's turn our attention to the challenge of discerning and fashioning a 'religion' more relevant to today's and tomorrow's world. As said, I suspect that many today cling to Christianity because they don't have a good replacement, just as back then disenchanted pagans honored their old gods before Christianity became prevalent. Whether this replacement might be a neo-Christianity—taking Pope John XXIII's *aggiornamento* to it's logical conclusion—or something altogether different will be explored in Chapters Ten and Twelve.

I'd like to think that years from now people will look back on today's Christian beliefs with the same sardonic condescension that we today look back on the Greco-Roman pagan beliefs, and wonder 'How could they have been so gullibly naïve as to believe all that stuff?' Indeed years from now they may see little difference between the Greco-Roman pantheon with many gods and goddesses, and the Christian 'pantheon' with a tri-une God, Virgin Mother, angels, apostles, saints and devils. Both had/have feast days venerating their gods and employ/ed statues, murals, coins or holy medals to remind devotees of them, and lit/light lamps/candles to honor them. Once you gain a detached perspective of Christianity—as many have—you can recognize the parallels. A major difference, as said, is that the Christian 'pantheon' has a tighter hierarchy as Constantine appreciated. Otherwise they're much alike.

Moving right along then, in the next six chapters I'll attempt to describe what I see as the pertinent concepts in our current knowledge of nature, including man: What the founding Christians' beliefs—in a flat-earth with heaven overhead, in a six-day creation, in God—are now changing into. Then the final three chapters will explore how I think we might employ these concepts to fashion a better world.

Part II

Science Concepts

Chapter Four

Some Fundamentals

Just beyond the settlement is a Wall of high craggy cliffs blocking our ascent to the Mountain. It looks impenetrable so none of the townsfolk have even tried to scale it. We almost turn back ourselves in discouragement. But as we get closer we see some possible routes up. There are cracks and outcroppings we grasp as we pull ourselves up to reach the next handhold, then the next and the next. At first we dare not look down from the dizzying height. But after getting used to it, we marvel at the grandeur, at the changed perspective it gives us. Alas we reach a pitch in the Wall that is beyond our abilities. We have to trust the skill of the mountaineers in our party and their equipment in order to scale this last overhang. Finally over the top ledge with the monster Wall behind us, we relax and confidently anticipate the high altitude climb ahead.

The fundamentals covered here are not those of the Christian Fundamentalist or other such believers.[1] Theirs are based on revelations in the Bible or the Koran (aka Qur'an). Rather the few fundamentals discussed here are based on our best current knowledge of our world. Unless you're already familiar with these concepts, this chapter asks you to make radical shifts in the traditional views of our world, paradigm shifts, to 'stand on your head' in order to invert your perspective. If they're new to you a gestation period may be required until you become comfortable with them, until you get acclimated. Or you may reject making some of these shifts at all, but at least you'll know there are different ways of 'seeing' our world. In a way our Catholic upbringing prepared us to accept mysteries we can't fathom like the Trinity, virgin birth, Heaven... Since as children we grappled with such concepts, our minds have been trained—or at least somewhat disposed—to withhold disbelief and to tentatively accept 'far-out' concepts (but now it's ok to be skeptical). These are not just 'mind games', they are fundamental realities of our world some of which we'll need in later chapters. We'll start with an easy paradigm shift.

"Sunrise, Sunset . . ."

Few people today still believe the Earth is flat and that our Sun and the other 'fixed' stars move across the sky, as people generally did in Christianity's formative years and even as late as the 1600s as Bruno and Galileo learned.[2] Even so we use expressions as though we still did, such as 'sunrise' and 'sunset.' Moreover even though we intellectually know the Earth rotates, most of us relate to the world as if the Earth is fixed and the skies move. In order to develop a feeling in our bones for the reality and shake off obsolete attitudes, let's try a mental exercise.

Imagine it's night at a small itinerant carnival set up in a field. We approach one of the rides, a Ferris wheel maybe fifty-feet high with double seats suspended around its circumference. We sit in one of the swinging seats and the wheel starts to rotate so that we're moving backward, then upward and then forward as we come around the top. As we crest over the top a distant bright streetlight comes into view. Now we could say that the streetlight is rising, if we regard the Ferris wheel as stationary and the streetlight as moving upward. But that's not a very useful way of experiencing the situation even though it's a valid perspective. It would be difficult to relate to the scene around us with such an egocentric point of view. Yet this is the way most of us regard 'sunrise'—the Sun 'rising' from below the horizon into the sky.

Instead, try to visualize and feel Earth's great mass rumbling around under our feet like a mammoth Ferris wheel. At dawn the Sun gradually comes into view as our location on Earth rotates toward it, at mid-day we're carried under the Sun overhead, at 'sunset' it's gradually hidden from view by the 'rising' horizon and at night we're carried around again under the stars.[3] So try to feel Earth rumbling 'round underfoot so you get in the habit of conceptualizing Earth this way.[4]

'Suction'

Another mental exercise regards Earth's atmosphere. The oceans, seas and lakes are the pooling of the Earth's liquid water in depressions in the Earth's solid surfaces by the force of 'gravity'. Similarly our atmosphere (*atmo*=vapor +sphere) is the pooling of air above the denser land and water surfaces by the force of 'gravity'. We live at the bottom of an 'ocean' of air. But we're generally not aware of the pressure of that ocean of air on us[5] just as fish in water probably aren't aware of the pressure of the water on them. Yet there are normally nearly fifteen pounds pressing on every square inch of our body. Try holding a fifteen pound weight concentrated on one square inch of your skin to get a feel for it, then imagine the cumulative force all over your body! Think of the wind as a stream of air flowing over you or of riding a bicycle as plowing through the 'ocean' of air.

When you put a straw into a glass of ice tea, put your lips on the other end and 'suck' up the tea, you may think you're drawing the tea up the straw. But the tea is being pushed not pulled. What you're doing is reducing the air pressure in your mouth below normal. Hence the normal air pressure on the tea in the glass *pushes* the tea up the straw. What is called 'suction' is another one of those obsolete,[6] misleading terms like 'sunrise' that distort our concept of our world.

'Gravity'

The compression of Earth's atmosphere is analogous to the compaction of the space around the Earth which in part explains 'gravity', another misleading term (at least in the way we're used to).

Hence this next mental exercise concerns 'gravity' and assumes you're seated while reading this book (not because you might be bowled over). Focus your awareness on the pressure your chair exerts on your buttocks, somewhat like you'd feel on your back from an airplane seat-back pushing on you during take-off. Now imagine that instead your chair is in an enclosed capsule in space far from anything. You're being pushed 'upward' faster and faster through space by a silent vibrationless rocket engine. If the 'push', the thrust, is just right, you couldn't detect the difference[7] between your space capsule chair and your reading chair even though in your reading chair you're sitting 'at rest', motionless. In other words the push of the rocket chair would be equivalent to the 'push' of your Earth chair—Einstein's (strong) principle of equivalence.

Instead of experiencing 'gravity' as your weight pushing downward, think of it as though your reading chair is being accelerated upward. Of course everything else around you would have to be accelerating upward too or else your reading chair would take off. In fact the whole Earth would have to be moving up, expanding, which is ridiculous. How could you be accelerating upward without moving?

Acceleration is when an object moves faster-and-faster or, put another way, moves through more-and-more space in less-and-less time. Think of 'gravity' as two things happening at once. The Earth's mass compacts the space around it similar to the way it does our atmosphere. You can think of it as space squeezing down, being contracted around the Earth. You're not moving up, space is moving down. But somewhat the opposite is happening with time. The Earth's mass is stretching out time around it, dilating time. So even though you're not moving, more-and-more space is moving down in less-and-less time.[8] Try imagining layers of space raining down ever faster (like fence posts going by ever faster as your car speeds up) while concurrently time is slowing, dragging (like a slow-motion movie).

The concept that neither space nor time are fixed but are both variables takes some getting used to.[9] Think of them as reciprocal: as space contracts, time dilates.[10] Or more prosaically, as space shrinks, time stretches. Hence the term 'space-time' and the expression "Mass warps space-time."[11] What we experience as 'gravity' is Earth's mass warping space-time. You might begin to get used to the idea by occasionally feeling the Earth, the floor, your chair ... pushing you up.[12]

Hey, you say, hold on a minute! If 'gravity' is the effect of space being compressed and time stretched, why doesn't it affect me and my chair the same way it affects the Earth? After all I'm in the same space-time 'atmosphere' as Earth. Why aren't I, my chair and all the weighted objects on Earth experiencing space-time the same way as the Earth[13] so that we aren't 'pulled down' by 'gravity'? Well, if you were in the rocket-driven space-capsule described above and slid off your chair, the accelerating floor would quickly catch up to you with a thump. Each and every weighted object's mass warps its own surrounding space-time, even subatomic particles must a tiny bit.[14] The space-time between you and the Earth is warped so that you're 'accelerating' toward the Earth while it's 'accelerating' toward you.

Our concept of 'gravity' has changed over the past couple thousand years. It's not Aristotle's 'body at rest' on the flat Earth, *terra firma*. Nor is it Galileo's and Newton's[15] attraction at a distance. And it may not be Einstein's warped space-time either but that's the best we know so far.[16] Warped space-time is not consistent with quantum mechanics so it too may be wrong. (As discussed in the note below 'string theory' attempts to reconcile relativity and quantum mechanics.) Before we touch on quantum mechanics though, we need to consider some other weirdness, namely light.

(Alright, so yes, maybe I did entice you to come this far, but as long as you're here now, why not press on? I never said it'd be easy—most worthwhile things aren't. Hopefully though, it's intriguing.)

Light

Our everyday experience of light doesn't lead us to suspect how marvelous and weird light really is. We switch on a 'light' to light up our surroundings so we're not in the dark. Sunlight lights up our world, warms and nourishes it. Nothing special there … or is there? The next mental exercise is one Einstein began when he was sixteen.[17] He tried to imagine what it would be like traveling with a beam of light. Some years later he concluded that from the light beam's perspective time would be so dilated that time would stand still and that space would be so contracted that the light beam would be everywhere at once.[18] (I don't pretend to fully grasp it either![19] But I find it helpful to extend the above description of 'gravity' and think of space as being compressed in front of the light beam thus dilating time.) This thinking led to Einstein's Special Theory of Relativity in 1905, and in 1915 to his General Theory of Relativity. Both have been subjected to many tests all of which tend to support these theories and none to refute them.[20]

By 'light' is meant not just visible light, but the whole spectrum of electromagnetic radiation from low-frequency radio waves—AM, FM, TV, microwaves[21]—through infrared, visible, ultraviolet, X-rays on up to very high-frequency gamma-rays. The back 'wall' of our eyeballs, our retinas are like small roving satellite dishes, but they detect only the narrow frequency band of light called 'visible', hence the quip "Looked at in this way, we are almost blind."[22] Our eyes and brain interpret these frequencies of visible light as colors: red, orange, yellow, green, blue and violet, and shades in between. Light consists of photons which are ill-defined, ultra-tiny packets of vibrating energy; the higher a photon's frequency of vibration, the higher its energy level.[23] A photon might be envisioned as a fuzzy, quivering dimple rippling through space-time.

So not only are space and time variable, but light somehow plays a unique, privileged role in defining time. Again from light's own perspective it exists outside of time, that is, for a light wave/photon traveling at the speed of light, time is so dilated that it doesn't flow and conversely space is so contracted that it doesn't exist.[24] (As you get used to the concept of 'gravity' as time stretching out as space is compacted by mass, then like Einstein try visualizing space being compacted as a particle travels faster and faster through it, so that time stretches out.) And somehow light establishes the ultimate limit of speed, so that it's generally believed that nothing can travel faster than light.[25] Moreover regardless of the motion of the observer, the observed speed of light, 'c', is constant (in 'gravity'-less vacuum). This constant defines the relation between energy and mass in Einstein's famous equation $E=mc^2$.[26]

But there's even more weirdness. Light behaves both as a wave and as a particle—the 'wave-particle duality'[27]—which leads us into quantum mechanics. An example of this weirdness is one of quantum mechanic's major mysteries, 'nonlocality', whereby two related particles that have become widely separated maintain some sort of instantaneous physical correspondence, connection, coherence or entanglement.[28] Another is the uncertainty principle—the more precisely a photon's (or electron's, or proton's, or even molecule's) velocity is determined the less precisely is its position known, and vice versa.[29] But is this uncertainty truly weirdness or just ignorance?[30] Maybe we just haven't yet found the perspective that will remove the ambiguity. That's why it's called quantum *mechanics*—quantum physicists know *how* it works but not *why*, just as a good mechanic might understand *how* something works and *how* to tweak it without knowing *why* it works.[31] In the past century over a dozen *interpretations* have been proposed to explain why quantum phenomena work,[32] starting in the 1920s with the Copenhagen interpretation. But that quantum mechanics does work is attested by many experiments[33] and by technology based on knowledge developed during that same period such as CDs and lasers.

Perhaps our minds are not capable of grasping, or have not yet evolved to be able to grasp, the quantum perspective, to make the shift to the quantum realm (more on this in Chapter Nine). The consensus among physicists is that in trying to understand smaller and smaller particles, the microscopic, we humans loose the ability to visualize what's happening, our intuition fails us. Instead we must resort to mathematics to describe and predict in this microscopic realm. It's said there's a divide, a chasm—between the *micro*scopic realm and this *macro*scopic world we inhabit—that can't be crossed by our intuition even with metaphor.[34] Hence it's recently been proposed that here too we must invert our approach. Rather than attempt to understand relativity and quantum mechanics from our perspective, some say we should adapt our thinking to the microscopic perspective in order to find ways of interpreting it into our macroscopic world.[35] It's believed that the fundamental laws of physics are quantum. Reality is founded in the microscopic and as it morphs, 'decoheres', emerges up to our scale of the macroscopic, only then are we able to perceive it with our senses and grasp it with our intuition. (Boy, is this reminiscent of the Catholic Church's 'mysteries' we were told we couldn't expect to fathom!?) Does this mean we should abandon efforts to understand? I'm not willing to yet, but I hope help arrives soon.[36]

There is one important physical system that is said to be impervious to decoherence—disappearance of quantum interferences at our macroscopic level—and that physical system is ordinary light. This makes the problem even more mysterious.[37] These characteristics of light and the microscopic may seem esoteric, of concern only to physicists and their ilk. Yet it is the light from our Sun that not only sustains our Earth's hospitality to most life as we know it, but the Sun's photons are the fundamental source of energy for most life and growth on Earth.[38] And photons from our Sun may have played a crucial role in the origin of Life on Earth (to be explored in Chapter Six). Probably we don't appreciate light's uniqueness because we're so accustomed to light, as we are to air pressure and 'gravity'.

Emergence

The above concepts (except decoherence) have all involved reducing the phenomenon in question to its component parts, its fundamentals. This is called reductionism[39] which has proved to be a very powerful and valuable approach or technique in grappling with nature. But in reducing a thing to its constituents something is lost. For instance, if we take a car apart, we can learn a lot about how it's made and how it works. We can see the body, the doors, the seats, the wheels, the transmission, the engine and so on. And if we take the engine apart, we can examine the pistons, the connecting rods, the crankshaft, the valves and so on. But we no longer have a car—we have a collection of car parts! If we're hoping to find what makes a car unique, its essence, we won't find it. In dismantling the car we've destroyed what made it a car. Until we put those parts properly back together, we don't really have a car except maybe in our imagination.

The quality that emerges when parts are properly assembled is called synergy or synergism wherein the whole is greater than the sum of its parts. As I'm using the term here, the key feature of synergy is not just that the combination of parts results in a more complex 'whole'—as some writers assert—that might simply be chaos. Rather the key feature of synergy is that the whole is more elegant in the sense of being ingeniously neat, simple or concise. The synergistic whole possesses supervenient properties that weren't in the parts. The synergistic effect of capabilities may arise from the type of parts that are combined and/or the way they're organized, arranged or coordinated.[40] A more rudimentary example than the car is a molecule. Molecules are composed of putatively identical protons, neutrons and electrons, but depending how many are combined and how they're combined, each kind of molecule will have unique properties.

The concept of emergence is relatively new and is now being studied[41] as an antidote to an over-reliance on reductionism's way of insisting on explaining everything.[42] Zealous reductionists deny the potential efficacy of emergence, of organization (maybe they're kind of like anarchists). But as seen in the above examples often the 'whole' can't be found in the parts—the whole *is* greater than the sum of the parts. In the following chapters we'll utilize both reductionism and emergence in an attempt to trace how our solar system and planet emerged, how life and organisms emerged, and how humans and consciousness emerged. The concept of emergence is essential to accepting the idea of a Life Urge, as we shall see later on.

Recap

Our world is not what it seems. And our words describing our world are often based on misleading, obsolete concepts which have to be unlearned and discarded in order to grasp a better understanding of our world. But even when we abandon obsolete concepts, we may not have new words, so we continue using the old ones. Indeed the term 'evolution' means 'unrolling' which is wrong as we'll see in Chapter Six. Quantum physicists use 'waves' and 'particles' even though there's no medium in which those 'waves' move and no solidity to those 'particles.' While we can't dispense with metaphors in thinking about nature, there's a risk of mistaking the metaphor for the reality, the map for the territory. It'd be nice if we could come up with more accurate words but in the interim we'll just have to make do. On the other hand maybe it's a good lesson—not only isn't the world what it *seems* to be, the world is not what it's *said* to be.

Here's another consideration. As Catholics we were required to accept unfathomable religious mysteries on faith. Now we're being asked to accept as yet unfathomed, and perhaps unfathomable, scientific mysteries maybe not on faith but certainly by putting our faith in scientists. The danger could be that we humans become more and more dependent on science and technology which fewer and fewer of us understand. And those who do understand (or purport to) become the new 'priesthood' dispensing advice, or recommendations, or decrees on the rest of us, which they say we would ignore at our peril. Therefore it behooves us not to be complacent, not to be science and mathematics 'agnostics', not to leave that responsibility to others. Rather it behooves each of us to become as knowledgeable as we are able. And who knows, it might just be fun. In the Dark Ages what little learning there was, was mostly the privilege/responsibility of the clergy. But in an enlightened free society, learning is not only the privilege but the obligation of everyone in that society, if we wish to remain free.[43]

Finally let me return to the question posed at the beginning of Chapter Two concerning belief in God. It should come as no surprise that I believe we need to invert our concept of God just as we've inverted some other concepts. Take the Ferris wheel example: while it may be conceivable to think of the streetlight as rising (like 'sunrise') it's not very practical. Even less practical is it to think of God as 'out there'—it's truly not as we'll see. Or take other analogies: what's known as 'suction' is not pulling but is just the opposite, it's pushing. And perhaps 'gravity' isn't a pulling down by the Earth but just the opposite, a pushing up by the Earth. These are misconceptions that science has turned around. Putting it another way, recall how the mysteries of quantum phenomena during the past century spawned over a dozen interpretations. But during the past three-hundred centuries, mysteries of phenomena that are called gods/God have spawned dozens of theisms—interpretations—from pantheisms through monotheisms. So just as physicists are searching for a perspective that explains quantum phenomena, we'll search for a perspective that explains God.

To gain that perspective, as said, I think the belief in a God 'out there' needs to be turned around as just the opposite, not 'out there' but 'in here'. It needs to be re-conceptualized, reinterpreted. My hunch is that what's called 'God' is something fundamental within all Life that emerges through each successive level of Life until that 'something' somehow eventually emerges into humans' heightened consciousness. Unfortunately at this last level it seems humans punt—that 'something' gets projected 'out there' by most Occidentals. By exploring what this fundamental 'something' is and how it emerges, my hope is to suggest ways for more people to reclaim it, to re-own it and to reverence it throughout all Life. As explained earlier, I'm calling this inversion of theism 'prototheism' ('proto-' = first in time, beginning, giving rise to, first formed, primary/per Merriam-Webster's dictionary). At the very least, prototheism could be a heuristic for elucidating a science of religion. But I'll argue it's far more than a science *of* religion; it marries science *and* religion by replacing revelation with research and clearheaded thinking. It tries to renounce the mystery and the mysticism, yet to retain the marvel of and reverence for Life.

This inversion is somewhat the reverse of the Copernican Revolution over four centuries ago, alluded to at the beginning of this chapter (and the note thereto). Until Nicolas Copernicus published his *De Revolutionibus* in 1543, virtually everyone accepted Aristotle's and Ptolemy's Earth-centered Universe as reality.[44] Their Universe placed the immovable Earth at the center with the Moon, planets, Sun and stars revolving around Earth in enormous concentric spheres called the firmament or heavens.[45] Copernicus inverted that—today only the staunchest religious fundamentalists hold such beliefs. So just as the Copernican Revolution inverted the focus of the universe from here to out in space, I believe we need to invert the focus of theism from 'out there' to 'within here' in our deepest being.

If the inversion I'm proposing is comparable to the Copernican Revolution, we might expect comparable reactions by the 'authorities' and by many ordinary people. As mentioned toward the end of Chapter Two, that realization—that the Earth wasn't the center of the universe, but was a 'ball' like the Moon somehow 'floating' in space—was very upsetting to most people back then. So much so that it was declared a heresy which brought on the wrath of the Inquisition. Similarly the realization—that there is no "Father in Heaven" thus overturning lifelong deep-rooted beliefs—could be very upsetting for many people resulting in reactions from denial to anger and rage before acceptance (which might never come). Near this book's end we'll explore how such reactions might be ameliorated.

Yet before that we need to arduously work our way to a well grounded idea of what that fundamental 'something' is 'in here'. That's what we'll be exploring throughout the next five chapters. Then you can decide if you like my conclusions or want to come up with your own, but at least you'll have the benefit of my spadework as said at the outset of this 'expedition', this quest.

Chapter Five

Earth's Beginnings

After the strain of scaling the Wall, we pause to rest and look around. Perched up here we can see back past the settlement to the forest we slogged through and the sea far beyond. And turning toward our future course we can make out the long challenging climb ahead and a distant prodigious cloud that shrouds the Mountain summit. While perched here atop the Wall we can read the history of the Mountain recorded in its veins of rock piled one atop another or tilted up at dizzying angles. We muse—How'd this all get here?

"In the beginning ..." was the Big Bang. At least that's what most cosmologists have come to believe. Their belief is based on several kinds of evidence. Perhaps the easiest to envision is based on the expansion of the Universe. The farther out into space astronomers look, the faster distant galaxies appear to be moving away.[1] If the galaxies are now moving away, they must have been closer together in the distant past. In space, far away equals long ago (the more distant the galaxy, the longer its light has traveled to reach us, so looking out into space is also looking back in time). Cosmologists extrapolate back to an initial starting point of our Universe as an explosion that was derisively dubbed the "Big Bang" when the theory was first proposed.[2] Another kind of evidence is the Cosmic Microwave Background radiation left over from the Big Bang—everywhere astronomers 'listen' in the Universe they detect faint radio waves and have concluded that they are the greatly cooled and diluted remains of the enormously hot Big Bang nearly fourteen billion years ago.[3] A third kind of evidence is the abundance of helium—there's too much to have been formed only in stars, as we'll examine below.

Before the Big Bang there was no 'before' because that's when time began for our Universe. (Asking what came before the Big Bang has been likened to asking what's north of the North Pole.) Some people are troubled by what came before and so to relieve that anxiety posit God as the "uncaused first cause." But aren't they doing what we discussed in Chap-

ter Two on gods/God? It seems to me that they're inventing a parent figure so they won't feel frightened, like a security blanket. Yet if they're willing to accept an "uncaused cause" with no beginning, why not call it the
Big Bang rather than anthropomorphize it as "God the Father"? We simply need to accept that we don't know what preceded the Big Bang (if anything) and probably can't know.[4]

A way of thinking of the Big Bang that I find useful is as an extension
of the concept of 'gravity' discussed in the preceding chapter. 'Gravity'
was described as the compaction of space and the stretching out of time.
For the start of the Big Bang take this description to its extreme where the
space of the whole Universe was concentrated in a tiny spot and time was
so dilated that it didn't flow—time stood still. (Under those extreme conditions physics may have had as yet unknown properties.) This tiny spot
contained all the (latent?) energy/mass of the Universe that ever was or
will be. Then for whatever reason (a quantum fluctuation?) space began to
expand faster than the speed of light and in the first split second[5] became
enormously hot and went through a very rapid inflationary epoch. I think
of this inflation as the reverse of the 'gravity' we experience here on
Earth—instead of space contracting, it expanded at a stupendous rate taking all the energy along with it. Some 4% of the energy transformed into
photons and elementary particles, mostly quark-gluon plasma, electrons
and neutrinos (*baryons*), and another 23% into proto-dark matter.[6]

Then as our primordial Universe continued to expand at a slowing
rate its concentrated energy thinned out in effect cooling. And as it cooled
quarks were able to combine mostly into protons and some into slightly
heavier neutrons.[7] With further cooling protons that could find neutrons
paired up with them—but still three-quarters were left single as the nuclei
of hydrogen atoms (*ions*). Most proton-neutron pairs (*deuterium* ions) further combined with each other to form the nuclei of heavier atoms, mainly
helium. Thus the visible matter of the Universe ended up three-quarters
hydrogen and nearly one-quarter helium.

With still further expansion and cooling the free electrons were able
to bind with these nuclei (*recombination*) so that the hydrogen atoms began
absorbing the photons bringing on the cosmic 'Dark Ages'. Not until nine-
hundred-million years had enough stars formed producing ultraviolet
light which reionized the hydrogen ending the Dark Ages. The photons
left over from the Big Bang could stream through space as the cosmic microwave background (CMB) radiation mentioned above. There are still
some three billion of these Big Bang photons for each photon we see arriving from the stars![8] They began streaming toward us 380,000 years after
the Big Bang.[9] During an over thirteen-billion year journey through ex-

panding space their temperature has been red-shifted down from 3,000K (Kelvin is Celsius degrees above absolute zero= −273°C) so that they now measure 2.7K.[10]

As mentioned, in addition to the visible matter there must have been much more *dark matter* and *dark energy* created somehow. What this dark matter and dark energy are no one yet knows but there are several theories.[11] Even though this dark matter can't be seen nonetheless it warps space so its effects can be detected.[12] Dark energy (negative 'gravity') is postulated from the accelerating expansion of space in the past five billion years.[13] Probably some die-hard theists will seize on the preponderance of 23% dark matter and 73% dark energy as evidence somehow for the existence of God once again turning to their "Father in Heaven" as the explanation of the as yet unexplained. More relevant to our prototheistic quest, if our world of baryonic matter constitutes only 4% of our Universe's matter/energy, how can we hope to answer the 'big questions'? Well, I don't know, but that's the world we live in and the only world we can deal with yet. Throwing up our hands in despair or to Heaven gets us nowhere. So let's press on.

Galaxy and Star Formation

When space expanded in the primordial Universe it wasn't completely smooth, it had slight ripples that can be seen in the cosmic microwave background radiation. One scenario for what happened next goes as follows: Think of the ripples in space as roughly analogous to ripples in a stretched, thin sheet of rubber and the dark matter as BB shot pellets spread out on that flat sheet. The weight of each BB slightly warps the sheet down around it so that, given a slight disturbance, the BBs began to roll together into bunches. This further warps the sheet around the bunches of BBs but stretches the sheet elsewhere.[14] Similarly in our scenario bits of dark matter collected in the ripples of the expanding space thus warping the space around each bit and enlarging the ripples. The ripples then gathered more bits of dark matter thus further warping the space around them. The localized warping of space slows down its expansion nearby but perhaps speeds up the expansion of the space where dark matter is sparse. As this went on eventually the dark matter formed halos herding the visible matter into proto-galaxies.

The visible matter was still a gas, its atoms racing through the space ripples until the ripples grew into 'troughs' and 'valleys' steeper than the visible matter's speed could surmount. The speeding atoms of visible matter were thus herded into narrow filaments, then into swirling clouds by the dark matter's halos' steeply warped space. The visible matter further warped the space of the clouds into whirlpool-like disks, huge pinwheel proto-galaxies with innumerable embedded swirling eddies. The closer to the proto-galaxy's center, the more numerous the eddies. Each swirling eddy steered its cloud toward its center increasing its disk's spin as does a twirling ice-skater by drawing in her arms. Each swirling eddy swept much of its cloud into its center forming a proto-star, often two or three spinning around one another.[15]

The accelerating speed of the atoms as they smashed into their eddy's center drove up the proto-star's core pressure and temperature enough to start nuclear fusion[16] in the more massive stars. Of course these initial proto-stars were mostly hydrogen and about a quarter helium from the Big Bang. A star with less than eight percent the mass of our Sun was too small to initiate nuclear fusion and will glow as a *brown dwarf* for many eons.[17] Slightly more massive stars could just barely initiate low level nuclear fusion and burn as *red dwarfs* for almost as long until they exhaust their hydrogen to transform into *blue dwarfs.*

A first-generation star about as massive as our Sun readily had its core temperature raised enough to initiate fusing the hydrogen into helium. The energy thus released sustained the core from further collapse and generated photons in gradually increasing amounts.[18] But after about ten billion years the central hydrogen is used up suspending fusion and the outflow of photons so that its now helium core is squashed and heats up further. This heat drives the fusion of the outlying hydrogen shell adding more helium to the shrinking core but swelling the middle layers. As the star swells its expanding surface's temperature cools so it becomes a *red giant.* Also as its energy output increases material is driven into space as strong 'winds' that reduce its mass by a quarter. At the same time its helium core is squashed further into an extremely dense *white dwarf* driving up its temperature even more and again initiating nuclear fusion this time of helium into carbon. This nuclear fusion quickly goes hyper and flashes away its red giant outer layer. Its remaining white dwarf core burns brightly for another hundred million years before it dims.[19] (This'll be our Sun's destiny.)

First-generation stars much more massive than our Sun begin with the same sequence but generate much higher core temperatures. They use their hydrogen a thousand times faster and go well beyond the carbon stage. The massive star rapidly fuses its helium core into carbon and oxygen squashing its core to ever higher temperatures. Great quantities of neutrinos are produced and escape into space. When hot enough the carbon fuses into magnesium which in turn fuses into still heavier elements.

As these nuclear reaction cycles progress, rapidly producing silicon, sulfur and finally iron, the fusion comes to a halt.[20]

The massive star now has onion-like layers of successively heavier elements starting from its outer hydrogen shell inward to its iron core. When this iron core grows above a threshold mass (about 1.4 Sun masses) it collapses precipitously going through a sequence that crushes the iron core's protons and electrons into neutrons. As soon as this massive core of neutrons collapses to its maximum density some of it bounces back driving a stupendous lopsided shock wave through the layers inside-out like shrapnel. It's called a *supernova* (type II).[21] The energy of the shock wave drives neutrons to synthesize a small amount of even heavier elements (lead, gold, uranium ...) and blows these—along with the fusion products and the unused hydrogen and helium—out into space in a vast heterogeneous cloud, a *nebula*. Such clouds seeded future generations of stars and planets which produced all the elements on Earth—'star stuff'.[22] The remaining core of neutrons (with an iron crust) survives as a speeding *neutron star* (sometimes becoming a *pulsar*)[23] or collapses further into a *black hole*.

Before leaving this section on galaxies and first-generation stars, black holes should be briefly described. These are concentrations of matter so dense that they warp space into 'whirlpools' so deep that not even light can escape from their 'wells'—hence the name black holes. But they can be detected by their severely warped space's effect on nearby matter and passing light, *gravitational lensing*, and more recently by x-rays radiated by matter as it's being swept into a black hole's 'whirlpool.' Most galaxies are believed to have immense black holes at their centers;[24] some are *quasars*.[25] Even more massive stars at the far edges of our Universe, nine- to fourteen-billion light-years away, are now thought to explode as *hypernova* briefly producing gamma ray beams as they collapse into massive black holes and disappear.[26]

In addition to learning that we have a black hole at the center of our galaxy, it's recently been learned that there's a vast ring of stars that wreathes our Milky Way perhaps the remains of another galaxy.[27] With all those stars and galaxies moving about it's inevitable that some of them would collide—it happened in the past and is expected to happen again in a few billion years when the Andromeda galaxy merges with our Milky Way galaxy.[28]

One further consideration to put our significance in perspective. There are perhaps ten- to a hundred-billion galaxies in our known Universe and up to a hundred-billion stars in each galaxy. Some of these stars appear to have planets orbiting them as does our Sun.[29]

Our Solar System

After a few generations of supernovas transmuting and spewing heavier elements into space, the local region of our Milky Way Galaxy accumulated a cloud with enough of all the natural atomic elements to spawn our Solar System.[30] Nearly all of this cloud was used to form our own star, the Sun,[31] through the process described above but with an important difference. While the heavier elements constituted only two percent of the cloud's mass, they were the seeds that somehow accreted to form meteorites, asteroids, and the inner planets, including our Earth. Just how this occurred is not well understood but the following simplified explanation illustrates how it might have happened.[32]

The heavier elements had been formed earlier by a few generations of supernovas into grains of dust swirling in the gas cloud of mostly hydrogen and helium. At some point the cloud began to collapse perhaps triggered by massive gravitational waves.[33] The cloud's gas was accelerated from a temperature of some 40K to well over 1800K evaporating the heavier elements' dust grains. Then as the heat dissipated into space the cloud re-cooled first condensing the less volatile molecules into frozen droplets, *chondrules*.[34] As the cloud continued to cool the more volatile molecules congealed in matrices around the chondrules or frost around whole globs called *chondrites*.[35]

As it collapsed the swirling solar-system-wide cloud gathered into a 'thin' protoplanetary disk revolving around the protoSun forming in a dense 'cocoon' at the center of the cloud.[36] Because the chondrites orbiting the protoSun were crowded together in the protoplanetary disk they likely collided. If the chondrites' collision wasn't so violent that it shattered them, they eventually stuck together forming ever larger clumps of rubble called *planetesimals*. The larger planetesimals' increasingly warped space began to sweep up the smaller ones in their vicinity forming protoplanets. Then as fusion started up in the protoSun's core it blasted a 'wind' of gas that blew away the dense cocoon so that the Sun's photons could shower the inner region of the disk.[37] Those planetesimals closer to the Sun 'boiled' away their free hydrogen and helium which wasn't 'locked-up' in chondrites.

Even though many planetesimals accreted into planets like Mercury, Venus, Earth and Mars, there are still many orbiting out there especially in the asteroid belt between Mars and Jupiter. Those that still 'fall' to Earth as meteorites reveal much about our solar system's formation.[38] In addition, tons of dust still shower Earth daily.

Early Earth

The newly forming Earth was heated some by the dim newly shining Sun but mostly by kinetic energy of the many planetesimals bombarding Earth. The heat partially melted the chondrites that had aggregated to form Earth. Most denser molecules such as iron sank toward the center while lighter ones such as silicates rose toward the surface.[39] Some may now still be fractionating and rising or sinking.

As the newly formed Earth orbited the Sun a planetesimal perhaps a tenth the size of Earth was traveling along a converging path. And the two collided. The planetesimal got the worst of it so that much of its iron center merged with Earth's. The collision splashed a like amount of Earth's molten surface material out into space some of which was lost and some eventually fell back to Earth. But about a tenth of it was held in a close orbit around Earth as the protoMoon. Initially the strung-out clumps of proto-Moon hugged Earth as they gathered into a single clump circling Earth every few 'days'. The Earth's and Moon's masses warped the space between them as the Earth rotated thus raising a tidal 'wave' of any fluid material on the side of Earth nearest the Moon. The drag of this tide slowed the Earth's spin while increasing the Moon's speed making the Moon's orbit gradually drift farther away in a lengthening circuit.[40] (Imagine that as Earth whips around it slings the Moon farther out.)

Because the Earth was still partially molten the huge dent from the protoMoon soon closed as did the craters made by the planetesimals still pummeling Earth.[41] Before long most of the larger planetesimals near Earth's orbit had been swept up and Earth could begin to cool. Still incoming though from the realm of our solar system's giant planets far from the Sun, swarms of colder planetesimals (*comets*) crossed Earth's orbit. Some were swept up depositing their frozen water and gas to feed our oceans and atmosphere. In addition their organic compounds may have been the feedstock for Life's eventual emergence on Earth.[42] This further cooled some of the lighter materials that had risen to near Earth's surface as a kind of scum. The cooling 'scum' began solidifying into crust on the seafloor riding on top of the molten mantle. Far underneath the mantle down near Earth's center the enormous pressure on the largely iron core two billion years ago begin compacting the high temperature liquid into a solid whose density is now twice what it'd be at Earth's surface.[43]

Earth was anything but tranquil. The gigantic tides raised by the close-in Moon not only dragged 'waves' across the surface as Earth turned but also churned the molten mantle underneath.[44] The latent heat convected from the solidifying iron core made the molten mantle boil up through the crust spewing gas and lava from multifarious volcanoes and vents. Somehow the volcanoes mixed seafloor crust with water producing a lighter crust on top of the seafloor crust thus depositing the first lands. All this turmoil under and in the forming crust broke it into plates and jostled them around on the mantle pushing them into one another. Above the surface the water from the out-gassing volcanoes and in-falling comets[45] steamed up the thick atmosphere of largely nitrogen and carbon dioxide. The water rained acid down on the newly forming land washing carbon compounds into the scalding oceans to settle-out nearby as sediment.

Then as now, Earth circled the Sun spinning like a tilted top (wobbling[46] a little perhaps initially from the protoMoon's impact). The young Sun's output was then maybe thirty percent less than what it is now so Earth continued to cool especially at the isolated poles. But some of the heat radiating out into space was retained by the 'greenhouse' effect of the thick atmosphere's carbon dioxide, methane and water vapor.[47] As Earth cooled not only could more crust[48] solidify but it was less jostled by turbulence of the now plastic upper-mantle underneath, by the receding Moon's smaller tides and by fewer incoming planetesimals. About three billion years ago the landmass growth accelerated so that ever more of the carbon dioxide in the rains was being washed into ocean sediment. But as long as moving tectonic plates plowed that ocean sediment back under the land, the resulting volcanoes at the margins recycled the sediment's carbon dioxide back into the atmosphere maintaining the greenhouse balance.

However recently it has been proposed that the balance may have been disrupted several times between 2,300– and 600–million years ago resulting in cycles of 'snowball earths' followed by 'hothouses.'[49] The scenario goes like this: Continent size islands had deployed around the equator where massive evaporation produced massive torrential rains.[50] These rains were removing far more carbon dioxide from the atmosphere than was being replaced. With the 'greenhouse' gone the Earth's infrared heat radiation escaped into space. As the oceans iced over from the poles the ice reflected more and more of the Sun's rays back into space and the temperature plummeted. Soon all water and land was covered with a thick shield of ice, a 'snowball,' at $-50°C$. But still carbon dioxide continued to be expelled from volcanoes poking through the ice, as well as from vents on the ocean bottom under the ice. With no rain and exposed land to wash out the carbon dioxide it slowly replenished the 'greenhouse' even denser than before. The heat from Earth's interior (by now including radioactive heating, *fission*) no longer all escaped into space. Not only did it melt the ice but the Sun could once again warm the exposed oceans evaporating water to intensify the 'greenhouse.' It turned Earth into a 'hothouse' of +50°C. Thus the cycle started over again and kept repeating until the wandering land-masses congregated forming super-continents such as Rodinia and Pangaea,[51] thus breaking the cycle.

All during this four-billion year travail Life emerged and evolved. Life was not only greatly affected by the changes in Earth's environment but Life also began to affect the environment, for example by producing free oxygen. Other examples will be described in the following chapters.

Restless Earth

Before getting into the following chapters on Life's origin and evolution, we need a broad understanding of what Earth was doing during that time: in the sea, on the land and in the air. First the sea.

Earth has two main sources of energy: by far the greater is the Sun which is gradually increasing its output while Earth's interior is gradually decreasing its.[52] An important outlet of interior energy is at mid-ocean ridges where molten basalt rises and solidifies, venting heat and matter into the water, as the ocean plates are nudged, jostled and pulled apart by the ever churning mantle underneath. Another important outlet is at the other end of the moving ocean plates at seafloor trenches where, having cooled and contracted, the ocean plates plunge (*subduct*) under the lighter continental plates to be recycled. There the friction and interior energy re-melt the basalt along with the sediments and water that are conveyed under. The subducting ocean plates shift and raise the continental plates near the margins causing earthquakes as along the San Andreas Fault and pushing up mountains inland like the Andes. Some of the melted mix of basalt and sediment can rise through the continental crust to the surface as volcanoes like Mount St. Helens.[53] The smoke, ash and lava from the volcanoes settle back to the surface on the lands and waters as sediment to be compressed over ages into layers of sedimentary rock as revealed in the Grand Canyon. Underneath ocean plates and continents are hot plumes rising in the mantle causing hot spots like the Hawaiian Islands and Yellowstone.[54] These can melt continental crust producing *batholiths* that cool into granite to be broken up, ground up and carried away or weathered away over the ages. Nevertheless continental crusts far outlast the constantly recycling ocean plates.[55]

The moving ocean plates also push the continental plates around or pry them apart. There seem to be 600 million year cycles of forming supercontinents[56] like Pangaea, then breaking them apart into new continents and large islands. Pushing them together can crumple and uplift the land, and raise mountains like the Himalayas.[57] Prying them apart can create oceans like the Atlantic. Even moving 'small' plates can have tremendous consequence like the Cocos plate moving the large Pacific island that became Central America closing the Isthmus of Panama, as will be discussed in Chapters Seven and Eight.

The Sun's energy makes Earth's weather. As discussed above, the Sun evaporates ocean water that rains down on the land, washing away surface crust and depositing it elsewhere. Or if the Sun's energy can't overcome Earth's heat loss,[58] the rain turns to snow and ice, sealing off the land and water. The Sun drives the ocean and air currents carrying heat and particulates around the Earth. Movement of landmass can change water and air currents creating deserts,[59] or rain forests, or glaciers at higher latitudes and elevations. Earth's diameter is usually measured from its surface but the atmospheric gases that hug the surface go out at least fifteen more miles to the ozone layer which screens the surface from ultraviolet-rays ever since oxygen invaded the atmosphere. Beyond, thin wisps of Earth's atmosphere extend hundreds of miles into space dragging on satellites. In addition 2,500 and 15,000 miles above the equator, trapped by the Earth's magnetic field, the Van Allen radiation belts deflect the solar winds and cosmic rays thus preserving that ozone layer.[60]

Still, debris from space penetrates this perimeter. As mentioned above, large amounts of dust shower Earth daily. Some of the larger dust particles ignite as they enter the atmosphere in meteor showers (shooting stars). Occasionally an asteroid, or its fragments, makes its way to Earth's vicinity and is captured by Earth's gravity.[61] Sixty-five-million years ago a seven- to ten-mile wide asteroid slammed into (what is now) Mexico's Yucatán Peninsula around Chicxulub. As the diverging shock waves re-converged on the other side of the globe perhaps they shook-loose the crust and magma erupting volcanoes in India's Deccan Trap. The combined outpouring of smoke and lava is believed to have caused the mass extinction of three-quarters of the species worldwide including the dinosaurs. Then thirty-five million years ago another three-mile wide asteroid is believed to have slammed into (what is now) Chesapeake Bay with not quite as devastating results. Smaller asteroids now and again show up such as at Manicougan Québec, at Sudbury Ontario, at Mason Iowa and at Barringer Crater in Arizona.[62] In 1908 at Tunguska Siberia a comet was thought to be the culprit.[63] Recently in the news was the American Museum of Natural History's 15½ ton Willamette Meteorite that fell to Earth some ten thousand years ago. The Clackamas tribe, with others, attempted to repatriate the meteorite as a Native American religious artifact (more on this later).[64]

Our Earth was first formed some $4\frac{1}{2}$ billion years ago and, at best, will last about that much longer before our Sun explodes. (It could be only two billion years until the Sun becomes a red giant possibly enveloping Earth.[65]) So say we're about half way through Earth's life. If we liken Earth's life to a 24 hour day, we're at noon. Our species, *Homo sapiens*, evolved on Earth putatively 200,000 years ago which would be less than two seconds before noon of Earth's 'day.' How then do we put our significance in perspective? We're certainly not the final culmination of Earth's long struggle to evolve Life as once thought. Rather we have 'inherited' the fruits of that long struggle with Earth's 'mid-day' yet to unfold. What are we going to do with our inheritance? Will we squander it or make good use of our species' 'day in the Sun'? It's too early in this book to try to answer that question but we should keep it in mind as next we trace the evolution of Life on Earth.

". . . from so simple a beginning . . ."

"... from so simple a beginning endless forms most beautiful and more wonderful have been, and are being, evolved." When Darwin penned those words in 1859 at the close of his *Origin of Species* he surely wasn't envisioning so far back as the Big Bang—that theory came a hundred years after Darwin—but he could have been. From such a simple beginning as the Big Bang it's astonishing how much diversity and complexity has emerged just in the chemical elements and compounds, and in the multiplicity of forms they can take. Because it's so common and routine we've come to expect it. But if we step back and take a fresh look we begin to marvel. Think of it—depending on how many identical protons and neutrons combine to form an atom, completely different properties can emerge. Oh sure, the Periodic Table arrays the atomic elements in families with similar properties, but that doesn't diminish the marvel at how the elements' differences emerge.

And that's only the start of the synergy—wholes *are* greater than the sum of their parts. Combining various atoms produces molecules with ever increasing complexity and unique properties which can change radically with changes in their energy level. Take for example something as simple as water, H_2O: Ten identical protons, ten identical electrons and eight identical neutrons in hydrogen and oxygen molecules spontaneously arrange themselves into a water molecule to do some pretty astonishing things—like two gases becoming a liquid.[66] Depending on how fast the water molecule and its electrons are moving—namely its temperature—it can act as a solid, liquid or gas (and more[67]). Unlike most other solids, instead of sinking in its liquid, ice floats on top of water. This un-usual behavior not only cools the drink in our glass—the ice cubes float in the warm liquid up top where the liquid cools and circulates to the bot-tom—it does the same thing on a lake. The lake's ice covering buffers the water below from winter's cold, delaying the freezing of the water thus sustaining the life below. Come spring it's just the opposite: the lake warms from the top down.[68]

If instead of the oxygen atom combining with hydrogen, it had paired with another oxygen atom becoming an O_2 molecule, its properties would be completely different. Or if instead the oxygen atom had one less proton, electron and neutron it'd be nitrogen, again with far different properties. Such trifling differences have profound results that we can eas-ily fail to appreciate because they're so common. And all these marvelous properties emerged "... from so simple a beginning."

And that was only the beginning.

Now there are those who see 'the hand of God' in all these unlikely coin-cidences and the order that pervades our Universe. This attitude is known as the "... strong anthropic principle, which assumes that everywhere and at any moment in the Universe, the physical laws are set in a way that allows for the emergence of conscious beings such as ourselves." "This is a teleological argument ... if we manage to compute the probability of each chance coincidence, and conclude that their simultaneous appear-ance is unbelievably unlikely, this becomes proof that the Universe has a grand design, oriented towards a definite purpose." This definition by Delsemme attempts to be unbiased even though he's skeptical, but Den-ton is unabashedly anthropocentric: "All the evidence available in the bi-ological sciences supports the core proposition of traditional natural the-ology—*that the cosmos is a specially designed whole with life and mankind as it fundamental goal and purpose, a whole in which all facets of reality, from the size of galaxies to the thermal capacity of water, have their meaning and explanation in this central fact.*" [Denton's italics][69]

Aside from its arrogance,[70] I have a few other concerns about this at-titude. As discussed in the chapter on gods, it strikes me as reaching for the ultimate parent figure to explain nature, which can be counterproductive to finding explanations ourselves. Secondly it strikes me as Pollyannaish, the opposite of paranoia, akin to Voltaire's Dr. Pangloss in *Candide*—"All is for the best in the best of all possible worlds." Thirdly a species only lasts at best a million years or so, probably including ours. If "... mankind [is the cosmos'] fundamental goal and purpose ..." what's going to happen in Earth's remaining four billion years after we go extinct? (as described a few paragraphs above).

To see 'the hand of God' in the order that pervades our Universe fails to recognize an important fact—nature continuously tries many experiments most of which fail, but we don't see most of those failures because only what works survives. 'Order' is what works; what didn't have order didn't work and so isn't around anymore for us to observe. In the 'survival of the fittest' what didn't fit, didn't survive. So we don't see much *disorder* in the Universe because it didn't make it.

Delsemme takes this notion a little further. In response to the argument that our Universe is 'tuned just right' for our emergence, he suggests that maybe there are many universes, *multiverses*, most of which are not 'tuned just right' for the emergence of conscious beings. (Of course we have no way of knowing yet since we can't contact them, science fiction aside.) Our own Universe just got lucky: somehow Life did emerge here.[71]

Chapter Six

Life's Beginnings

As we trudge up the long gentle rise toward the distant Mountain heights, we see lichen clinging to the rocks, tiny flowers pushing up out of cracks, a small critter scamper off toward the jumble of boulders somehow making its living in this unforgiving environment. Somehow Life will find a way. Then we see it, a stunted but glorious tree tenaciously rooted among the rocks, its leafy branches reaching up into the clear morning air. The so ordinary wonder of it leaves us dumbfounded. Why does it grow? What ubiquitous urge compels all its kind to reach ever upward defying gravity?

Before exploring the origins of Life, we need to ask ourselves: What is Life? What is the defining difference between life and non-life? Because we may feel we just know intuitively, we may not bother thinking about it much. A person, animal, plant … is either alive or not; we just know. Oh there may be gray areas where we have to check for vital signs but if there are none we pretty much know they or it is dead. Simple as that—or is it?

First of all, we now recognize that there are different levels of life. In recent years we've come to accept that a person's body may be alive even though they're 'brain-dead'[1] with no hope of recovery—they're no longer a 'person.' Yet most of the billions of cells that constitute a living human body can be kept alive indefinitely until someone 'pulls the plug.' And many of their organs are still alive and viable if promptly transplanted to another person. In addition while a person is fully alive there are bacteria, say in their guts which are not only alive but essential to digest food.[2] Even when their body is dead a 'lower' level of life, microbes take over to decompose their body, yet these are somehow different from the bacteria in their guts. Then there are the viruses which technically aren't alive … and so on. So in discussing life we need to make clear which of the many levels we're referring to.

Then how are we to determine when Life first began? To do that it seems we need a clear definition of what constitutes Life. Yet is that realistic? In the previous chapter the age of Earth was cited as 4.56 billion years.

But that's the age of meteorites that fall to Earth which are the same kinds of planetesimals from which the Earth first accreted. Until a lot of planetesimals had accreted over time into a proto-planet large enough to be called Earth, we can hardly say that Earth began. To count the Earth's age from the age of the free planetesimals in space is like counting the age of a person from the ages of the egg and sperm before the two even united into a *zygote* from which that proto-person grew.[3] There's a lot that has to happen before that proto-person will be able to meet the usual biological definition of Life: separately viable and capable of reproducing. Gosh, a person's well into their second decade before they meet those criteria.[4] Maybe it's only in retrospect when we can see the outcome that we can retrace the Life process back to its beginning—to predict from the outset what'll produce synergy is dicey. Thus, in exploring when Life on Earth emerged I'm not going to be too finicky about a strict definition but instead focus on those events that led to successful Life at its various stages and levels.

Steps Towards Life

Where?

In seeking Life's beginnings, maybe because we're surface dwellers we're likely inclined to think of life emerging somewhere on the surface of Earth or in its shallow waters, a surface chauvinism. *Genesis* spoke of inert clay, Darwin envisioned "... a warm little pond" and most of the research since Miller's groundbreaking experiment[5] has been premised on life originating at Earth's surface. But so far there are few plausible explanations of how that might have happened.[6] The problem is that today even the simplest cell requires developmental instructions like RNA (*RiboNucleic Acid*) far too complex to have evolved undisturbed in the turmoil of Earth's early years. Consequently some have proposed that the instructions came from outer-space arriving in a meteor or comet (*panspermia*[7]). But all that does is transfer the question to a venue that's currently inaccessible to research (perhaps it's a ploy to promote funding for space research). Another alternative has been argued in recent years that I find more plausible, and incidentally is compatible with extra-terrestrial life, namely that life started deep in the crust of terrestrial planets.

Recall from the previous chapter that the terrestrial planets were initially formed from the accretion of chondrites in planetesimals or meteors. The carbonaceous chondrites brought hydrocarbons as well as amino acids.[8] Assuming that the primordial Earth was only partially molten, the hydrocarbons in part survived as the so called 'fossil fuels' (methane, petroleum and hard coal) in the pores of Earth's crust.[9] As the hydrocarbons migrated towards the surface, it's proposed that Life emerged deep in Earth's crust. Evidence of living indigenous microbes is seen in oil wells over four kilometers deep which seems unlikely to have come from the surface.[10] This realm is called 'the deep hot biosphere'.[11] How 'in hell' could life possibly have started down there?

Compared to Earth's surface there are several advantages Earth's crust has as an incubator: Within the depth that might be suitable where currently thermophiles flourish, perhaps down as far as ten kilometers, there's an immense amount of volume under both land and sea.[12] While rising magma would make much of it inhospitable, a vast volume still remained which was sheltered from volcanic debris, storms, harmful rays, asteroids and other nastiness at the surface. The tiny pores/fissures in the crust provide nanoscale niches, compartments or vesicles (micro-'test tubes' or 'petri-dishes') to sequester developing proto-cells thus initially forgoing the need for membranes (the term 'cell' originally derived from 'jail cell'[13]) yet keeping them in contact with the minerals in the crust walls and near the flow of nutrients.

Why? How?

One scenario for the origin of Life might have the primordial hydrocarbons and amino acids, together with water[14] and minerals from the surrounding crust, selectively combining to form more complex molecules perhaps as a defense against the early Earth's heat and/or deep crust's pressure—"the best defense is a good offense." (A half-mile down the pressure of just water is 87 times atmospheric, too high for water to boil.) In effect they would have been overcoming the heat by absorbing it as the energy to bind available molecules into more complex molecules better able to withstand the heat and pressure—a kind of rudimentary metabolism. The crust's crystal patterns on their compartment walls might have functioned as templates[15] to facilitate the assembly of complex molecules, a kind of rudimentary replication.[16]

There must have been many failures before there was any success. Driven by the heat, molecules were continually and randomly rearranged into different combinations (mutations). Occasionally a particular combination provided resistance to the heat and survived, the rest didn't. The ones that survived sometimes were able to repeat the trick and produce duplicates, to reproduce. Stated another way, those which evolved *traits* that improve their *fitness* to the environment were *selected* to survive and reproduce; at least until the environment shifted and they had to evolve even hardier traits.

If all this sounds tenuous and haphazard, it was. Too often in the literature evolution is described from our human perspective as though it had a planned outcome, *teleological*, as though there was a design with a purpose. There wasn't—it just happened, over and over and over ... But every once in a great while something worked. The odds were tremendously against success but because there were so many 'players', occasionally a player would succeed. More than likely, different players succeeded in finding different parts of a solution to Life, different parts of the puzzle which, when pieced together, gave them a solution to rudimentary Life. In other words, those few successful players not only got help from templates but then pooled their talents as described a little further on. And even if bad luck culled those, others emerged to take their place. Life somehow found a way.

Actually Life probably found several ways, else how could 'they' pool their talents if there were only one player? (Sure, one could have emerged, its offspring mutated, and then the successful ones have incestuously pooled their talents.) If the Earth's crust was so congenial to Life's evolution and there were gazillions of players, several compatible viable solutions could well have been found. Or for that matter the same superior solution, even though very complex, might well have been found more than once, maybe many times.[17] Some argue that Life was far too complicated to have evolved more than once. But I'd argue just the opposite—If Life could evolve once, then it could have evolved more than once, perhaps many times. In other words if Life was possible, then it was possible to happen more than once. And if Life wasn't possible, then it wouldn't have happened at all. But whether Life emerged just once or many times, Life did emerge.[18]

Some More Help

There is a phenomenon currently being studied called *collectively autocatalytic systems*[19] which may also have assisted. Autocatalysis describes how at a certain critical level of complexity a system catalyses its own growth through feedback loops, it takes off and takes on a 'life of its own.' Autocatalysis has been observed in specially designed light bulb networks and computer programs as well as in natural systems such as the Belosov-Zhabotinski reaction.[20] Clearly these systems are not alive in the usual sense but nonetheless exhibit behavior we attribute to Life.

Another phenomenon may also have contributed. *Self-organized criticality* is the study[21] of complex systems that gradually build up to a critical point, then abruptly change. The analogy used is a pile of sand, or snow on a mountain slope which unpredictably lets go as an avalanche. Sometimes an avalanche can be triggered, say by gun fire. Similarly a species may grow until it's poised way out of balance, then some minor or major catastrophic event forces evolution; also known as *punctuated equilibrium*. In the present case a colony of complex molecules may have grown in the pores of Earth's crust until perhaps shock waves from an asteroid or earthquake, or radiation from radioactive decay precipitated their mutating to a new level of fitness.

Still another phenomenon is *quantum superposition of states* wherein a *micro*scopic fundamental particle remains suspended in two or more complementary positions—two or more places at once—or any other complementary state, until some *macro*scopic intervention. It may be for example that a small molecule both *does* and *doesn't* combine with a larger molecule until some macroscopic event forces a 'decision'. The small molecule by itself may not confer any evolutionary fitness value to the growth of a larger molecule and so by itself would not be favored for selection even though it's a crucial step in a whole series of steps. What this means for the evolution of ever more complex molecules is that the whole series of steps can be tentatively combined and not combined until the 'proposed' complex molecule is put to a macroscopic test and proves the value of the overall combination. Thus unbelievably improbable complex molecules could emerge.[22]

Life's Emergence

Whatever the impetus for the initial growth, it's obvious from the existence of living indigenous microbes in the deep hot biosphere[23] that somehow it did happen. Within just a few hundred million years after Earth's formation Life emerged. What may have started as a defense response against early Earth's harshness became a conditioned reflex, a 'habit,' an algorithm, a 'way of life'—*rea*ction became *pro*action.

Molecules became ever more complex and better able to cope with their environment or to invade other environments, first by internalizing the templates and elaborating them to catalyze more complex molecules, second by adopting membranes (petroleum bubbles?) so they could venture forth from their fixed compartments to exploit new opportunities, and third by combining their template with the template of a different complex molecule (gene-splicing) in order to gain more flexibility to cope with ever more challenging environments. I'll elaborate on this scenario of steps shortly. Of course at this early stage these steps were not taken 'intentionally', they just happened by chance against overwhelming odds.

The scenario I'm sketching of course may not be quite how it happened or where it happened. Yet even though it's somewhat speculative, it's based on some sound scientific work as cited in the references—it seems to make the most sense, it's intended to show the plausibility of the emergence of life from non-life, somehow, somewhere.[24] (Incidentally if Life could emerge in Earth's crust then perhaps it could also emerge in the crust of similar planets. And since they started with the same ingredients and similar conditions, they might even have found the same solution.) And let's not quibble at what point pre-life qualified as 'Life,'[25] rather let's continue pursuing those steps that may have led from pre-life to Life.

However before we do I'd like to clarify an important issue. Until very recently most scientists in the field have maintained that all life on Earth evolved from one common ancestor.[26] This was not only based on Darwin's theory but supported by both fossil and genetic evidence. The 'tree of life' could be traced back down the many 'twigs' to small 'branches' growing out of ever larger 'branches' until a common 'trunk' was reached representing the common ancestor of all life. Diagrams abound showing such a lineage. But now the 'tree of life' model, at least at the earliest stages, is being replaced by a reticulated model more like some vines I've tried to dig up and chop out—the roots all grow together and the 'branches' tangle and seem to graft onto one another. Life's history is now seen as a common ancestral *community* of primitive cells.[27] Early on there was a lot of gene swapping and cohabitating going on that spawned cellular cocktails and communes (*symbiosis*).[28]

Venturing Forth

Let's complete the scenario I've been describing. A key step was the evolution of a complex macromolecule (aka *protobionts*[29]) that could function as a portable template. Rather than being dependent on its compartment wall's crystal patterns as a template to fit molecules into a useful order and shape, a complex macromolecule had to evolve that could provide the pattern itself. This complex macromolecule not only had to have shapes on its surfaces that could hold various loose molecules in place and link them together, it also had to make copies of itself—a tall order indeed. The candidate complex macromolecule for this role of portable template is known as rRNA, *ribosomal RiboNucleic Acid*.[30] Because rRNA is unstable at higher temperatures (such as found at mid-ocean vents) it must have evolved in strata of Earth that are within a suitable temperature range.[31]

With the evolution of rRNA the complex macromolecules were not only freed from the ridged templates on their 'jail cell' walls and thus were able to elaborate more versatile templates, they were also freed from the 'jail cell' itself to wander through the myriad pores in Earth's crust. But like Adam & Eve leaving the Garden, the rRNA was 'naked,' and it dare not venture forth naked in that world. It needed to evolve a 'bag' or membrane either of petroleum or from *lipid* and *protein* molecules it fabricated.[32] The 'bag' also protected it and the other proteins that the rRNA 'learned' to evolve to suit other needs that arose. It also 'learned' to multiply by 'cloning' itself. And as the rRNA metabolized simple molecules into proteins, its 'bag' started getting too full. The rRNA had to make a copy of itself, divide up the contents of the 'bag' and pinch off the 'bag' into two equal parts with an identical rRNA in each part (unless the rRNA copy was not quite identical, that is, had mutated). It could now truly be called a 'living molecule,' *autopoietic*, able to actively maintain itself. For a while it was an 'RNA world' at least until the prokaryotes came along.[33]

Prokaryotes

Many living macromolecules stayed deep in Earth's crust and continued to evolve there—a very rough estimate puts today's mass of subterranean life perhaps greater than the mass of all life at the surface.[34] But back then some of those living rRNA molecules would have migrated upward exploiting newly-habitable unpopulated realms nearer the surface by evolving en route to thrive at lower pressures and temperatures. Incidentally this scenario solves the riddle mentioned earlier of how complex Life could have emerged from scratch in all the turmoil near Earth's surface: Maybe it didn't, maybe it migrated there, not from outer space but from Earth's depths. In the past few decades heat-loving microbes (*thermophiles*) have been observed in many environments all the way from hot vents at the mid-ocean ridges where sea floor divides over $1\frac{1}{2}$ miles down, on up to surface hot springs such as Yellowstone's. These microbes are in the broad 'kingdom' *prokarya*, simple cells without a nucleus (*pro-*='pre' + *karyon*='kernel' in Greek).

We need to get a little technical. The key distinction between the living rRNA molecules described above and prokaryotes is DNA, *DeoxyriboNucleic Acid*. DNA evolved from RNA. When unfurled most RNA is like one side of a zipper whereas most DNA has both sides (you've undoubtedly seen pictures of the DNA double-helix). The 'backbone' of their 'zippers' differs slightly as their names imply. In addition both have four nucleotide bases that form the 'zipper teeth' but in RNA one 'tooth' is uracil whereas in DNA that 'tooth' is thymine.[35] RNA still provides the template to assemble the molecules of protein into their proper order. But whereas the rRNA did it all by itself, in the prokaryote the RNA assembles (translates) protein in a tiny 'factory' called a *ribosome*. Also whereas rRNA replicated itself, in prokaryotes RNA is made as needed by the DNA partially 'unzipping' at the desired gene and copying (transcribing) the 'teeth' sequence into a length of mRNA (messenger RNA). The rRNA in living molecules gave up its freedom so that more information could be stored with greater security in a longer loop of 'zipped up' DNA. Thus prokaryotes gained both versatility and stability.[36]

In recent years the term 'prokaryotes' has been revised to comprise at least two domains, *archaea*[37] and *bacteria*. (There is some evidence that even older domains went extinct.[38]) This distinction is based on analysis of the variety of rRNA genes in ribosomes of various prokaryotes. But this same analysis reveals much gene swapping (transfer) that went on, and still goes on, among the various prokaryote types.[39] Today, for example, gene swapping gives bacteria the flexibility to adapt rapidly in order to cope with our antibiotics. Back then gene swapping enabled prokaryotes to adapt and colonize every niche on the entire Earth, in its crust and to a much lesser extent in its atmosphere.[40]

Life first emerged on or in Earth nearly four billion years ago[41] perhaps as archaea living on hydrocarbons deep in Earth's crust. Some archaea migrated to the crust's surface and obtained their energy by converting carbon-monoxide and -dioxide into methane which (later assisted by methanogenic bacteria) became a significant constituent of Earth's early atmosphere promoting a 'green-house' which compensated for the still dim Sun.[42] Other archaea that migrated to hot springs 'learned' to live on hydrogen sulfide by the trick of using the Sun's photons to extract the hydrogen and combine it with carbon-dioxide to make glucose.[43] Some bacteria—purple and green—similarly used the Sun.[44] Nearly a half-billon years on some of these bacteria adapted both the purple's and green's processes but instead used some of the Sun's photons to tear hydrogen from a far more abundant source, namely water.[45] Because these blue-green *Cyanobacteria* supplied themselves and the purple bacteria with glucose,[46] both should have thrived except for a problem: Cyanobacteria produced toxic molecular oxygen as a waste product and started polluting both the atmosphere and oceans in what eventually became an 'oxygen holocaust.' The purple bacteria living nearby were flexible enough to adapt to oxygen's toxicity as *proteobacteria* which we'll meet again.[47]

Because we're so dependent on oxygen for breathing we may overlook how nasty it can be. We've learned to deal with oxygen's rapid oxidation in fires and explosions, and its slow oxidation in rusting and rotting. Cyanobacteria's prokaryote neighbors also had to 'learn' to deal with oxygen, if not by dying than by hiding or evolving in a kind of 'arms race.'

But at least they had a long time to adapt because it took over one-half-billion years before oxygen's production outpaced its consumption by the dissolved iron in the oceans and by the methane, ammonia and hydrogen in the atmosphere. By two billion years ago the surplus of these molecules had pretty much been oxidized and oxygen could begin to accumulate at least in the atmosphere.[48] Somewhat before then, maybe as long as three billion years ago,[49] a new domain of life began to emerge which eventually augmented the oxygen build up.

Eukaryotes

Perhaps it was a branch of archaea that first 'learned' the trick of co-opting others to do things it couldn't do for itself—it would go far in this world. It might have gone something like this: The archaea shed its hard shell so it could ingest nearby molecules through its membrane. Then it 'learned' to contour its membrane at first to increase surface area for ingestion, and then so it could engulf molecules as well as bacteria in order to digest them inside its membrane. But some bacteria weren't digested, instead they were co-opted by the archaea to do things it couldn't, such as utilize oxygen. However to protect its DNA from these intruders the archaea further contorted its membrane to enclose its DNA in a nucleus—the 'karyote' in eukaryote. ("Oh what a tangled web we weave, When first we practise to deceive!" [sic] But with practice one gets good at it.) Having 'learned' this trick it continued aggrandizing until the known eukaryotes grew ten to thirty times bigger across than bacteria[50] (even so most are far too small to see with the naked eye). Thus through a strategy called *symbiosis* this chimera became a new domain of cells, a *eukaryote*[51] (*eu-* = 'true' + *karyon* = 'kernel' in Greek) sometimes called *Eukarya*.

Let's be a little more specific about some features we'll need to know later on. From their archaea parents the eukaryotes retained the membrane and perhaps *actin fibers*[52] as 'scaffolding' to support and contort the membrane including forming an envelope to sequester its DNA in a nucleus as mentioned.[53] The eukaryotes captured various bacteria and enslaved them as *organelles* ('little tools') by transferring most of the captives' DNA also into the cell's nucleus. Perhaps the most notable captives were the proteobacteria mentioned above which became *mitochondria* and 'burned' oxygen as the eukaryote's energy 'factories' as well as enabled it to survive the coming oxygen holocaust.[54] Another may have provided a tail (*flagellum* or *undulipodium*) which increased mobility.

A while later one of these eukaryotes captured still another kind of bacterium also mentioned above, the blue-green cyanobacteria. It enslaved them as *chloroplasts* to absorb sunlight in order to metabolize carbon dioxide, and at the same time producing its own oxygen for its mitochondria, dumping the excess oxygen as waste. So together these photosynthesizing bacteria and eukaryotes established the prevalence of oxygen in the Earth's atmosphere and waters. This enabled the dominance of the aerobic lifestyle: the reciprocal partnership of the oxygen producing and oxygen consuming eukaryotes. Today most all eukaryotes are aerobic (an exception is the parasite *Giardia*).[55]

Sex

We need to talk a bit about sex (not just the birds and the bees), the process of exchanging genes, namely DNA segments, and about the process of multiplying. Multiplying for prokaryotes and their captive organelle descendants is a simple matter of 'unzipping' the DNA and making a hopefully identical copy. Then the cell divides everything up and splits into two daughter cells, it's called cloning[56] or cell fission, as described above for rRNA living molecules. Single cell eukaryotes multiply basically the same way, for the most part, but because they have far more genes they must be more orderly and so to multiply they use a process called *mitosis*. Even the multicell eukaryotes employ mitosis to clone cells in order to multiply, except when they initiate a whole new multicelled organism, then they use sex to exchange genes.

Exchanging genes between prokaryotes is done by swapping, transferring copies of DNA between cells[57] which facilitates evolving. However most single-cell eukaryotes, called *protists* or *protoctists* and sometimes *protistans*, relied more on capturing prokaryotes, symbiosis, to acquire different genes as pre-packaged traits in organelles and so evolved more slowly for a couple billion years.[58] But maybe as long as a billion years ago some single-cell eukaryotes began fusing their off-spring together in a kind of mutual symbiosis. They evolved 'sex' whereby their two reproductive cells fused into one cell which ends up having two sets of genes. But this created a problem for the next fusion: if each parent cell had two sets of genes, then the next generation's fused cell would have four, and the following generation would have eight, and so on. To solve this problem they learn to first divide their reproductive cell in a way that each reproductive cell had only one set of genes (*haploid*). When it fused with a reproductive cell of the other sex it would then have just two sets of genes (*diploid*).[59]

Sex became a way of not just exchanging genes between two cells but of first shuffling their whole suite of genes, all their DNA, called *meiosis*.[60] It's as if two different decks of cards were shuffled together then somehow separated again so that the two new decks were a blend, but with each having a complete set of cards from aces to deuces. Similarly meiosis provides the sex cell with a complete set of genes, a 'full deck,' blended from the parents' two sets of genes. Thus the sex cell, called a *gamete*, will have a unique set of genes which produce unique traits. If two gametes (from separate parents) fuse through sex to form a composite cell called a *zygote*, it will have two 'full decks,' two sets of genes just as its parents do, but unique blends.[61] The zygote then multiplies into cloned cells through mitosis developing a unique organism. Those organisms with traits that conferred greater fitness may flourish—until later cells evolve more competitive traits.[62]

This raises another issue. When a cell clones itself does the old 'mother' cell die and the two new 'daughter' cells begin life? If we say the mother cell dies, then in our bodies when we clone new cells for growth, do the old cells die? If so then are our bodies continuously dying? Alternatively since the 'mother' and 'daughter' cells are identical (barring mutation) we could just as well say the 'mother' cell's life continues and that she produces one new daughter cell. This way the 'mother' cell's life continues indefinitely until she or the whole organism dies. So this is the opposite end of the question raised at the beginning of this chapter—When does life start? Now we're asking—When does life end? Clearly we have a new life when a zygote forms from male and female gametes, but the parents don't die, at least not then. Eventually however the parents do die and with them all their cells with their unique set of genes never to be cloned again[63] (or maybe they will the way gene technology is advancing). We'll explore this issue further in the next chapter on multi-celled organisms, primarily animals.

Starting about a half-billion years after Earth formed and for the next three-billion years, two-thirds of Earth's existence to date, only single-cell life existed as archaea, prokaryotes and then eukaryotes. And for maybe as long as two-billion years, even though many eukaryotes joined together into colonies, they existed essentially only as single cells—protists or protoctists. Then seven- or eight-hundred-million years ago some eukaryotes evolved into multicelled organisms,[64] the *Grand Climacteric*, the subject of the next chapter. But before we leave this chapter let's recapitulate where we've come so far.

Hey wait a minute, you say, Wasn't this the time of a 'Snowball Earth' discussed in the previous chapter? How could photosynthesis prevail if the Earth was all iced over blocking out the Sun? Well yes, but no one ever said it was easy; life had its ups and downs, literally. The theory of punctuated equilibrium cited earlier in this chapter might suggest an answer.

Such a catastrophe would wipe out much of the population that had flourished until then. But obviously enough survived—maybe hanging on somehow around volcanoes thrusting up through the ice—to seed a fresh population that was reinvigorated because of the trial.[65] When the ice melted they could rapidly take full advantage of the open field with little competition and an abundance of carbon dioxide, a 'free lunch.' Obviously somehow somewhere the eukaryotes' Sun-driven oxygen producing/consuming partnership survived because they went on to found the multi-celled kingdoms.

Recap

OK, on with the recapitulation. There are a number of key events we can see in the above description of Life's beginnings: The key basic ingredients were supplied in 'stardust' from outer space as Earth first formed or soon after (in geologic terms). As they packed together some of these molecules were impelled to take 'defensive' actions against the harsh conditions of the early Earth, defensive *re*actions that once in a great while led to solutions resembling life-like behavior. Because there were an unimaginable number of these molecules reacting over millions of years, many life-like solutions likely were found, implying that Life, even if only remotely probable, must have emerged many times.[66] But because of the harsh conditions and fierce competition, Life must have been snuffed out many times too. However a few of those life-like solutions prevailed perhaps because they were able to pool their talents, so that what eventually survived was a 'tree of life'. We have examined that tree's tangled 'roots', microscopic single-cell organisms many of which are still with us today out of sight—that is, smaller than our unaided sight can see—and mostly tucked away: Out of sight and out of mind.

In time's broad sweep, the pattern has been for consecutive levels of synergy to evolve wherein at each level 'the whole was greater than the sum of its parts' and the 'wholes' at one level became the 'parts' of the next higher level in nested hierarchies. Thus long before they came to Earth, protons, neutrons and electrons had combined into atoms, and atoms into simple molecules. Eventually some of these molecules further combined in ways that conferred life-like behavior. Then these macromolecules somehow added capabilities whereby they clearly became living cells. And some of these cells co-opted other cells as symbionts which conferred functional advantages and a qualitatively richer life. At each higher level of increased complexity, unexpected synergy emerged with properties not found in the constituents—higher levels of Life emerged.

Most of the research on Life's beginnings addresses the question of 'How'? How did Life get started? This is certainly an important question. Yet just as important is the question 'Why'? What motivated[67] or impelled these molecules to go against entropy and take on behaviors we call 'Life'? Not only what got them started but continued to impel them? What gives them the 'spark of life'? A century ago the doctrine of 'vitalism' was advocated—it proposed that there is some 'vital impetus' in nature, an *élan vital*,[68] infused by God from the Beginning which throughout evolution passed from parents to offspring. Vitalism has now pretty much been rejected, though the concept of the 'soul' still has its adherents.

Rather, many scientists now think the behavior we call 'Life' started randomly. Why'd it start? I suspect the reason why it started was that complex molecules simply stumbled on ways of coping with extreme conditions to avoid being torn apart by them. They stumbled on ways of converting the threat into growth, say by converting the high temperature activity of heat and pressure, or the 'sting' of the Sun's photons,[69] or the ferocity of acids and oxygen. They survived and grew by co-opting the threat and turning it to their advantage. A complex molecule that 'eats' lesser molecules as a reaction to hostile conditions, eats its way towards the threat—it 'grows'. A present day example is the way plants' leaves absorb the energy of the Sun's photons by 'eating' carbon dioxide, that is, assimilating the Sun's energy by using it to convert the carbon (with water) into plant growth toward the Sun.[70] Back then that's what worked and got replicated, and continues today.

Back in Hadean times some four billion years ago the molecules that 'learned' to thrive on adversity were the *extremeophiles*. Yes, the Hadean Earth was indeed a harsh chaotic environment. But if there were enough 'oases' where the heat from the meteors' impacts didn't completely fry all the carbonaceous chondrites, they would have had the chance to find Life in niches at the edge of that chaos by converting the harsh conditions into growth, into Life.

I suspect that what began as a defense became a conditioned reflex and then a way-of-life. What started as random *re*actions evolved into aggressive programmed *pro*actions once successful behavior patterns were learned. They not only had to learn the behavior but had to learn to sense the threat or opportunity in order to trigger that behavior. Rephrasing this in synergistic terms, the chaos threw molecules together in all sorts of combinations. Every once in a great while, some molecules would stumble onto a combination that produced unique properties that were more effective in coping with the chaos, what could be called synergy. A few of these combinations may have incorporated ways of replicating themselves and, *voilà*, Life emerged. They evolved what I hesitantly call an 'Urge to Life'—a Life Urge—but that's what it acts like.[71]

This key point bears repeating. It's not vitalism with its *élan vital* infused by God, but a 'neo-vitalism' wherein a Life Urge emerges spontaneously perhaps as a reaction for coping with harsh conditions which evolved into a programmed proaction. Instead of *re*gressing under harsh conditions they *ag*gressed, they were *urged* forward by aggressive, assertive learned behavior, a rudimentary *Urge* to Life.

The notion I'm exploring throughout this book is that this 'Urge to Life' is somehow felt or 'sensed' in even the simplest living cells and percolates on up through each higher level of Life. This Life Urge is so intrinsic to all living things, the *sine qua non*, that we may take it for granted and overlook its presence. Eventually on up at the human level it creeps into consciousness but it's so intrinsic we may not realize it and appreciate it for what it is. Instead, like most other phenomena we're exploring, I believe it's been misinterpreted. This 'Urge to Life' has been sensed and experienced as marvelous, mystical, numinous emotions—which some call 'faith'—and thus misconstrued as 'God.' My notion is that this 'Urge to Life', peeking or budding or bubbling or bursting into consciousness, is the prototheistic root of the belief in God. And like other misinterpretations it needs to be turned around, inverted. I believe it needs to be understood as emerging from our deepest, most fundamental emotion—the Life Urge, to live!—and then owned as the expression of our primal Self. Certainly it shouldn't be projected out of ourselves onto an illusion of 'God' out there.[72] It's too precious to be thrown away or even given away! It's our one and only Life!

In the next chapter I'll elaborate and trace how this notion of an 'Urge to Life' continued its emergence on up through the evolution of multicelled organisms, especially animals. In tracing the evolution of ever more complex Life's emergence, we're looking for a central trend in order to ascertain Life's trajectory in later chapters. To decide whether you agree or have a different interpretation, I'd suggest you diligently scrutinize my sources and thought process as we go forward. Be picky!

Chapter Seven

Animal Evolution

Resolutely trudging ever onward and upward (and often downward in order to go farther upward) we're now shrouded in the cloud that blankets the Mountain heights. Any step could bring disaster as we groped our way along the narrow path with the abyss gaping below and the threat of rocks tumbling down from above out of the mist. But an agile-winged raven frolics on the updrafts among the crags saying "grock," whatever that means.

In this chapter we need to cover a great deal of ground to trace the progress from multicelled life's beginnings to human evolution. So we'll only barely touch on plants and fungi, and concentrate on animals. Even so we'll look at only a few animals in order to understand how animal cells communicate and develop into organs and organisms, and at how those organisms evolved in their environments. One of the main concepts we want to glean from all this is an inkling of how the Urge to Life might percolate on up in us humans.

But first a *caveat*. I confess I found it difficult to get a handle on this chapter because initially I had scant knowledge of genetics. This fast changing field is complex[1] and I only wanted to grasp its concepts. So unless you're already familiar with the subject or willing to struggle to learn it (including delving into some of the references), you might just skim this chapter only concentrating on the recap at the end.

We have explored how Life perhaps emerged and evolved into three domains or kingdoms of single-celled organisms: archaea, bacteria and eukaryotes. Although some single-celled eukaryotes aggregated in cooperative linkages such as algae, they did not perfect the trick of specializing cells and coordinating them as *multicelled* organisms, the *Grand Climacteric*, until less than a billion years ago.[2] For their first two billion years eukaryotes had existed essentially as unicellular organisms at most linked together in *meta*cellular chains or networks (some sponges?). But once they learned the multicell trick, they began the long perilous evolution to ever more complex and varied forms, during the most recent fifth of Earth's existence so far.

The multicell trick is to turn various cells into specialists by making them somehow different, to *differentiate* cells, and then dedicate them to specific coordinated functions. Most eukaryote cells have a full set of genes but in a differentiated cell only certain of those genes are active, that is, are *expressed* to make only those proteins it needs to perform its dedicated function. For example muscle cells contain *actin* and *myosin* proteins so that the myosin can grab the actin filament and pull on it to contract the muscle.

The eukaryotes diverged as multicellular arguably into three new kingdoms: animals, plants and fungi, for a total of five kingdoms[3] (or six if you count archaea, or eight if plants comprise three kingdoms—these are not just cataloging issues[4]). The animal kingdom diverged initially in the seas and had evolved thirty-some basic body forms, *phyla*, by the time of the Cambrian 'explosion' some 550 million years ago.[5] However while the animals were the first to diverge they didn't colonize land until perhaps 425 million years ago,[6] well after plants and fungi had gone ashore. There wasn't much point in animals' going ashore until there were some plants or fungi there to eat. When they finally did, initially there was less on shore that could eat them.

Plants first came ashore some 470 million years ago (probably the liverworts[7] evolving from ocean algae) and eventually diverged into fifteen phyla with perhaps a million species. The flowering plants were the most recent phylum to evolve some 130 million years ago. Virtually all plants[8] photosynthesize using the Sun's photons indirectly to separate hydrogen from water which they then combine with carbon dioxide into organic compounds used for their growth.[9] This provides an additional source of carbohydrates and free oxygen essential to all animal life as well as to fungi.[10] (Animals which existed before plants, ate single-celled organisms or each other.)

Fungi evolved after animals but probably before most plants and may have enabled some plants' adaptation to land similar to the way they aid plants now by providing nourishment to the roots. And while we may think of fungi as related to plants in fact they are closer to animals not only in using oxygen but in having cell walls of the same material *chitin* as insects' exoskeletons. But fungi differ enough from both to have their own kingdom consisting of three phyla and perhaps one-and-a-half million species.[11]

Of the thirty-some animal phyla originating in the seas, only four have members which then evolved to live exclusively on land: some 'insects' (including spiders and centipedes: arthropods), a few snails, some worms and some chordates including us vertebrates (even so some later returned to the sea, such as whales[12]). The small percentage of animals that successfully immigrated from water is understandable given the difficulties of adapting to land: The loss of buoyancy required strengthening limbs, and oxygen-rich air greatly altered breathing and posed the risk of desiccation under an unscreened Sun.[13] Rather than an abrupt transition from sea to land, evidence suggests that four legged salamander-like animals living in marginal swamps, in order to escape water predators, crawled onto shaded patches of land more and more, until they eventually evolved to live there.[14]

Animals are the most diverse in form of all organisms by virtue of having the greatest variety of specialized cells. Consequently animals have the most complex junctions between cells to regulate the flow of materials, energy and communications. We will first survey how cells produce the desired proteins to specialize their functions and how they communicate to coordinate those functions. Then we'll look at some of the ways evolution works to produce the various forms of animals.

But throughout our survey it's well to keep in mind that all animals, for that matter all living things, are made up of three basic ingredients: atoms, energy and information. All through an animal's life atoms are constantly being replaced so that from one year to the next in a sense it's a different animal. Energy too flows through the animal as does information. What is essentially constant throughout that animal's life is the basic organization of the information, energy and atoms.[15]

Animal Cells

Recall that a eukaryote cell stores the basic instructions for making protein and other components in the double strands of DNA in its nucleus. To make say a protein, the section of DNA that encodes that protein, its *gene*, is first copied, *transcribed*, onto a strip of mRNA (messenger RNA). The mRNA is then sent out of the nucleus into the main body of the cell, the *cytoplasm*, to a tiny 'factory', a *ribosome*. In the ribosome the mRNA in turn matches three of its 'teeth' or nucleotide bases at a time, a *codon*, to three 'teeth', an *anticodon*, of a tRNA (transfer RNA). Each tRNA fits just one of twenty-some amino acids.[16] Each chosen tRNA has fetched its amino acid from the cytoplasm 'soup' to be assembled in the sequence prescribed by that protein's gene back in the DNA. The long sequence of amino acids then somehow folds up into that protein's unique shape.[17] Thus the information in DNA is transformed, *translated*, from a linear code to a three-dimensional shape, from the *genotype* or *genome* to the *phenotype* or *soma*.

However this simplified description doesn't capture the marvel of the process or the intricacy of the results. Unless you have your own copies, a perusal at your local library of a few copies of the weekly professional journals *Science* or *Nature* will picture protein shapes of unbelievable complexity that are produced wholesale by the myriad of cells that make up even the simplest of animal organisms. And there are trillions of cells that make up our human body. It's easy to be overwhelmed by the complexity.[18] But over the past couple hundred years science has been teasing out some of the few basic rules[19] that nature has used over the past four billion years to create this complexity.

There are many distinct proteins, some hundred thousand in us humans.[20] The very short ones are sometimes called *peptides*. Those proteins that can function as catalysts are called *enzymes*. A protein's shape determines its function, "form follows function," that is, the three-dimensional shape of the protein enables it to mesh with another protein or smaller molecule to perform the desired function. For instance in the muscle example mentioned above the myosin's shape enables it to grasp the actin's complementary shape and pull on the actin filament. Some proteins (*allosteric*) can be flipped to an alternate shape by inserting a specific molecule thus altering their function or, in the case of myosin, making them do work.

A wide variety of proteins are embedded in a cell's wall, its *membrane*. In most cells, as with myosin or actin, the proteins attached to the inside of the membrane define the cell's shape and thus its dedicated function.[21] These can attach to other proteins in the membrane which bond cells together. Still other proteins protruding through the membrane control the flow of materials in and out of the cell. These not only include nourishments, wastes and other cell products, but signal particles such as calcium or hormones. Then there is another group of proteins that resides in the cell's nucleus which control production of that cell's proteins and other products described above. These are the regulatory proteins of that cell's active genes.

It seems that the development of an organism, in very broad terms, proceeds something like this: There are undifferentiated *stem*[22] cells initially in the embryo organism (and later in some of its various organs such as bone marrow), that is, cells which are not different from one another. These undifferentiated cells receive signals to repeatedly divide into copies of themselves, *clones*,[23] and then differentiate into a specific type of cell. Apparently the signals first instruct each developing cell's DNA to produce the regulatory proteins only for those genes which are to be expressed and thus can be activated.[24] (All the other genes in the differentiated cell thereafter remain silent normally unable to be activated.[25]) Next the regulatory proteins receive signals to produce the proteins and other products needed to perform that cell's dedicated functions as described already. These differentiated cells aggregate in their respective organs' locations in the developing organism: muscle, bone, skin, heart, blood and so on, and begin to function passing materials among themselves including signal particles.

The signal particles take many forms including molecules such as hormones and ions such as calcium. Some signals pass in or out of a cell through controlled channels in its membrane. Others dock at complementary receptors on the outer membrane where the signal particles' shapes trigger relays through the membrane into the cell. The mechanisms used to accomplish all this unambiguously can get quite complex.[26] The signal particles travel between remote cells in the interstitial fluid or the blood stream. But for fast transmission over relatively long distances higher animals evolved nerve cells, *neurons*, whose *axons* can be several feet long and carry signals electrically. Even so, neurons usually employ signal particles, called *neurotransmitters*, at their multiple terminals called *synapses*.[27]

I find it helpful to think of four general levels in an organism. First the structural: each cell body with all its components as well as aggregates of these cells that form the tissues, the soma, plus their nutrients. Second the regulatory: all the signal particles that direct what a cell will become, when it will and where—that is, its differentiation and sometimes its death, *apoptosis*. Third the operational: the other signal particles and nerves that communicate between the organs to control their operation. And fourth might be extensions in the world outside the organism: the signals such as sounds and pheromones used to communicate, and 'tools' such as birds' nests and bees' hives, that is, behavior and the extended phenotype (on this last, a little more later in this chapter and a lot more in Chapter Eleven on Tools).[28]

Evolution's Ways[29]

Much of the writing about evolution uses terms like 'design' that imply evolution is deliberate, either that there's a master designer, namely God, or that a lineage of animals deliberately changed to adapt to their changed environment. For example the latter implies that certain mammals grew more hair to cope with a colder climate. Granted using 'design' can be a shorthand way of describing what happens from our human point of view accustomed as we are to engineering, but it's misleading. So I've endeavored to avoid such language at the risk of clumsier descriptions (it's like trying to avoid saying 'sunrise').

Rather the way evolution is believed to work is by a two step itera-tive process of variation and selection.[30] First, in a population of animals different individuals might have variations in various traits, say some have more hair (or fur) and some less. If the climate where they live gets colder more hair should be an advantage and less hair a disadvantage (if they lived in a warming climate the reverse might be so). The climate would favor those individuals with more hair so that they are better able to survive. Those with less hair might die out. Thus that climate selects for the trait of more hair, the second step in the evolutionary process. If they pass on to some of their offspring the trait of more hair they too would be selected to survive and reproduce. And so with each generation that mam-mal's lineage might evolve to have more and more hair until they reach the optimal coat for that climate.[31] (This process is referred to as *adaptation* but it's misleading to infer that the animals deliberately 'adapt' as we might.[32])

Variations come about through sex[33] and mutations. Recall that in most animals' fertile sex act each parent contributes one complete set of genes. Each parent has two full sets of genes (diploid) which they shuffle and divide into one full set, a full 'deck', (haploid) for each of their sex cells, called *gametes* (or sometimes called *germ* cells). Note that each ga-mete's set of genes is a mixture or crossing over of that parent's two sets of genes, called *recombination*.[34] Through sex the parents fuse their gametes into one cell initially called a *zygote* which now has two unique full sets of genes that will be duplicated via cloning in every cell in that new individ-ual's body.[35]

But even though two particular genes in each set code for the same general trait, not all genes are created equal. The variations of a gene are called *alleles*. (Examples of alleles in humans are the genes for eye color and for blood type.) One of that gene's two alleles may be *dominant* and thus be expressed more than the other *recessive* allele.[36] Within a popula-tion's gene pool a particular gene may have many alleles with varying de-grees of dominance but each zygote only gets two of them from the shuf-fle of its parents' sets—the luck of the draw. So even though some of the alleles may be recessive they can still get expressed if the zygote 'drew' two recessive alleles. This is more likely to happen in a small inbreeding population. Thus small isolated populations are more likely to evolve unique traits. But unique traits only evolve from unique alleles which came about through mutations.

Mutations in genes can arise from mistakes in transcribing the DNA, from reverse transcription or from assaults on the DNA.[37] Most mutations are either harmless or harmful, only a few are beneficial. As an analogy con-sider the effect of a 'mutation' in mi typing this draft. The spell-check should have caught it. In this case it's a harmless mistake but other mistakes could harm the sentence's meaning; it's highly unlikely that a mistake would improve its meaning. Similarly the DNA's 'spell-check' transcription machinery is very thorough but it's not perfect.[38] The vanishingly few mistakes that do get transcribed probably are harmless. Even if they are harmful they only get passed on to the offspring if the mutation is in the sex cell where even then they may make the offspring unviable and so die out. However occasionally the mutation may prove useful, though maybe not immediately. The mutated gene may get passed along through generations and multiplied as a new recessive allele until some environmental change gives it a competitive advantage, and so it gets chosen, selected to flourish.

Reverse transcription is more controversial. During the past century it has been a dogma of genetics that information only flows one way, from DNA to RNA and to protein, as described above. (The dogma was to some extent a reaction against Lamarck's hypothesis of the previous century.[39]) But there are a couple problems with this dogma. If Life arose in an RNA world, how did the information later evolve into DNA? Sometime, somehow it must have flowed back 'up stream.' Secondly, in recent decades it's been discovered that viruses can invade the nuclei of cells and implant their RNA or DNA into those cells' DNA. If viruses can do it, there may be other ways.[40] One of the other ways discovered in the past half century is 'jumping genes' which not only change position in the genome but scatter multiple copies of themselves thus increasing their odds of reproduction.[41] Still another proposed way is adaptive mutations via quantum evolution.[42] Once again such mutations could only be passed on to offspring if the mutation were in the sex cell.

A third cause of evolutionary mutations is chemical or radiation assaults, *mutagens*, on the DNA of sex cells. Again such mutations are passed on only if they are benign or beneficial, otherwise they die out with the host. Today we're familiar with the dangers of hazardous chemicals in air and water pollution, in food additives, toiletries, medicines, and on and on. Well, the ancient volcano and meteor debris not only killed off many species but also polluted the air, water and plants so those animal that survived ingested chemicals thrown up in the debris. Some might work their way past the survivors' defense systems perhaps into their sex cells' DNA causing mutations a few of which might prove beneficial in the post catastrophe world.

Today we're also familiar with the carcinogenic hazards of ultraviolet radiation from direct sunlight. The ozone layer discussed in Chapter Five screens out most of the ultraviolet radiation.[43] Even more pernicious for our DNA is the higher energy X-rays and cosmic radiation screened by the Van Allen belts which are generated by the Earth's magnetic field. But as mentioned in note 60 to Chapter Five, the Earth's magnetic field reverses periodically. If the magnetic field collapses each time it flips, do the Van Allen belts collapse too allowing cosmic and X-rays to penetrate and inundate Earth which also break down the ozone shield thereby allowing UV rays to bombard Earth? Thus during such magnetic flips radiation may have induced genetic mutations causing an increase of variations in the gene pool from which evolution could select.[44]

Evolution is resourceful; minor mutations, tinkering, can bring about major changes. For example the same basic *hox* gene[45] that regulates the development of body segments in fruit flies also regulates the development sequence of vertebrates. Moreover variation in the regulation of development timing, called *heterochrony*,[46] can use the same components to evolve major differences. Take for instance forelimbs: the human arm, the dog front leg, the bird wing and the dolphin flipper all use most of the same basic bones but by varying their growth rates achieve dramatically different *homologous* structures.[47] "Timing is everything," not just for comedians but in evolution too (then maybe evolution is a comedian judging from some of the results it cobbles together). These variations on a theme enabled paleontologists to reconstruct evolutionary history before DNA tools became available.

Mutations are continuously occurring in a species' cells, sometimes more frequently than at other times, but they're regularly occurring. Whether they affect the evolution of that species' lineage though depends first on the remote chance that the mutation is in a sex cell that gets reproduced and second on what's happening in its environment. If the mutation conveys no advantage it may die out sooner or later. But if the environment is changing too then that mutation may prove beneficial, as in the above example of hair versus climate, and so that mutation gets selected. However this may be a little misleading—it's not just the mutated gene that's selected but the whole organism—unless that organism survives the gene won't either.[48] Hence the adage: The organism proposes and the environment disposes.

Death is constantly occurring too, so a youngster with a minor advantage due to some mutation might not initially be able to compete against an established adult, say for mates, but eventually that adult will get old and die.[49] Then the mutation's advantage can get passed on. Even more pervasive is when death on the massive scale of extinction clears the field and frees up resources for the survivors. This happened when the dinosaurs were wiped out putatively by the huge meteor that hit Mexico sixty-five million years ago as mentioned in Chapter Five. What was a catastrophe for the dinosaurs though was the mammals' great good fortune by removing competition allowing the mammals to flourish[50] (perhaps with the help of a "methane burp" ten million years later[51]). Of course the dinosaurs had benefited similarly from a previous mass extinction at the end of the Permian some 250 million years ago when half of shallow-water marine and four-limbed animal families, as well as most insects and plants, were suddenly eliminated.[52] Fifty million years later the dinosaurs got lucky again when they somehow averted the catastrophe that decimated most of their competitors.[53]

After all, other individuals are part of the environment too. This is especially operative between predator and prey: As some members of the prey evolve traits to avoid getting eaten by the predator in order to pass on those prey traits, some predators must also evolve more effective traits in order to catch and eat prey, and pass on their predator traits—a kind of arms race called *coevolution*. But such escalation doesn't work if the predators' arrival is sudden not allowing the prey enough time to evolve adaptations. An example also from Chapter Five is when some three million years ago the Cocos tectonic plate moved east out of the Pacific carrying a large island and pushed up against the Caribbean plate. It closed the gap between North and South America forming the Isthmus of Panama.[54] This provided a land bridge for placental predators to invade the South with a devastating impact on the marsupial predators there.[55] (Closing the gap also may have brought on the Ice Age as will be discussed in the next chapter.)

In addition to *natural selection* such as by climate, habitat or competitors, there's *sexual selection* by mating pairs. For instance a female bird might be attracted to a male by his fancy feathers, his song or his turf, and so selects him to mate with. And thus they pass on those traits: his feathers, song or resourcefulness along with her attraction to them. If those traits are also selected for by nature (or nature at least tolerates them) they may come to characterize their lineage and perhaps segregate their lineage into a distinct species. The trait that evolves to be sexually selected may have no direct relation to natural selection, in fact may be a detriment, the 'handicap principle'. The classic example is the peacock's tail feathers: they not only waste energy to grow and drag around but can be an impediment in eluding a predator. But they're a sexual display that signals he is so hardy he can waste energy on them. The peahen's eye has evolved to detect the feathers' iridescent colors as an indicator of good genes and selects him to mate with.[56] (We'll look at hominid female preference in the next chapter.)

Speciation

So when do the variations among individuals of a species constitute different species? The prime criterion is when such bisexual individuals can no longer breed offspring that can successfully breed second generation offspring. For example a horse and donkey (ass) can mate and produce a mule, a usually sterile hybrid. So the horse and donkey are separate species but the mule is not, it's only a hybrid. When populations of a species are separated geographically or otherwise for a long enough period that their mutating genomes drift far enough apart so that they can no longer successfully breed, they become separate species. Perhaps some of their genes' alleles mutate enough to become unique and separate genes.[57]

However there's a second criterion—the species' own sexual preference—they can successfully mate with a close species but they don't, usually. The much celebrated finches of the Galápagos on isolated islands have evolved a variety of specialized beaks to exploit different foods. For example the several species of ground finches have evolved specialized beaks each suited to different size seeds. While the differences between these species may appear miniscule to us, they know and mate almost exclusively within their own species. However the seeds' abundance or scarcity swings as that island's climate alternates over the years from wet to dry and back again. Thus the populations of each species will rise or fall with the climate. In lean years the few individuals of different species who do interbreed can produce hybrids that thrive. If that lean climate persists long enough those hybrids might become their own new species.[58]

Abrupt changes in the environment can induce rapid (in geologic terms) changes in species, again called *punctuated equilibrium*.[59] Typically a small population of the species that had been isolated and evolved will become the founder species when an abrupt change decimates the old static population. Then the founder species flourishes unchanged until the next environmental change decimates them; species' equilibrium is 'punctuated' by abrupt environmental changes.

The evolution of species over eons is sometimes characterized as a ladder but in many ways it's more like a bush. One of the classic examples of such evolution is the horse of course.[60] The horses we know today arose in North America some eighteen million years ago from a small browsing multi-toed ancestor, the *parahippus*. Over the next seven million years they branched into some thirty species (*clades*[61]) of grazers. Like a bush, out of the base grew 'limbs,' then 'branches,' then 'twigs' and so forth with variations in body size, teeth and toes some of which evolved into hooves.

Then all of these branches died out in North America except for one, *Equus*, that somehow migrated to Eurasia and Africa (back across the Bering land bridge?) to evolve into what we know today as the horse, donkey and zebra. So to characterize the evolution of the horse as a 'ladder' of ascending successive species is to ignore all the other 'twigs' of the 'bush' that got 'pruned,' whether through "bad genes or bad luck" I don't know. (A similar ladder has been mis-portrayed for human's evolution as we'll explore in the next chapter.) Rather, most animals evolved ever branching clades and though many went extinct, many of their varied descendants are still with us today.

To reconstruct the 'bushes,' until recently paleontologists relied on fossils and the geology where they were found. For example dating the age of the strata where the fossil was buried gives a clue to its geologic age—fossils found below it are older. And fossils of other species found with it that are known from other locations imply its ecology, and so forth. But recently genetic tools have added a whole new dimension. By sampling the fossil's DNA and comparing it with the DNA of suspected relatives, its pedigree can be inferred. An analogy is Xerox copies: If you have several copies of the same page but some have more smudges and specks than others, you can surmise that the dirtier ones are copies of the cleaner ones and by careful inspection can probably determine their sequence. Similarly more mutations in the DNA imply more recent species. And common genes in different species imply common ancestors. New genetic tools are enabling paleontologists to refine the 'trees' constructed from the fossil records. For instance by comparing gene sequences researchers recently surmised that the hippo is the closest living relative to the whale.[62]

Understandably genome sequencing projects to identify genes, their alleles and functions are currently all the rage, and rightly so. Deciphering genetic codes is solving old mysteries and promising a newfound understanding of nature, a veritable Rosetta stone. It's reminiscent of the early 1800s after Linnaeus' nomenclature scheme launched naturalists, including Darwin, on voyages throughout the world to identify and classify species (*systematics*). Genetics is based on the premise that genes and their environment determine organisms and their operation. But is that all? Some argue that genes, organisms and the environment are in a reciprocal relationship in which all three are both cause and effect.[63] Admittedly science can only do so much and right now genetics is most promising (and potentially profitable garnering pharmaceuticals' funding).[64] Sidelined are other proposals that address issues genetics ignores. An example is the far-out 'morphic resonance' concept[65] wherein, as I understand it, presumably each organism emits and receives 'fields' from their kind which not only influence their development but enable communication between them. Trouble is there's no known medium for such 'fields,' but "... absence of evidence is not evidence of absence." We'll explore this further in Chapter Nine on consciousness.

There are several schemes for conceptual hierarchies of animals, systematics is just one.[66] The food chain is another basically tracing how energy from the Sun is converted by plants into carbohydrates and then by animals into protein. This food chain scheme of course places us humans at the top (provided we ignore that when we die it's the microbes' turn). Still other schemes trace the increase of information, complexity or synergy.[67] But it's not just a question of more information or greater complexity but the emergence of higher levels of synergy. A phone book has lots of information and a junk pile has lots of complexity. But information and complexity must add up to more than the sum of their parts to cross a threshold that emerges at a higher level of synergy (or synergism). Of course one of the problems in using synergy as the criterion is how to detect and measure it; we humans have an innate sense for synergy, often called 'elegance', but science requires more than just intuition (more on this in Chapter Nine).

Animal Senses

It seems that any natural phenomenon that can be used for sensing has been adapted by some animal somewhere. The term *Umwelt* is sometimes used to describe an animal's world from its perspective, its niche excluding extraneous phenomena it hasn't evolved senses for, like human's blindness to ultraviolet light.[68] Let's briefly survey some phenomena and how they're utilized.

We've discussed ions and molecules including hormones which pass information between cells within an organism. Molecules are used similarly outside of organisms. Scents and pheromones are carried by the air between land animals to signal such emotions as anger, fear and sexuality (we humans are marketed scents to mask such signals although apparently we don't consciously sense pheromones). Other molecules carried by air enable animals to smell food, familiar surroundings or noxious vapors. Mosquitoes smell their victims' carbon dioxide. Still other molecules in water and food are sensed by taste, for example salmon taste their home-waters in swimming upstream to spawn. Smell, olfaction, was perhaps the first sense to evolve.[69]

Air and water also exert pressure as discussed in Chapter Four which fish and other sea animals can use to sense depth and perhaps birds can use to sense altitude. Rapid variations of air and water pressure, that is pressure waves of varying frequency, can be sensed as sound. The frequency of pressure vibration is perceived as the sound's pitch. Some animals hear a wider range of pitch than we do, for example bats for echolocation—some narrower such as reptiles.[70] And sounds can be manipulated into coded signals such as insects', frogs', birds' and whales' songs, wolves' calls and human's speech. (Speech will be discussed further in the next two chapters.) Also it was recently discovered that many animals communicate with vibrations through the ground over long distances—this is believed to be how the earliest land animals 'heard'.[71]

Gravity and, more broadly, inertial changes can be sensed to tell which way is up and how our body's movement is changing as well as to control limb movements (proprioception).

Electromagnetism covers a wide range of possibilities. Static magnetism, namely the Earth's magnetic field, is used by migrating birds, salmon and bees for navigation and positioning.[72] Pulses of static electricity are used by electric eels and some fish to prey, navigate and attract mates.[73] As electromagnetism vibrates with increasing frequency, also discussed in Chapter Four, it first passes through the radio frequencies but I'm not aware of any natural use of this range.[74] Next up, the infrared range is used, for example by pit-vipers such as rattlesnakes to locate prey. The 'visible' range is so called because it's visible to us humans as well as many other animals. We perceive these electromagnetic frequencies as colors perhaps more discriminatingly than most other animals. But our lineage lost the ability (probably as the first nocturnal primates) to see ultraviolet light as can birds, fish, amphibians, reptiles and some mammals; so while they see a broader spectrum, we see finer.[75] Moreover advanced cephalopods, ants, bees and some spiders can see polarized light.[76] Beyond the UV range I know of no unaided usage of higher frequencies (no natural X-ray vision). A few people claim to see auras which we'll explore in Chapter Ten.

But are there other kinds of signals that we're not yet aware of, consciously, that is? For example some dogs seem to know when their humans are coming home even though there seems to be no apparent way of their knowing. Most of us have had the experience of thinking of someone, then the phone rings and it's they.[77] It seems to happen more often with someone we're fond of. Might prayer work this way? We'll explore this further in Chapters Nine and Ten.

Most signals sensed by higher organisms are transmitted through nerve cells, neurons, to other cells. The reaction of the cells receiving the signals can be quite rudimentary such as hair follicles erecting to expand fur thickness for warmth. In addition nerve cells can bundle together into a cluster, called a *ganglion*, to operate as a simple brain. In us humans, as well as other higher animals, ganglia are strategically located throughout our bodies near their target organs or along our spine to control unconscious functions.[78] And of course nerve cells mass together at the top of the spine to produce brains.

Virtually all signals processed in ganglia and brains don't rise to the level of consciousness. The signals are processed by complex programs that have evolved through trial and error to deal with the information just as a computer might. But there is some evidence to suggest that some animals may do more. For example a humming bird will harvest nectar from a large array of blossoms, with frequent rests, without going to the same blossom twice. Does the bird somehow put together a map, a *representation*, of the array? We'll address this question further in Chapter Nine on consciousness.

Recap & Trend

So far in this book we've traced how elementary particles combined to form molecules with unique properties not possessed by the constituent particles—emergence. We've seen how molecules might have found ways of arranging themselves into macromolecules that produced the life-like behavior of simple cells. And how the macromolecules might have evolved into archaea and bacteria with internal chemical signals to control reactions. How bacteria perhaps merged into archaea to achieve the cooperative society within a eukaryote cell using even more intricate intracellular chemical signals and processes.

And in this chapter we've traced how eukaryote cells joined together, specialized and cooperated as multicelled organisms, the Grand Climacteric, exchanging chemical signals between cells to coordinate growth and behavior. We've also mentioned neurons, nerve cells in more complex organisms that, in addition to internal chemical signals, employ electric signals coursing through their long axons to then send out chemical signals from their multiple synapses to other cells including those in ganglia and brains. But so far we've only hinted at what brains can accomplish for higher levels of synergy.

Throughout the four billion year story of Life on Earth many of the players remained essentially unchanged, virtually unmutated while their cousin cells mutated into ever more complex variations to find viable niches in their environments. So today we still have with us many archaea, bacteria and unicellular eukaryotes as well as multicellular eukaryotes.

While time and again individuals had to pass competitive tests in their environments, cooperation among them often facilitated passing those tests. The cliché of the "selfish gene" may resonate with the competitive ethos of our society, but cooperation plays an important rôle.[79] In fact the selfish gene might better be characterized as the 'resourceful gene' ever finding ways to fulfill its Urge to Life, trying anything and everything. Life will find a way. "More of this anon."

Chapter Eight

Human Evolution

Still we wearily trudge ever farther up the Mountain under our heavy packs, the thin mist-filled air laboring our steps, ever at the mercy of uncaring nature. What are we doing up here! We feel humbled though when we think back about early humans' struggles to survive under far harsher conditions with their primitive equipment, contending with fierce predators... Well, maybe we're not so bad off after all.

To put human evolution in perspective let's again use the analogy of a twenty-four hour day. Recall in Chapter Five we didn't put the present at the end of that day, at midnight as do most such analogies. Instead we supposed that Earth's now only half-way through its life-span of, say nine billion years from Earth's formation until it's destroyed by the exploding Sun's death-throes (though it could happen sooner). Earth's $4\frac{1}{2}$ billion years so far would be twelve hours putting us at twelve noon. Thus the dinosaurs' extinction some sixty-five million years ago would have been at 11:49:50am, about ten minutes before noon.[1] If our species *Homo sapiens* emerged no more than 300,000 years ago[2]—that's a little past 11:59:57am, less than three seconds before noon. But maybe it was only 100,000 years ago, about one second. Then how long before our species goes extinct? Using this twenty-four analogy it seems unlikely that our species will get our proverbial fifteen minutes of fame—that'd be nearly a 100 million years! More likely, only fifteen seconds—that'd be about $1\frac{1}{2}$ million years total, a fair tenure for a species.[3] That'd give us at least another million years, if we're lucky and don't do ourselves in before then, taking most of the other higher species with us.[4] In order to speculate in later chapters about where our species might be heading we need to first get a good understanding about our species' recent tenuous presence here on Earth—where we came from and how we got here—what this chapter's about.

Our taxonomic class, the mammals, first appeared two-hundred-twenty million years ago,[5] blossomed with the demise of the dinosaurs and flourished after the 'methane burp' of fifty-five million years ago.

Mammals[6] first evolved in a nocturnal niche and so are fur-bearing (generally), warm-blooded vertebrates characterized by their females' mammary glands (as a male I'm ambivalent that our taxon's eponym is the female breast).[7] Within the mammals, our taxonomic order, the primates (as in prime!), emerged perhaps eighty million years ago most-likely as tiny, nocturnal, insect-eating tree shrews, although an alternative places early primates on the ground. Over the next fifty million years they evolved binocular vision and hand-like paws for their life in the trees, along with social skills for life in a troop. Some shifted their diet to include fruits and leaves, and so forty million years ago re-evolved their lost color vision for day-time use.[8] Hand-eye coordination for agility in the trees together with social interactions favored the evolution of relatively larger brains. Extant primates include tarsiers, lemurs, monkeys, apes and humans.[9]

Hominids

The reconstruction of human's precursors has been torn between intense interest and paltry data. Until recently the paucity of fossils saw theories being constructed based on minimal evidence only to have those theories shaken or toppled by the next fossil dig.[10] Egos, reputations and funding agencies understandably demanded results which perhaps persuaded researchers to stretch their interpretations, but as a consequence eventually those agencies helped fund improved methods. Increasing numbers of fossils along with refined excavation techniques, radiometric dating and biomolecular clocking have helped improve the situation, if not entirely remedied it.

Here's a sketch of what's generally believed to be the scenario leading to humans, a brief overview before we examine in more detail. Go back some twenty million years to when, due to climate change, the unending forests begin to recede in eastern Africa. Soon after, some proto-apes successfully emigrated out of Africa, across the newly-formed Arabian landbridge and radiated throughout southern Eurasia, but then mostly died out except in Africa or some may have returned.[11] As the forests further receded into isolated stands of woodlands among encroaching grasslands, some proto-apes were forced to come down from their trees and evolve for living on the ground much of the time. From the time that the ape and hominid lineages diverged some seven- to five-million years ago,[12] many species of human precursors emerged—at least fifteen experiments. But today only our species remains, *Homo sapiens*. All the other branches were pruned, went extinct, vanished leaving only their fossil remnants similar to what happened to the horse in the previous chapter. The great apes faired a little better leaving four species today: the orangutans, gorillas, chimpanzees and bonobos (pygmy chimps), our closest living species.[13]

Currently the earliest known fossils of human precursors are represented by 4.4- to 5.8-million year old fragments of *Ardipithecus*.[14] Next are the 4.2-million year old jaw and tibia of a crude (knuckled?) upright walking species, *Australopithecus anamensis*. Walking upright is a hallmark of hominids. Next are the many 3.9- to 2.9-million year old fossils of *Australopithecus afarensis*, of which Lucy is the celebrity.[15] From australopithecines ('southern ape') a line putatively branched off, the genus *Homo*, that eventually led to us humans. Meanwhile the australopithecine branch continued on for two million years in some six species with a variety of skull shapes; some males were very robust with a bony crest atop their skulls to anchor powerful jaw muscles (*Paranthropus*).[16] The brain-case size for Lucy's kin averaged 400 to 500 cubic centimeters, only a third the size of *Homo sapiens'*. But by some 2½- to 1½-million years ago all the australopithecines had died out.

A recent find, tentatively named *Australopithecus garhi*, is a leading candidate for the earliest *Homo*. The 2.6-million year old *A. garhi* fossils were found in association not only with chipped-stone-tool use but with tool-making. Moreover the raw material that was chipped to make the stone-tools is not found near where the tools were found. From this evidence it's inferred that stone-tools were toted around, not just improvised when and where needed as do chimps. Of course this circumstantial evidence may be overturned with the next fossil find. The point is that making and using tools favored the evolution of brains and concurrently facilitated getting food from scavenged carcasses to fuel those energy-expensive brains. Probably long-since-perished wood clubs and spears along with thrown stones enabled the users to drive off predators and other scavengers from a carcass, like jackals and vultures.[17] Then their stone-tools enabled them to cut off its meat and break-up its bones and skull for the energy-rich marrow and brains that few competitors could access. Coupling exercising the brain with feeding it enabled the evolution of larger brains,[18] the hallmark of *Homo*.

Following *A.garhi* there were at least seven *Homo* species. So far the longest around was *Homo erectus*,[19] some 1½-million years (the jury's still out on how long *Homo sapiens* will be around). *Homo erectus'* brain-case ranged 800–1200cc (*Homo sapiens'* ranges 1250 to as much as 1700cc).[20] They radiated out of Africa all across Eurasia. Whether *Homo erectus* led directly to *Homo sapiens* or through an intermediate species (*Homo antecessor?*), or whether *Homo sapiens'* line split off before *Homo erectus* is being debated.[21] Also debated is, if *Homo sapiens* emerged from *Homo erectus*, was it only in Africa or also concurrently in Eurasia ('Mitochondrial Eve' vs. Multiregional).[22] Another now extinct *Homo* species that emerged a little earlier than *Homo sapiens*, perhaps with a slightly larger brain-case (~1520cc), was Neanderthal (aka Neandertal) which we'll touch on later in this chapter and in later chapters.[23]

That's the scenario as I write.[24] But new interpretations and finds are coming at a dizzying clip so probably what you're reading here is already somewhat outdated.[25] Even so, we can draw some insights from it to fit into the conceptual prototheist framework we're putting together. As a way of dealing with the limited and changing data, I'll describe what seem to be plausible explanations which should enable you to envision a most likely process of human evolution.

We're not nearly as unique as was once thought. Not only were 'cousin' species acknowledged only in the past hundred years or so. But more and more those characteristics that were thought to make humans unique were seen in other *Homo* species, as well as are seen in some other 'lower' animals. So human's 'uniqueness' may not be a difference in kind but of degree. For instance take tool-making cited above as a distinguishing characteristic: Birds make nests, bees make hives, and spiders make webs, some very elaborate, but from instincts not deliberation or learning. But chimps and ravens for instance do deliberately make tools. Or take language, another of our distinguishing characteristics: some birds, gerbils, wolves and dolphins have evolved elaborate vocalizations.[26] Even consciousness: several other animals display behavior that could be interpreted as consciousness. Certainly we humans have evolved and developed these characteristics to a much higher degree but maybe that's all—or have we crossed a threshold of 'critical mass'? What we do know is that we humans have evolved a suite of characteristics that gives us flexibility to deal with varied, unusual and changing situations.

But just as we've seen from earlier chapters, human evolution favored the development of some characteristics at the expense of others: trade-offs. For example humans can see finer hues of color in the visible spectrum but not into the ultraviolet. And our hearing may be more acute in the mid-registers but we totally lose the upper registers where dogs and bats excel. Human's early primate ancestors gained binocular vision at the expense of diminished smell. So while humans are superior in some things, we're inferior in others. The question becomes, superior for what?[27]

At the risk of seeming repetitious, the following three sections will first look at some external forces that drove human evolution, then at some internal factors that shaped us, and finally at social pressures and a likely scenario for the emergence of language and culture. It seems that it's simplistic to look for one or even a few pivotal causes that led to us. There's undoubtedly a whole suite of forces and factors that operated mutually to evolve humans (and probably not all of them are yet known). To help appreciate the interplay of these we'll go over the description of hominid evolution from these different perspectives. Of course what I've gleaned from my reading may be somewhat speculative but it's intended to give you a sense of how our evolution most likely progressed. One other *caveat*: in order to see our ancient ancestors as plain folks, I'll use familiar terms like guys, gals and kids.

External Forces

Climate played a formative role in hominid evolution. It's argued that the closure of the Isthmus of Panama, cited earlier, had profound consequences for the climate of Africa and Europe. But that was only a 'recent' episode. For fifty million years the climate had been getting colder with ever greater swings in temperature and rain due largely to cyclic variations as Earth orbits around the Sun and to plate tectonics carrying continents northward. Australia had split off leaving Antarctica isolated in the gyre around Earth's south hub to collect water vapor from the oceans which condensed into huge glaciers. Africa collided with Eurasia some sixteen- to twelve-million years ago closing the Tethys Sea and thus forming the Mediterranean which periodically was left high above the lowered oceans depleted by the glaciers' build-up. Then between 6.4– and 4.6–million years ago the Mediterranean periodically dried up along with what became the Sahara and Arabian Deserts.[28] To the south in Africa, plate tectonics also raised highlands in the west which lifted the easterly Atlantic winds dumping their moisture into rain forests. But in the east the now dry winds left arid plateaus with volcanoes, like Kilimanjaro, periodically spewing ash across the land.[29]

Indictment of the Isthmus of Panama goes as follows: When the Isthmus finally closed some three million years ago, it cut off the current into the Pacific from the Atlantic's water that had flowed northwestward across the equator where evaporation had left it saltier. Instead the warm salty water was diverted to flow toward the northern Atlantic further evaporating, cooling and concentrating salt as it went. As it neared the Arctic the denser saltier water sank to the bottom, stalled and turned back south taking its remaining warmth with it. This deprived the Arctic Ocean of the warm less-salty current that had flowed farther north before the Isthmus closed, so it froze-over year round. Moreover the moisture from the evaporating northerly flow precipitated, forming glaciers. When the cold periodically deepened as Earth's varying orbit reduced sunlight, the glaciers thickened and crept south across Eurasia and North America bringing on the Ice Ages. Africa also felt the chill.[30]

So now let's take another look at hominid evolution this time from the perspective of climate change. Imagine a sequence that putatively went something like this: Around six million years ago as the climate cooled and dried, the forests receded into woodlands interspersed among grasslands. Some apes, compelled to venture onto and across grasslands, perhaps raised up onto their hind legs for better views but knuckle walked like chimps.[31] As they increasingly scavenged on the grassland they used their forelimbs less for support and more to gather (including using sticks to dig tubers?) and to carry their finds back to the woods where in the trees they could feel safer from the large predators then prevalent (except from leopards' ancestors). Upright posture (aided by walking sticks suited to hands accustomed to tree limbs?) on the open grassland also reduced their exposure to the Sun overhead and increased their exposure to cooling breezes. They could spend more time in the open foraging in mid-day while competing predators sought shade. Thus the australopithecines evolved a physiology that optimized their versatility for both woodland and grassland as the climate alternatively favored one or the other. They could gather, or walk and tote, or climb as needed, each satisfactorily enough. It served them well for a couple million years without the need of a particularly large brain.[32]

Then three million years ago the Ice Ages climate further diminished the sheltering woodlands. Our distant ancestors weren't banished from the Garden of Eden, the Garden was banished! With less woodland to retreat to, predators culled australopithecines and other woodland animals. Then as prey populations plummeted many of the predators themselves may have died off (sabertooths went extinct?[33]) This may have been the respite that provided a window for the transition from australopithecine to *Homo*. Those animals that survived were forced to adapt to live more in the open grasslands.[34] A little faster and a little smarter may have made the difference between being eaten and surviving to pass on those traits—like the joke about the two guys and a grizzly, you only need to run faster than the other guy.[35]

What might have happened is that mutated genes[36]—long carried in australopithecines' chromosomes as recessive alleles—would occasionally be expressed in larger headed 'freaks'. These might have been discarded, either accidentally or intentionally (per note 32). But when the australopithecines were deprived of trees, among many initial disadvantages, one advantage was that such 'freak' infants were more easily held on to and cared for on the ground. And with the decimation of the australopithecine population and probably a reduced birth rate under the harsh conditions, they could no longer afford to lose an infant even if 'defective'. If infants were infrequent and thus precious, troops that didn't sustain every one they could may have died out. As the big-brained 'freaks' grew to adults, they were a little smarter and had a better chance to survive and raise more 'freaks'. (Concurrently bipedalism and other traits further evolved.) Recurrent Ice Ages tested the survivors every few generations culling the less fit.[37] And so the mutation may have flourished and *Homo* evolved.

Still they had to deal with predators and find a new way of life. One salvation was to 'walk softly and carry a big stick' (paraphrasing Teddy Roosevelt's dictum). Not only did one branch of hominids eventually learn to make stone hand-axes and become more adept with those 'sticks' mentioned already,[38] they perfected walking. Eventually one species evolved with somewhat larger brains atop tall, slender, long-legged bodies: *Homo erectus*. Putatively as resources on the expanding grasslands became more dispersed and seasonal, they were compelled to walk ever farther toting their young kids and stuff, opportunistically seeking food and water—migrating nomads. *Homo erectus* got so good at it that by sometime over a million years ago they had walked beyond Africa into much of tropic and temperate Eurasia.[39]

Internal Factors

While *Homo* shaped crude wood, fiber and stone tools, those tools 'shaped' *Homo*. Let's look closer at how this may have happened. As the woodlands receded soft fruits and leaves were less available. As grasslands expanded, fibrous stems and roots were the main choice among plants. To chew such courser foods some australopithecines evolved massive teeth and jaws powered by muscles wrapped around their skull and anchored to the crest along the top (sometimes called *Paranthropus*). Alternatively others started using stones to break up the course food before chewing it (the first 'processed' food) thus avoiding the requirement for massive teeth and jaw muscles. This alternative had three advantages: It was more flexible—tools can be 'evolved' more readily than body parts—so when needs changed tools could be more quickly adapted. And beginning three million years ago needs changed frequently as the terrain fluctuated between woodland and grassland putting a premium on flexibility. Secondly the hand/eye coordination of hammering and manipulating stones (along with throwing them) fostered brains.[40] Thirdly the skull and jaws were less constricted by massive structures so the brain and pharynx were freer to expand.[41]

This third advantage needs elaboration. Recall the concept of heterochrony, described in the previous chapter, whereby varying the rate of development of a body component can produce major differences, such as seen in the forelimbs of humans, dogs, birds and dolphins. Heterochrony varied the shape of hominid heads, inside and outside.[42] Mutated hox genes (genes that orchestrate growth rates) in a few individuals must have sometimes prolonged juvenile brain growth[43] resulting in slightly enlarged brains and skulls. That may have gotten them marginalized as freaks. Those 'freaks' may have hung-out with other such 'freaks' interacting and mating so their joined alleles initiated a line of such big-headed 'freaks'. Eventually the freaks' big mutated[44] brains and interactions facilitated innovations such as tool-making and proto-language. And hand/eye manipulation of tools exercised those brains inducing a reciprocal development of tools and brains. Similarly with proto-language. Better tools, 'language' and brains enhanced the freaks' abilities to survive and pass on those traits as suggested previously.[45] And so it goes.

Heterochrony similarly affected the pharynx in the upper throat. Expansion of the pharynx was at the expense of an even shorter lower jaw crowding the rear teeth and increasing reliance on 'processed' foods (tool use). It also lowered the rear of the tongue, and the epiglottis and larynx in the throat so today we can no longer swallow and breath at the same time once we're past infancy.[46] But the extended pharynx in conjunction with an agile tongue and lips, and controlled breathing greatly augmented the sounds that could be produced with the vocal chords.[47] In conjunction with concomitant evolution of hearing, the enhanced vocal abilities facilitated communication within the troop and eventually led to language, a hallmark of humans.[48] (We'll elaborate on this toward the end of this chapter.) The manipulation of sounds further exercised the expanding brain just as hand/eye manipulation of tools was doing. A more developed brain enhanced survival so those traits could be passed on to offspring, the Baldwin effect.[49] And on it goes.

(Neanderthals apparently didn't have such an expanded pharynx and thus it's surmised that their language was more rudimentary[50] as were their tools[51]. But their brains were comparable to our ancestor's, so what were they using their big brains for?[52])

But as *Homo's* heads enlarged, the problems of birthing and childcare grew more demanding. As *Homo* babies evolved enlarged heads their mothers had to evolve enlarged birth canals, but there's a limit. As heads evolved ever larger, the solution was for the baby in effect to be born 'prematurely'. At birth contemporary humans' brains are about 300cc or so, whereas the brains of newborn chimps, a 'near relative' species with similar adult size, are less than 200cc. But at birth humans' brains are only twenty-five percent of their eventual adult size whereas chimps' brains are about fifty percent along. So it's been said, in order to produce comparably developed infants, that human's gestation should not be nine months but as much as twenty-one.[53] But of course that's not how we evolved because newborns' oversized heads killed them and their mothers. Mothers who instead gave birth 'prematurely', survived to pass on the trait to their offspring, else our line would have gone extinct. Evolution's solution was to transfer some prenatal development on to postnatal. Chimps attain 95% of their adult brain within two years while humans take five or ten.[54]

Social Pressures

Parenting of big brained infants shaped social interactions in the troop and thus was another important factor that shaped hominid evolution. All species of mammals in the wild care for their infants while they're being nursed—the mother doesn't have much choice. And many species care for infants in a troop such as chimpanzees and elephants, some include the bonded father such as in a wolf pack. As the *Homo* species evolved ever larger brains, the duration of childcare and training was extended (*altricial*) from a few years to over a decade. Other mammals, like puppies and kittens, are dependent for a few months, but not for a dozen years. Mothers with fetal and infant children were incapacitated somewhat so needed help in getting high-energy food to feed their energy-expensive progeny (the adult human's brain is only 2% of our weight but uses about 20% of our energy and a growing child's uses even more, nearly two-thirds for newborns[55]). Their progeny also needed protection and transport. The solutions that evolved are surmised by a kind of 'reverse engineering'—by speculating over fossils and artifacts, by extrapolating back from our current behavior and by studying extant aboriginal peoples.[56]

What's generally believed is that males who abandoned australopithecine's philandering ways[57] and paired with females were more successful in raising children to pass on their evolving genes. Females bonded male partners by evolving a perpetual state of sexually receptivity but concealed estrus; that is, unlike most other mammals, *Homo* females evolved to be horny even when not ovulating.[58] Females' concealed estrus reduced competition among males for mating rights avoiding undermining cooperation among males essential to the troop's survival.[59] Concurrently *Homo* shifted from the primate eat-as-you-go hand-to-mouth feeding strategy to hunter-gatherers.[60] Stereotypically mothers stayed close to camp 'gathering' roots, bugs[61] and berries while fathers ranged far and wide 'hunting' meat. More likely, all able adults and children foraged in groups, near or far, toting their booty back to a sheltered encampment for processing. Reciprocal sharing or exchange deals insured all members were fed as long as some had success.[62]

Reciprocal sharing also forged bonds ("I owe you one") strengthening cohesion in the troop. Strong bonds proved valuable in encounters with predators and roaming gangs as they ventured into disputed lands. Thus some argue that *Homo* evolved not only through individual selection but also group selection. That is, groups with altruistic members were more likely to survive and prosper than groups with only selfish members. And even though altruism may benefit other members' progeny as much or more than the altruist's (if the altruist is killed), nonetheless the altruistic traits are perpetuated. For example, self-sacrificing fathers who die defending the troop not only enable their own children to survive but other members' children as well.[63]

Somehow the troop acquired members (or at least their genes in sperm) from other troops to diversify their gene pool.[64] Inter-troop pairbonding is the romantic's preference. Alternatives range from exchanging[65] members with neighboring troops to build alliances against roving gangs, all the way to taking captives, although some readers might not see much difference. Early on, it'd seem, populations were too sparse to tolerate many lethal rivalries—survival was better served by cooperation. Cooperating in childcare in an extended family may have also facilitated raising more children than did the australopithecines in spite of *Homo's* extended childhood.[66]

Cooperation requires a mutual understanding among troop members via communication. This is true of all species of social animals to some degree and is believed to have contributed to the evolution of their brains, particularly mammal's neocortex.[67] The mutual understanding of troop members required not only developing a knowledge of each member's personality and idiosyncrasies but also required mapping the interrelations among members. Most importantly it required evolving what's called a 'theory of mind'—mind reading—by putting one's self in the other person's place or 'shoes' to infer what they're thinking, their intensions.[68] (In the opening chapters I argued that this became their model for our early ancestors' understanding of nature. That is, they assumed that each item in nature was alive and had its own personality and idiosyncrasies even though mostly invisible, hence were 'gods'. They dealt with these 'gods' the same way they had learned to deal with the other members of their troop and with the strangers they encountered. We'll explore this further below and in Chapter Nine.)

Communication initially was similar to other social species: postures, gestures, vocalizations, and facial expressions sometimes known as 'body language' or mimesis. And indeed it led to proto-language and the evolution of our brain as will be described in the next chapter. Improved communication enabled extended troop size and cooperation with neighboring troops.[69]

Leaders arose who facilitated cooperation based on their know-how, charisma, hunting skills, peacekeeping or whatever, but dominance was suppressed judging from extant hunter-gatherer egalitarian societies (at least among adult males). Nomadic foragers prize freedom. A leader was 'first among equals'. The rank-and-file retained parity, they 'dominated' by suppressing upstarts through whatever means were warranted including ostracism or execution if all else failed.[70]

Domestication

Leadership of other male members may have been muted but not leadership of other animals, namely domestication. Just as brains enabled *Homo* to make and manipulate tools and other members of the troop, their brains enabled them to capture and manipulate other animals. The story goes that hunters took wolf-cubs (or wild-dog pups) back to their encampments for the kids. As the cubs grew they imprinted on the hunters as they would have on the alphas in the wolf-pack's den, and then stayed with the troop as guards and hunting 'dogs'. It's believed that domestication of dogs began perhaps as long as 135,000 years ago, but more likely 40,000 or only 15,000 years ago.[71] A similar thing happened much later with goats,[72] but there was a price: the goats had to be guarded and herded from one grazing site to another as the seasons changed. So the goats ended up 'domesticating' their humans who changed from nomadic hunters to herders. Then next *Homo* domesticated plants (by planting a hybrid that couldn't propagate naturally)[73] with even more confining consequences: the nomads had to stay-put while the plants grew in order to guard them from hunter-gatherers (human as well as other animals)—they changed from herder-gatherers to peasants beginning some ten thousand years ago.[74] Eventually it led to settlements and civilization. (Of course, a misogynist might argue that domestication started way back when *Homo* women first got men to bond with them—the women tried to 'domesticate' the men. And they're still trying to, even today.)

But long before they domesticated animals and plants, back while they were still hunter-gatherers a momentous event happened—they domesticated the fire-god. Imagine the consternation among the troop's elders when some smart-aleck kids first captured and brought fire into the encampment. Fire, that rained from heaven as lightening or volcanoes' spew, angrily burning up grassland and woods—everything in its path. Not only were the kids 'playing with fire' but they were defying a god—sacrilege! "They'll get us all killed!" But of course that's not what happened, usually. They learned to domesticate the fire-god and it became their friend. As long as they treated the fire-god right, the fire-god kept them warm, cooked their food, lighted the darkness and warded off predators. It changed their lives dramatically and permanently. The hearth became the symbol of home.[75] Actually the earliest evidence of the use of fire dates somewhere around a million years ago.[76] The user was *Homo erectus* and so once again my fanciful dramatization is exaggerated—hyperbolized—they had not yet evolved language, only vocal-sounds, facial-expressions and hand-gestures. And they probably had only vague notions of gods, but then, gazing into a campfire on long nights may have induced hypnotic states, conjuring a 'person' in the fire.[77]

Domestication, particularly rudimentary agriculture, fostered at least three seminal concepts in *Homo*'s emerging mind: They could manipulate not just tools but nature—not only the soil to plant seeds but the plants and animals as hybrids. Second they had to control resources, land and animals, in order to produce (hence myths were created about their gods bequeathing the land to them in perpetuity). Third, just as new plants didn't sprout unless seed had been planted in the soil, new animals weren't born unless males' seed had been 'planted' in females.[78] Since the seed was the active constituent, not the soil, men believed that they had 'souls' but women didn't (per some male Greek philosophers). You can see the mischief these concepts spawned, even unto today.

Recap & Elaboration

So now let's consolidate the external, internal and social factors as well as expand on some of them to get a composite picture of human evolution. We have seen how climate fluctuations over the past few million years drove species, including our ancestors, to evolve adaptations to ever changing environments. Some lineages evolved adapted body forms to cope with their changed environment only to have it change again obsoleting that body form. Those lineages that couldn't re-adapt their bodies soon enough, went extinct. Rather than rely just on evolving body form, our lineage followed a somewhat mixed route that favored flexibility and the use of artifacts, extensions external to the body, namely tools or culture.

The apes that became our australopithecine ancestors adapted to receding forests by evolving bodies that could both climb trees and walk somewhat upright on the grasslands. They probably foraged using 'found tools', sticks and stones, then toted their booty back to safety in the trees. As the forest further thinned they had to abandoned trees and adapt to living more in the open through greater reliance on tools. Some evolved enlarging brains which made them more adept in tool fabrication and use as well as intra-troop coordination. But enlarging brains put an increasing burden on mothers to supply their children's greater energy needs during prolonged childhoods. The primary solution was to entrain the fathers to provide support, which eventually lead to us, *Homo sapiens*.

Here again is the likely scenario, elaborated, of how that evolved. And to help see them as just plain folks, let's use today's vernacular of 'guys' and 'gals'. Whereas mothers bond with their offspring in their wombs and at their breasts, males had no such attachment to their offspring. Indeed guys had little way of knowing whether offspring were theirs and probably didn't even know that sex caused babies! Guys were mainly interested in sex and so contested to ply gals who were sexually receptive with gifts like food (bonobos males do). Gals who could prolong their receptivity prolonged the gift giving (bonobo females do[79]). But the gals who most needed food were those who were pregnant or lactating, and were least able to forage for themselves with dependent children. Because they weren't sexually receptive they weren't getting gifts from guys. They could only get male support if they could convince the guys they were sexually receptive, whether they were or not.

Some paleoanthropologists believe the 'battle of the sexes' may have played out something like this: Gals who evolved concealed estrus (instead of swelling pink or red genitals as in chimps and bonobos) yet could be sexually receptive might initially fool the guys. The theory goes that only those guys who were attracted to pink and red signals, and romanced her until that gal was fertile, passed on their genes along with that penchant in their male offspring. So then non-fertile, pregnant or lactating gals, in order to get those guys' attention, began faking it by marking themselves with ocher[80] or other red coloring followed by receptivity. Soon all the gals started faking it together so all those guys didn't just concentrate on the one or two naturally pink or red fertile gals in the troop. Now each guy had to choose which gal to romance and probably paired with just one. So when the guys got the red signal, if they wanted sex they had to go hunt up food, preferably high protein meat.[81] The full moon became the time for the end of the hunt and for feasting, dancing, romancing ... or perhaps crashing parties in neighboring troops. Those gals who really were fertile passed on their trait of ovulating with the Moon and so perhaps the trait was selected to evolve.

Now with more or less exclusive access each to their own gal, guys no longer had to compete with each other for sex and could go off hunting together with less fear of being cuckolded. Consequently a guy not only bonded with his gal but after time also with her (his?) kids.[82] Guys who stuck around and supported them were more likely to raise successful offspring to carry on their traits.[83] But a guy's traits would only be passed on if he chose an able mother, so guys inherited an eye for swivel hips and full breasts (intuitively selecting for child bearing and lactation), and hearty spunk (for toting kids and fending off predators while foraging), plus friendly female kin (for backup). Gals turned on to guys who were 'wild types,' adventurous and vigorous, (good hunters) rather than layabout lotharios or bullies.[84]

But was that all? Were gals only interested in good hunters? In addition it'd be nice if he were also resourceful and intelligent (to deal with unique problems and opportunities), loyal and considerate (to be a good companion and father), witty and a good lover (so as not to become boring) and so on. How could she judge such characteristics beforehand and not just go by what turned her on? And to win the gal he fancied, a guy not only had to infer what she wanted (still a problem today) but evolve displays that would convince her that he had those characteristics (like the peacock's tail feathers in the previous chapter).[85] The solution that's thought to have evolved was proto-language: By signaling each other with vocalizations, facial expression, gestures and body postures they could exchange information and form judgments before committing. So like the peahen, females shaped males by arbitrarily specifying characteristics and mating with males who displayed them. If several gals wanted the same such guy and he were willing (and sneaky), his traits would spread rapidly down through generations and evolve further as they went.[86] Of course those characteristic had to be viable: Sexual selection proposes and natural selection disposes, eventually.

It perhaps was in female support klatches were proto-language and culture further evolved. In order to coordinate fertility signaling and extended childcare, women had to communicate with both body decoration and proto-language. But they also needed to learn deception (Machiavellian intelligence). And of course they 'gossiped'. Their kids picked up the proto-language and elaborated on it so when the kids grew up not only could the daughters carry on these practices but sons could better coordinate their hunts, tool skills, planning etc.[87] Thus enlarged brains were favored. (We'll expand on language evolution in the next chapter.) The species, *Homo sapiens*, was so successful that our ancestors radiated out of Africa and eventually dominated the Earth.[88]

Theism

Now with an understanding of how we humans likely evolved, let's reconsider the ideas put forth in Chapter Two—Gods, on how theism may have arisen. Theism probably arose along with language through the combination of three factors: Early humans may have believed that, just as all animals—dogs, birds, game, fish, insects and humans—behaved autonomously because they were alive, it intuitively followed that all objects in nature which also seemed to behave autonomously were alive—fire, wind, brooks, volcanoes, earthquakes ... Secondly just as early humans learned to read the concealed intensions of their fellow humans (the 'theory of mind' mentioned earlier) as well as the intentions of other animals, they tried to read what they thought were the concealed intentions of 'live' natural objects (animism[89]). Thirdly as language dawned they might have believed that the 'talking' they 'heard' going on in their heads subvocally, was coming from those 'live' natural objects. Thus they might have believed that those 'live' natural objects were speaking to them, were telling them their intentions so they didn't have to guess.[90]

Also recall from the chapter on Gods that early humans, from childhood on, were strongly influenced by their parents and ancestors even after the elders died. In preliterate societies, elders are the repositories of knowledge. The elders' 'spirits' continue to 'speak' to their descendants giving advice and admonitions. The lessons and myths learned from the elders lived on in their descendants' vivid imaginations. Later, settled societies deified their deceased leaders.

So just as they learned to deal with humans and other animals, they learned to cajole, manipulate and 'handle' these natural objects with prayer, ritual, sacrifice and fetishes. For example, in the chapter on Gods and in this chapter, I describe how they might have dealt with the fire-god. Also it's been suggested that women believed their menstrual ritual not only induced men to go hunting but induced the Moon goddess to grow full.[91] Language enabled them to not only give the objects names but also the spirits they believed dwelt in the objects. We know some of the names of gods, goddess, nymphs and satyrs from Greek and Roman mythology, as well as from other ancient literate cultures such as Egyptian and Sumerian.

How might such theistic beliefs contribute to fitness, to survival and reproduction, and thus be favored by natural selection to evolve? All other animals have survived in the same natural world but none seem to have adopted such elaborate theistic beliefs. But than none seem to have evolved the degree of consciousness and self awareness that we have either, nor the extensive use of tools and other artifacts.

Perhaps a way to answer this question is to consider three ways of knowing: magic, myth and science.[92] By 'magic' is meant those activities where if you blindly follow the prescribed procedures, it usually works 'as if by magic' even though you don't understand why it works—a kind of 'cookbook' approach. Animals will follow this approach from instincts when they build bird nests, spider webs, beaver dams ... But with the dawning of consciousness, some of our early ancestors may have asked why it works. They may have come to believe that a spirit or god controlled the process and prescribed the ritual in the same way that as children their parents and elders in the troop had arbitrarily prescribed behaviors. So a myth was passed on down by parents and elders which worked well enough and provided a plausible explanation given their limited understanding of nature. With language and ritual both the magic and myths could be conveyed which were useful for survival. Scientific explanations weren't used until their understanding of nature became more comprehensive and reliable.

An example might be helpful, say, 'how to start a fire.' With the 'magic' approach we're told to get some dry tinder and place it on a dry sheltered spot, then get some small dry pieces of wood and put them on top, then strike a spark into the tinder and gently blow on it until the tinder glows and flames start, and so on. With the 'myth' approach we'd follow pretty much the same routine but as a ritual: implore the fire-god to come to our hearth (altar), offer it tinder and wood, breath prayers into the offering, and so forth. With the scientific approach we'd still follow the same routine but we'd understand that the tinder and wood have to be dry or else too much heat would be used up evaporating the moisture before the tinder could reach its ignition temperature, that the spark has to be hot enough to heat the tinder to its flash point, that our breath supplies oxygen so the heat can oxidize the carbon in the tinder and wood which must be loosely stacked so the hot flue gases can rise up through, and so forth.

We still use the 'magic' approach in many things we do that we don't fully understand—that's how I deal with my computer. And though I don't believe in 'myths' I'll sometimes say 'prayers' to the computer 'god' (well maybe they're not prayers, more like curses). If I'm stuck some of my adult children can act as 'priests' to propitiate the computer 'god'. Because they have a scientific understanding of how the hardware and software work, they don't have to curse (quite as much). (I'm not really that computer incompetent but it illustrates my point.)

It's my contention that our early ancestors initially worked by 'magic' much like the other animals, maybe subconsciously. But as consciousness dawned and they began to wonder about nature, they used the same model they saw in their troop—that is, they projected 'life' into the natural objects and related to them as parent figures, as described above and in Chapter Two on Gods. Their 'gods' conception was a way of dealing with the terror of the unknown natural world around them—their surrogate parents would look after them if they were good. These myths were ritualized and elaborated as they were passed on down the generations. The myths that were effective in dealing with nature were preserved, those that weren't were either modified or abandoned. Until scientific methods came into wide use—chiefly in just the past few centuries—our ancestors survived and prospered largely by using 'magic' and myths.

What the above description leaves out, indeed ignores, is the mystery, the wonder, the numinous which even today many look to religions to provide. My suspicion is that the 'mystery' arises out of the tension between our conscious and our unconscious mind as we shuttle between them. We'll explore this more fully in the chapter on 'Religion' after we've an understanding of our brain/mind from the next chapter.

Even today, though science offers a far better understanding of nature, many people still use 'magic' and myths to deal with their world. Indeed, not just unsophisticated people but many in the highest levels of business and government are able to be effective in their daily affairs by espousing the rules prescribed by their religions without being distracted and confused by wondering and worrying about deeper issues and ultimate realities. Though quite analytic in the secular areas of their life, they seem to bracket off their religious life from any questioning. It's at a higher level than our early ancestors' belief in natural spirits, but it may still serve the same function. More on this in the final three chapters. Before then in the next chapter we explore how consciousness may have emerged.

Chapter Nine

Un- to CONSCIOUSness

The mist that has shrouded us so long now gradually begins to break here and there. Views fade in and out. Occasionally we glimpse the rocks around us and stretches of the narrow precarious trail ahead as we switch left and right traversing up the steepening Mountain. It's scary but wondrous.

The past four chapters could be viewed as setting the stage for this chapter. We now look at how the whole evolutionary process became aware of itself, became reflexive, conscious.[1] First we'll briefly look at how animal 'minds' generally operate and how human minds build on them. Then we'll consider in more detail how human brains seem to operate and produce consciousness. Finally we'll take a preliminary look at culture's role. Throughout our explorations don't get so caught up in the science that you lose your awe of the astounding activity that must be going on up here in our heads—again consider that even though it's only two percent of our body's weight, our brain consumes some twenty percent of our body's energy so there must be a lot going on up there.

Animal 'Minds'

A major impediment for us humans in attempting to understand other animals' 'minds' is our anthropomorphism. We are aware of the thinking going on in our own heads and so we tend to interpret other animals' behaviors that appear to be the result of their consciousness as actual consciousness. If the other animal is a fellow human who shares a common language, we can talk to them and confirm that they too are consciously thinking. But unlike the fictional Doctor Dolittle we can't "… talk to the animals." Yet we try—to our dog, cat or horse—and at times it seems they understand us. It's our way of knowing and relating so naturally it's our initial attempt in relating to other animals—at least the 'higher' animals, maybe not insects—tho' I do. (As children we talked to our dolls or stuffed toys.) Perhaps anthropomorphism, carried to the extreme, is the same tendency that our early ancestors used to imbue natural objects with life and consciousness which became the gods, as we've discussed several times already.[2]

But if we truly want to understand other animals we have to resist anthropomorphic tendencies and attempt to know them on their terms. What we'll learn is that, though they may not be like us with conscious minds, we're much like them in our unconscious minds. The kinship we feel for other animals need not be anthropocentrism as much as somehow connecting with them on some mutually compatible unconscious levels.[3]

Then at what level in this hierarchy of information exchange does consciousness arise? Asked another way from an evolutionary perspective, at what level is consciousness needed or even useful for the system to function? Certainly not in the somatic cells or even the nerve cells, neurons. Even bundles of nerve cells such as ganglia have evolved algorithms that program unconscious reactions to stimuli.[4] Only as billions of nerve cells cluster in a 'critical mass' at the top of the spine is consciousness manifest and only unequivocally in humans and even than only in a limited way. And only in humans does consciousness clearly have a functional benefit necessary to the species' evolution. But maybe we're using too narrow a definition of consciousness; maybe we've been narcissistically defining it so that only we humans qualify (you don't suppose ... ?!!) If other animals are conscious too than we're not so special that God chose us as the pride of His creation and "sent down his only begotten Son to redeem us."

The question of other animals' consciousness, self-awareness, has been extensively researched in recent decades. Animals perform amazing feats both in the wild and in captivity which from our anthropocentric perspective surely seems to clearly demonstrate self-awareness. They recognize us and other animals, they find their way in their home territory and even in strange territories, they have long memories, some even use tools,[5] and on and on. But it's been shown that these feats don't necessarily need the animal to be consciously aware of what it's doing.

Vertebrate animal behavior has been explained as 'association formation'—the animal learns to make associations between events, between stimuli and responses. It's believed that "Animals possess devices that detect dependencies between events in their worlds, and form associations between internal representations of those events." Various animals might have different representations of events—for instance a dog's representation would rely more on smells and a bee's more on UV light. However 'internal representations' of those events don't necessarily imply or require a conscious mind. The evolutionary significance is that "The ability to form associations will allow an animal to uncover ... 'the general causal structure of its world'." "All vertebrates ... form associations ... in ... a way that suggests that the role of association formation is to take advantage of the causal nature of the universe so as to predict events that have not yet occurred."[6] In other words since animals move, they need to predict the outcome of their movements in their world; so their brains learn to emulate their world in order to increase their chances of success.[7]

What's obvious though from the intelligence and vast complexity of animal 'minds' is that they must have a wealth of internal representations, emulations, in their 'minds' and an amazing ability to form associations among them. Their internal representations and association formations may all be unconscious but nonetheless are impressive.[8] Moreover, although ours may be the most advanced,[9] much of our human mind appears to operate unconsciously the same as theirs.

An argument against other animals' consciousness is that, in spite of ingenious and persistent tests on a variety of animals including apes and parrots, "... animals cannot master even the rudiments of human language."[10] Because language is such a clear indicator of consciousness, the lack of one casts doubt on the other.[11]

Another critical test of self-awareness that has been devised uses a mirror to judge whether an animal seems to recognize itself—dogs, gibbons and some monkeys don't seem to; some parrots, baboons, chimps, orangutans and perhaps dolphins and elephants do.[12] But than autistic children clearly recognize themselves in mirrors but don't seem to possess other forms of consciousness. So the jury's still out on other animals' consciousness. Some neuroscientists resolve the issue by proposing degrees of consciousness: humans and some other animals have 'core-consciousness' whereas only humans also have 'extended-consciousness' (more on this in note 1 and later). However the issue here is not so much determining when other animal's unconsciousness becomes consciousness as assessing when and how ours does.

Human Minds

As discussed in the last chapter, perhaps a mutation lurking in Australopithecine genes initiated the 'abnormal' growth of brains. But brains are expensive energy-wise so they'd damn well better have been good for something or else their continued expansion wouldn't have been favored by evolution.[13] And they were: Larger brains enabled our wandering bipedal ancestors to locate and map scarce resources in harsh environments. Large brains, in conjunction with dexterous hands, enabled them to fashion and use tools. Large brains enabled group coordination in camp, in hunts and foraging, in long treks ... as told in the last chapter. But some other animals do those things too—traverse vast territories, build nests, coordinate activities and what have you—without benefit of our ancestor's degree of cognition. Nonetheless larger brains benefited those functions by enabling greater flexibility and so it seems hominid brain growth was favored by evolution.

As hominid brains continued to enlarge they perhaps crossed a Rubicon, a threshold of 'critical mass' wherein synergistic complexity caused a few internal representations to tentatively emerge into hominid's fragile conscious as hesitant, half-formed thoughts. It was perhaps like a vague fleeting feeling we may sometimes get from a smell or taste that we can't place, that we 'can't quite put our finger on'. As an internal representation drifted in and out of consciousness (so the argument goes) it could be captured, held in mind, by assigning it a sound from their increasingly agile vocal tract. Like other animals our ancestors had been using sounds and gestures as signals with ever increasing specificity. Naming with vocalizations—words—facilitated sharing their thoughts with any of their fellows who were experiencing the same changes. Using shared words served to fix the thoughts in mind, as well as to exercise the vocal tract and aural sense. (Recall from the previous chapter how heterochrony was expanding both the brain and the pharynx, but not without some expense and risk, so again the benefits must have been worth their costs.)

Along with the emergence of internal representations as thoughts *of* events and things came the emergence of association formations as thoughts *about* the relation between events, things or ideas; one being about the other, subject and predicate, a sentence.[14] Speaking sentences further exercised their mind, as well as their voice and hearing, promoting those organs' mutual evolution. "It is probably not a coincidence that what is special about humans is that we outsmart other animals and plants by cause-and-effect reasoning, and language seems to be a way of converting information about cause-and-effect and action into a signal."[15] Those hominids who developed a facility for language improved their chances of survival and of successfully rearing progeny possessing those same traits, and (so goes the argument) thus consciousness evolve.

While language certainly helped to propel the evolution of consciousness, (others argue) there was a more fundamental cause of consciousness' emergence.[16] After all, the thoughts in our minds are not just those that are expressed in words. Without resorting to words, our ancestors probably were able to visualize a tree, a path down to a stream, and a rock by that stream ... They probably imagined if that rock could be chipped into a hand-axe or a branch of the tree used to dig or to hit. They probably visualized and speculated where the stream might flow, imagined what might be downstream and mused 'What if ...' . They must have imagined non-word sounds, like a bird's call. And like us, they undoubtedly were aware of ineffable feelings all without benefit of words. So it's argued that language is just one manifestation of a more fundamental capability that had earlier emerged as consciousness.[17]

Nonetheless words do facilitate thinking, say abstracting from the visualization of a specific tree or rock to the generalized category of any tree or rock. And we're conscious of even more abstract ideas such as numbers—the idea of 'three' can be abstracted from three trees or three rocks. Moreover externalizing the idea of 'three' into a symbol for '3'—its numeral (more likely 'III')—facilitates manipulating the ideas.

Thoughts may also have enhanced a consciousness of Self. At the cellular level our immune system distinguishes self from nonself[18] and brains do it unconsciously[19] but thinking enhances it. If there's a separate object 'out there', then might there be a different object 'in here': Me, Myself? Am 'I' distinct from it, and from you and from them[20]—Self-conscious? As mentioned in the previous chapter, it's argued a 'theory of mind' evolved that not only enabled one to be aware of what was going on in their own mind, but to infer what was going on in another's mind,[21] referred to as Machiavellian intelligence (poor misunderstood Niccoló[22]). Just when the concept of Self emerged is debated[23], but emerge it certainly did.

The major part of our Self that we're conscious of is our ego. We're unaware of our unconscious, of the unimagined wealth of internal representations and associations beyond our ego's reach. Indeed some believe we have two cognitive systems: the basic animal internal-representation/association-formation *implicit* system and an *explicit* ego system that emerged from the first.[24] Like other animals we have no conscious memories of those unconscious operations and experiences.[25] Consequently our ego can become arrogant, hubristic, thinking it's the whole deal, insistent on being in charge, on top (as is our neocortex).

Freud's 'iceberg' analogy is helpful to illustrate how our mind shuttles between consciousness and unconsciousness. Picture an Arctic iceberg floating off Greenland. What we see is only the tip; most of the iceberg—up to ninety percent—is below the surface gradually lost from view the deeper down in the ocean it goes. Our unconscious mind is like the mass of the iceberg out of sight in the depths, largely inaccessible to our conscious mind. Our conscious mind is like the tip, only a small part of our total mind. But because it's all we're aware of, all we 'see', we tend to think it's the main part of our mind. Still we catch fleeting glimpses a little ways below the surface. This part just below the surface—coming into view, then fading—is like our *sub*-conscious mind, out of our immediate thoughts but more or less available. Some say that at most we have only a few thoughts clearly 'in mind' at a time yet we can usually juggle or shuttle several thoughts between the conscious and subconscious parts of our mind. Sometimes though we lose them: "What was I talking about?" "It's right on the tip of my tongue." (As I'm leaving my house, if I feel I'm forgetting something, I probably am. So I go back in the hope it'll 'come to mind.' Or, if I can't think of a name and offhand admit it out loud, it's as though my subconscious says "Give up? Here it is" and the name pops 'into mind'.) However unlike our subconscious, our unconscious is way below the surface largely inaccessible to our conscious mind, at best only hints through dreams, fantasies, music, and so forth (we'll pursue this at length in the next chapter).

(The iceberg analogy may not work for other animals. If they have little if any consciousness, there'd not be much tip above the surface, only water washing over the mostly submerged mass just below the surface.)

Like other animals most of what goes on in our mind, does so beneath our conscious and stays there—such as blood pressure control—but a little of what goes on in our mind does make it into our conscious. In addition to our subconscious, just mentioned, some refer to our *pre*-conscious. The preconscious concept recognizes that our unconscious processes data before it's presented to our conscious. For instance, as you read this page you're mostly unaware of how your mind decodes the ink marks in order to identify specific words from the thousands stored in your memory, or how it deciphers and connects them into coherent thoughts.[26] When we speak we don't pay much attention to what words to use, in what order, how to move air over our vocal cords, move our tongue and lips, gesture ... Similarly we write, walk, drive ... in fact most of the things we do are done more or less automatically by our sub-, pre- and un-conscious mind.[27] Thus, since most of our mind and even more of other animals' minds are unconscious, much can be learned about ours by studying theirs.[28]

So then, what is the human mind and where is it? It's not just the brain or just some parts of it, say the left hemisphere with an 'interpreter' or in the basal ganglia.[29] Could it be that our individual mind is the manifestations of our brain and all its extensions—not only the nerves throughout our body but all the information exchange between our cells that percolates up through those nerves as well as through our body fluids?[30] Those manifestations are our *un*conscious, our *pre*conscious, our *sub*conscious and our conscious that function pretty much automatically in us (and other animals) to process and store information, and (at least in humans) to present a tiny bit of it to our awareness—what's been called our body/brain/mind continuum.

Moreover it can be argued that our mind extends beyond our physical body. Try pressing your finger on this page you're reading. You experience the hardness of the page at the tip of your finger as though your mind, your awareness, is at the tip of your finger. Now take a pencil and press its tip on the page; your awareness of the page is now at the tip of the pencil beyond your body. Is your mind at the tip of the pencil? Or focus your eyes on a word on this page; it seems that your awareness is out here on the page.[31] Now briefly close your eyes. Your image of that word is held seemingly in your eyes until you reopen them and it's back on the page. Does your mind shuttle between the page and your eyes? As you look out the window, say at a tree, your mind is out there with the tree. You know that the tree is out there—if you went out to it you could hug it and hear the wind up in its branches, and if there were other folks there they'd confirm it (unless you're all delusional)—so there's no doubt at all that the tree's out there. But again, while looking out your window at the tree, if you close your eyes, the tree's image is held in your eyes. Similarly with sound: if you're listening to musicians, the music is there at their instruments; but when their music stops you may still 'hear' it in your head.[32] In Chapter Two this process was called 'projection' (more on this shortly).

Now let's consider a 'radical' concept. In this book the pattern we've been tracing arising throughout nature is synergistic complexity. It seems that minds are a furtherance of the emergence of synergy first discussed in Chapter Four and elaborated in subsequent chapters. How's that? Recall I used the example of a car that we'd taken all apart so that it was no longer a car but only a collection of car parts. If we reassemble those parts properly, the car will re-emerge—the whole car is greater than the sum of its parts—that's synergy. Throughout nature we see nested hierarchies of ever increasing synergistic complexity: subatomic particles combining into atoms having unique emergent properties, then atoms into molecules, molecules into crystals and proteins ... proteins into living cells, and cells into evermore complex organs and organisms. And with each higher level, properties emerge that are often unexpected and unpredictable. The efficacy of each level's emergent properties is tested in its environment of other molecules, cells and organism in order to select only those combinations that fit their environment and can successfully reproduce themselves.

This Darwinian process of synergistic complexity and selection eventually led to brains, and in just the last few million years at most, to brains that are conscious. The radical concept is that the same process that led to conscious brains is what operates to produce that consciousness in those brains—Neural Darwinism.[33] Does it? From the complexity of an organism's neurons—in its nerves and brain structures—can a mind emerge which has the intriguing reflexive ability to perceive synergy? Just as, say a tree assembles its myriad molecules and cells in a synergistic way so that the 'tree' emerges, a brain through its senses gathers myriad photons that are reflected from the tree and somehow assembles those data synergistically into an integrated representation of that tree, a gestalt. Through a synergistic process in the brain, a gestalt emerges of that tree. (At least we know that gestalts emerge in our human minds; whether any other animals form gestalts or only form representations is an interesting question but not really pertinent to our endeavor.) Put succinctly, synergistic complexity is how entities emerge in the world; likewise synergistic complexity is how our brain integrates data to form gestalts of those entities. (We'll play with this concept some more shortly.)

Primitive Brains

In order to express their Urge to Life most organisms—from the simplest single cells to complex multi-billion celled entities—are compelled to reach outside themselves into their environment. They must carry on a balancing act between sustaining and enhancing their internal operations, and dealing with their surroundings—their inner-self versus the outside 'world', their interior versus the exterior, their organism versus the objects.[34] To do this they obtain and process information both from their interior and from the exterior, and somehow choose a course of action expressing their own idiosyncratic Urge to Life.

Let's briefly review what was discussed in earlier chapters about how an organism processes data. Cells react to external stimuli as well as take in ions and molecules through their membranes. These trigger processes in their nucleus and organelles, perhaps controlled by the *centrosome* of animal cells' cytoskeleton.[35] Cells also routinely pass signal particles like ions and hormones among themselves in response to stimuli in order to control their internal operations or to affect other cells, nearby or remote. Stationary multicell organisms such as plants evolved vascular systems to transport water, nutrients and signal particles long distances, defying gravity to reach for the Sun's photons.

Mobile multicelled organisms, namely animals also evolved vascular systems that transport signal particles such as hormones. But movement requires faster remote coordination so some signal particles engage nearby branching nerves cells, neurons, which rapidly transmit the signals electrically to higher levels through long axons. The higher level may be a ganglion—a bundle of nerve cells that processes data—nearby or next to a vertebrate's spinal cord as part of the autonomic nervous system. Or the nerve cells may transmit the signals through even longer bundles of axons leading all the way on up through the spinal cord[36] to the masses of nerve cells in a brain where predictions are made to optimize the organism's success.[37] Whether near or far, either way the signals are processed and sent back down to other organs' cells in the body to control their operations, both autonomic and muscular. At these various levels this is done mostly without conscious awareness or control.

How our human brains work is inscrutable compared to how our limbs work. We human vertebrates are endoskeletal animals and can see the outlines of our muscles and tendons at work. But we're exoskeletal in our heads and spines so our brains and central nerves are encased out of sight.[38] Moreover we can palpate individual muscles and some of our internal organs but not our brain's parts. Consequently to study human brains scientists have resorted to assessing the effects of damage on brain parts, what's lost, in order to assess what those parts do. Some probe brain parts during open brain surgery on conscious patients and ask what they experience. And now powerful brain imaging machines are enabling scientists to see what parts are active during various tasks.

Where we are currently in our understanding of the mind is perhaps akin to where astronomy was in Copernicus' and Galileo's day or where biology was in Darwin's and Mendel's day. While much has been learned about the brain in recent decades[39] there's still a long way to go, so trying to follow the explanations is challenging. Moreover there are differing opinions on what many brain parts do and what's worse, some parts are called by several different names. So bear with me. I'll try to tell this complex story with as little complexity as I can, and admittedly I'll be favoring my own point of view.

Where our upper spinal cord forms into clumps of neurons, nuclei, as it nears our head is called the brainstem (aka hindbrain). These nuclei select which ascending spinal cord signals warrant attention, control autonomic (vegetative) functions such as our heart rate and blood pressure, as well as other functions, and control the sleep/wake cycle by dispersing signal particles, hormones (aka neuromodulators), into our brain.[40] (Our upper brainstem bifurcates along here so the following brain structures are in pairs, roughly symmetrical right and left.) Nuclei and bumps (*colliculi*) attached to our brainstem process primitive aspects of sight and hearing. Perched atop our brainstem is the *thalamus* which relays to the cortices (the lumpy gray-matter) almost all incoming sensory data (except smells and pheromones[41]). The thalamus (Greek for 'chamber') is a complex of nuclei.[42] The thalami together with the adjacent *basal ganglia*—which mediate perception and movement respectively—are ancient brain parts which predated the evolution of cortex.[43]

Encircling our thalamus is our *limbic system* (*limbic* is Latin for 'belt'), including our *cingulate* and *entrorhinal cortices*, and *amygdala* and *hippocampus*. The limbic system putatively produces primitive emotions (*e* = outward + *movére* = to move), drives and behaviors through both neural connections and hormone production.[44] Our hippocampus also plays an important role in the formation of long-term memory.[45] Attached to the back of our brainstem is our *cerebellum* which coordinates movement of our body by mediating between the executive systems of our brain, our spinal cord, and our muscles and their sensors.[46] All of these too are done involuntarily without conscious awareness or control.[47]

The most primitive brain components, the 'reptilian brain'[48] are mainly concerned with survival and reproduction by sensing and controlling an animal's body in stereotyped responses ('fixed action patterns'= FAPs[49]) to what's sensed in the environment outside its body. The reptilian brain senses and controls what goes on in the guts (the internal milieu[50] and viscera) and how the body moves (the vestibular system and musculoskeletal frame). Above the reptilian brain the 'old mammalian brain' (aka paleomammalian), mainly the limbic system, as said, is generally thought of as the emotional brain where unconsciously fear, anger, joy and so forth are processed.[51] The primitive brain enables a 'lower' animal to think in its primitive way. The primitive brain also houses the brain's clocks.[52]

We tend to disparage the primitive brain perhaps because most pictures show the massive outer brain with the inner brain structures buried beneath out of sight. Also the outer brain is our neocortex, largely unique to mammals and most expanded in us humans, the part that distinguishes us as human, after all. But it could be argued that the neocortex is an auxiliary of the primitive brain, that the Life Urge wells up from all the cells in the body as drives and emotions—urges—in the primitive brain, and that the neocortex simply provides more thought-out alternatives for expressing those urges. For example take the mammalian defense reaction: An emotional stimulus into the sensory thalamus exits in two pathways: directly to the amygdala (low road) and round-about through the cortex to the amygdala (high road). In the direct pathway the amygdala makes a crude hair-trigger assessment and 'sounds general quarters' triggering defensive actions: blood pressure, stress hormones, freezing, or whatever. Meanwhile the cortex makes a slower but more discerning assessment and either endorses the amygdala's actions as warranted or curtails them as an overreaction.[53] Indeed some believe that the primitive brain can activate the neocortex but not vice versa—the neocortex can inhibit the primitive brain but can't directly activate it.[54] Thus the neocortex might be viewed either as the primitive brain's auxiliary or as the entire brain's executive.

Note that the primitive brain is not just reactive but is very much proactive, intentionally affecting processing in the outer brain as we'll explore shortly. Our primitive brain components are what mediate how vertebrates like us unconsciously sense and express our Life Urge welling up within ourselves. As such they constellate our preconscious Self or *proto*-self.[55]

Brains have been likened to analog computers, more apt for the lower brain components than for the upper brain. In fact, the farther along the evolutionary tree and more recently evolved (generally up and forward), the less our brain works like a computer—the more it's 'soft-wired' and uses 'fuzzy-logic'. The reptilian brain and to a lesser degree components in the old mammalian brain are modular, determined by genetics and programmed ('hard-wired') to respond stereotypically. But unlike current computers the upper brain is more dynamic and more plastic, especially the newer frontal regions. More than a 'blank slate', it continuously 'wires' and 'rewires' itself throughout life but especially in infants and children in a learning process we'll describe shortly.[56]

As mammals evolved more extensive upper brain matter, the neocortex, it enabled more extensive processing of sensory data and devising of alternative behaviors. The neocortex has evolved its greatest extension as yet in humans enabling extensive interconnection of the billions of neurons of the neocortex and the primitive brain thereby enabling our extended consciousness. Still the primitive brain remains the core *sine qua non*, without which the neocortex 'icing' can't operate.[57] Ironically while the neocortex is the more advanced part of our brain, it appears to be the less complex: The pictures in texts on human brain anatomy[58] show the primitive brain as a complex of specialized structures but the neocortex is shown as just an extensive furrowed thin-sheet of gray matter.

Brains into Minds*

The vertebrate brain is crowned by the *cerebrum*[59] which as said, exhibits the greatest proportional expansion as the various mammal species' brain size increase relative to their body size. Our human brain is proportion-

*The next twenty-six pages get rather intense so you may want to first skim them up to 'Symbols, Music & Language', then come back here.

ately three- or four-times larger than chimpanzee and Australopithecus brains due primarily to our expanded cerebrum—particularly the frontal and temporal lobes—in the past half-million years.[60] The outer shell of the cerebrum is the *cerebral cortex* (aka neocortex, *cortex*[61]=bark). Familiar pictures show the neocortex in folds capping the human brain from front-to-rear and side-to-side. Our cerebrum is divided in half by a fissure front-to-rear down the middle (the right-brain/left-brain lateralization) thus forming 'hemispheres' (though they're really more like quadrispheres). The halves are interconnected by a thick band of axons, our *corpus callosum*, deep in the center of the fissure, just above our thalamus but below our cingulate cortex.[62] The rear part of our neocortex receives and processes sensory data—visual starting at the very rear, auditory on the sides, and tactile and other across the top—comparing incoming sensory data with previous experiences. The frontal parts handle motor functions including speech as well as higher intellectual functions.[63] Even so, the processes going on in our neocortex are mostly un- or pre-conscious.

So how do such brains become minds? Well let's try a metaphor. To grasp new ideas a metaphor is useful to bridge the mental gap from the familiar to the strange (indeed metaphors play a crucial role in our brain as we'll see later). The difficulty in grasping new concepts is compounded if we can't come up with a cogent metaphor. For instance it's been said that the operation of the heart wasn't fully understood until chambered water pumps were invented providing an appropriate metaphor. In recent years a great deal has been learned about brains and at least one Darwinian metaphor has been proposed[64] (the analogy of the computer falls far short as mentioned already). So let me describe a metaphor that I find helpful and hopefully you will too.

Let's set the stage with a whimsical analogy. Imagine a vast tropical rainforest broken by many streams into many areas each with slightly differing ecologies. Tightly packed trees reach up into the canopy where their branches entangle. Their roots disappear down below the forest floor. Up in the canopy many plants grow where their branches and vines entwine in the trees' branches. Troops of monkeys live in the canopy, leaping from branch to branch as they forage for fruit and fresh leaves, raise their young and live out their monkey lives, generation after generation. Imagine however that each new generation of these monkeys has adventurous youths with a penchant to cross the streams and migrate through the forest, say south to north, so that each new generation of them must adapt to new areas as they go. If these young monkeys colonize an area that suits them, or the ecology of the area shifts in their favor, those monkeys will be selected to prosper. If the reverse occurs, they'll fail. So as they migrate, both the forest's and the monkeys' attributes will vary favoring some species of monkeys over others. Normally you might not notice the monkeys up in the canopy scurrying about but if they get excited they'll raise a ruckus, screaming and shaking branches, their howls reverberating through the forest (imagine if they synchronize!). When one troop invades another's area excitement escalates especially in the dominant troop. Then they'll get your attention.

Now keep my monkey metaphor in mind as we explore human brains. Our human neocortex, the gray matter just under our skullcap and meninges, is like a microscopic 'rainforest' where the 'trees' are the billions of *pyramidal* (aka *apical* or *projection*) neurons just a couple millimeters or so tall, only ten-millionths the size of real rainforest trees. And our neuronal 'trees' grow in dense clusters relatively much closer together than in a real rainforest. The pyramidal neurons' 'branches' (*dendrites*)[65] reach up into the 'canopy' where more billions of other *stellate* (star-shaped) neurons grow and entwine. In comparison to the real rainforest, our neocortex 'rainforest' is vast—it's all crumpled up to fit inside our skulls but if it were uncrumpled and laid out flat, it'd be about two square feet, and then if the 'trees' were spread apart like the real trees—scaled up it'd be equivalent to many Amazon rainforests.[66]

Whereas the rainforest trees and plants get their energy and nourishment from the Sun, air and water, the neurons get theirs through the blood/brain barrier via their many surrounding *glial* cells.[67] And just as in the rainforest where some trees flourish while others languish, in our neocortex some neurons grow and spread while others shrivel.[68] The pyramidal neurons' 'roots' (axons) travel across the 'forest floor' to nearby neurons or go down 'belowground' into the brain's white matter (*myelin*) where they extend long distances to connect with remote areas of the neocortex or with primitive brain structures such as the thalamus, limbic system and cerebellum.

But even though young children at times may act like they have monkeys running around in their brains, they really don't. Instead what are running around in brains are nerve impulses (and Cem-fields, more later). Unlike the monkeys scampering along and leaping between branches, nerve impulses travel electrically inside the 'branches'—the dendrites and axons—and 'leap' across at synapses mostly via neurotransmitters. (Recall from Chapter Seven that neurotransmitters are signal particles—ions and molecules—used to communicate between cells.) Of course there are proportionately many times more nerve impulses through the neurons and their synapses than there are monkeys in the branches. When monkeys travel along the branches, the branches shake and toughen; when nerve impulses travel through the dendrites and axons, they writhe and strengthen especially at the synapses. Significantly when nerve impulses repeatedly travel through neurons their dendrites' shapes are altered; indeed the nerve impulses shape the neurons which in turn affect subsequent nerve impulses, and on and on recursively. In addition, like forest monkeys that travel mainly in the canopy of their own area with some coming down to cross streams into a new area, nerve impulses also concentrate in their own area but send representatives into another area 'belowground' through axons to other neocortex areas and primitive brain structures.

Not only is the neocortex 'forest' extremely shrunk, but so is its time: whereas a monkey generation is a few years, a nerve impulse 'generation' is a few tenths of a second or less. And just as monkey varieties and species, generation after generation, can prosper or dwindle, nerve impulses can be reinforced and multiply or be inhibited. They 'mutate' too through chaotic processes and adapt to different areas of the 'forest'. And while both monkeys and nerve impulses scamper back-and-forth in their local 'forest canopy', nerve impulses can also travel relatively great distances at great speeds, not only between cortical areas (visual, auditory, motor, prefrontal ...) but also to and from other brain structures (thalamus, cerebellum ...) as well as to and from other central and peripheral nerves throughout our body.

Our neocortex 'forest' has many different specialized areas, regions and subareas (aka modalities). For example there are at least twenty some visual areas on either side of the rear brain (*occipital lobes*) where nerve impulses from our eyes are parceled out and categorized.[69] The primary visual area V1 receives the impulses in a skewed map depicting the visual images and preliminarily categorizes them as to shape, movement, color and so forth. The impulses are multiplied and forwarded by category to specialized areas for parallel processing. For instance, while area V4 is further selecting for colors, other areas are simultaneously selecting for shapes, motions or distances. Like monkeys migrating into a new area of the forest, as nerve impulses enter a specialized area of the neocortex those with traits that fit some of the neurons there are selected to prosper (they find their niche). To illustrate, nerve impulses that are somehow coded 'red' will be favored by neurons attuned to red so the 'red' neurons strengthen and multiply the 'red' impulses.[70] Those neurons are also invigorated facilitating subsequent restimulation which not only aids short-term memory but, especially in the developing brains of young children, actually sensitizes that area of the neocortex to interpret what's being seen.

Aside from the obvious, is there an important distinction between my monkey metaphor and neuronal nerve impulses? The monkeys exist individually to live and reproduce (just monkeying around ... so to speak), and collectively to perpetuate their species. The nerve impulses may do these things too (on an infinitesimal timescale) but don't they also have an important mission in support of the whole organism? Whereas the forest probably would survive without the monkeys, our organism won't survive without its brain with its nerve impulses—we'd be brain-dead. So while the nerve impulses may 'evolve' as individuals and 'species' (nerve patterns), how is their interest subverted to serve the organism? Maybe nerve impulses' relation to the brain is more like bees', ants' or termites' relation to their hive, nest, or colony.

Further Speculation

Let's set aside my monkey metaphor for a while and, if you're up for it, look more closely at what may actually be happening in our neocortex 'forest'. (Bear in mind that, though neurons may be special kinds of cells, neurons still have all the complexity of basic eukaryote cells described in Chapters Six and Seven albeit with their membranes extending in long tubules.) Picture a pyramidal neuron with its dendrite branches reaching up from its body and an axon extending down. Start at one of the dendrite branches where an abutting synapse from some other neuron's axon releases neuro*transmitters* into the synaptic gap or cleft between them. Any ambient neuro*modulators* in the gap will influence which neuro*transmitters* cross over to and are picked up by our downstream neuron's dendrite producing an electrical wave down our dendrite's branch. As the wave form travels down the writhing branch it's perhaps either amplified or attenuated by that branch much like a tone through a trumpet. Meanwhile other upstream neurons' synapses with their own unique pulses also have been triggering corresponding waves in our dendrite's other branches. When all these waves meet at the branch joints, or crotches, as they travel down the dendrites they combine into complex waves. When these complex waves reach the neuron's cell body they generate composite trains of pulses in the axon that are sent on to its downstream synapses.[71]

The nerve impulses leaving the neuron at its axonal synapses are composites of at least three factors: 1) all the nerve impulses received from preceding upstream neurons' synapses, 2) modulated by ambient neuromodulators at the synaptic gaps and 3) shaped by this neuron's dendrite branches. The nerve impulses from preceding upstream neurons were similarly formed. They may have come from upstream sensory areas (visual, auditory ...), from primitive brain components (along with neuromodulators), from prefrontal areas or from spontaneous neuron cycling or idling.[72] Previous nerve impulses through the neuron shaped its dendrites and synapses which then shape subsequent nerve impulses which in turn further shape dendrites, and so on in a repetitive learning process thereby forming memories.[73]

Nerve impulses traveling through a neocortical area usually migrate in large groups and organize into patterns as they go. (Like a large troop of monkeys migrating through the forest but the monkeys would have to organize into formation, phalanxes, like a vast army on the march.) The nerve impulse patterns traverse neocortical areas that each constitutes a 'map' depicting that area's perspective skewed to detect central features. For example the primary visual areas V1 and V2 have a 'map' on which are displayed the nerve patterns of the perspective as seen by the respective halves of the eyes' retinas. The 'map' is like a distorted grid on which the eyes' 'views' can be laid out, but the 'views' are not a picture of what the eyes see, rather they're the nerve impulse patterns. As described above, as the nerve impulse patterns are parceled and forwarded to successively more specialized visual areas, each area in turn has its own 'map', though perhaps in a distorted form idiosyncratic to that brain, our own unique synthesis.[74]

Thus the waves of sensory data from an object are segregated according to their attributes and migrate through the brain's specialized subareas reinforcing or attenuating those attributes as they go.

Binding

So that's how the sensory data are dissected to reinforce each attribute, but how are they reassembled to depict the composite scene? Particularly when you consider that the newly incoming saccadic waves of signals from the eyes are continually changing not only as the visual scene changes, but as the eyes, head and body reposition themselves. Just as your computer's color printer does when properly aligned, the respective patches of each 'map' must all register so each individual shape has its proper color, movement and other features. Well, we know that as the various subareas are processing in parallel there's much back and forth 'talk' between subareas in the form of synchronized impulses. Axonal nerve impulses are spikes of electrochemical energy. The spikes are arranged in an irregular sequence, an encoded train of spikes (like a bicycle peloton), followed by a rest, then another train and so on. Nerve impulse trains are sent in bursts.[75] In an active neuron the bursts are at a rate of 35 to 75Hertz (bursts per second) called 'gamma oscillations', nominally 40Hertz.[76] Nerve impulse patterns from corresponding patches that are coded for color, form, motion and other features are thought to bind together by synchronizing their bursts. It's like a group of different musical instruments playing on the same beat. Different patches of the 'map' might each have their own 'beat' (still at the same tempo) so they don't interfere with one another. In addition to the synchronized bursts there's evidence of 'neural transients' where non-synchronous brain areas nonetheless somehow act in tandem.[77]

The wonder is that the pieces can all be put back together again so we experience a composite scene, that somehow all the specialized visual areas are patched together as if in an assembly area. But are there such assembly areas in our brain? The answers seems to be yes and no. Yes, there are multisensory assembly areas both in the limbic system where the gist of processed data from each of the senses is combined into a whole and in the posterior parietal (association) cortex.[78] For instance an object's visual data are combined with its auditory and olfactory data. But no, there seems to be no pre-assembly within the individual sense areas; the refined data are somehow bound into a harmonized composite before being sent to the limbic system.[79] An alternative speculation described in the next section, is that electromagnetic fields induced by the nerve impulses blend together.[80]

Thus mammalian brains somehow experience all the refined visual nerve impulse patterns as composites, as gestalts, as if a quartet were playing in our brain so the various instruments blend into one melody. Specifically, as speculated at the end of an earlier section, the brain through its visual senses gathers myriad photons, say that are reflected from a tree, converts them into nerve impulses and through the Darwinian processes described above somehow assembles those data synergistically into an integrated representation of that tree. It may not be very satisfying to say that it's a synergistic process, but that's what it seems to be. They self-organize critically perhaps by the process described in Chapter Six. Perhaps the nerve impulse patterns that best fit that neuronal environment compete with other patterns to find their niche through recursive 'evolution' in our brain. In nature slightly different varieties, via mutations and sex, are produced from which their environment selects those with the 'best fit' to reproduce the next generation of varieties from which nature again selects 'best fit' and so on. Chaos in our brain produces slight differences in nerve impulse patterns, 'mutations', from which the 'best fit' in their basin of attraction/landscape (explained below under Volition) is selected to multiply into slightly different patterns, again selecting for 'best fit' and so on. And still these processes are all at the un- or pre-conscious level.

This same basic Darwinian process is likely utilized in most areas throughout our neocortex as well as in many of our primitive brain structures. In sum, as the visual nerve impulses move forward through the neo-cortex 'forest' all the visual attributes are first matched. Then they are com-bined, through coordination in the limbic system, with other sensory data such as auditory[81] and olfactory. As the 'evolving' impulse patterns invade successively more specialized areas they encounter trials of their synergy, of their 'plausibility'. Our brain tries to form gestalts, to make sense of the candidate representations. For example our brain applies visual, auditory and motor tests as in the prosaic quip, "It looks like a duck, squawks like a duck and walks like a duck, so it must be a duck!" Generally our brain tries not to present a representation to our (non-dreaming) consciousness until it's been recognized and categorized (abstract art purposely circum-vents this criterion[82]). And if there are alternates only one is presented at a time, such as the drawing of a vase that alternatively can be seen as side-view silhouettes of two faces facing each other.[83] Or if part of the view is missing or hidden, our brain infers what needs to be filled in to complete the gestalt.[84]

Emerging Consciousness

So how's consciousness emerge from all that? Continuing our spec-ulation, somehow as the harmonized nerve impulses began to dominate their neuronal 'environment' with their reverberations, they begin to emerge into consciousness. (It's perhaps like my metaphorical monkeys escalating one another's excitement by howling in unison back-and-forth throughout the forest.) Some believe there's a threshold intensity of these impulse reverberations in our brain that constitutes consciousness; an in-tensity level of diverse, integrated nerve impulses coursing back-and-forth through the neurons of our neocortex, limbic system and thalamus.[85] It's not the neurons themselves but the nerve impulses through the neu-rons;[86] not the anatomy but the physiology. (Think of the filament in an in-candescent lightbulb: as the electric current increases, the filament starts to glow.) And it's not just an intensity of 'noise' but of 'harmony'—there must be synergy to produce a gestalt that emerges into consciousness, weakly or strongly.

At first this may seem too simple. Yet I can't help but wonder, maybe naïvely, if the 'hard problem of consciousness'[87] that philosophers and neuroscientists are struggling to untangle is a kind of 'Gordian knot[88] of consciousness'.[89] As I understand it the 'hard problem' asks a reductionist question, 'How does the material of the brain produce a subjective experi-ence?' But as discussed in Chapter Four this is an emergence question.

Cutting the 'Gordian knot of consciousness' may be to simply recognize that our brain's reaction to synergistic nerve impulse patterns is what we experience as conscious. In other words is consciousness how we experience emergent synergy in our brain?[90]

Alternatively there's speculation that consciousness may be an attribute of an electromagnetic field, the em-field, that is induced by the nerve impulses coursing through neurons. (You're probably aware that an electric current in a wire induces a magnetic field around the wire, even if the wire's covered.) With so many neurons, even though the nerve impulses in each induce only a weak electromagnetic field, if synchronized the cumulative effect can produce a significant electromagnetic field, which within limits it's argued, is experienced as consciousness, called a Cem-field (aka *cemi* field: conscious electromagnetic information field). Accordingly the Cem-field produces mind whereas the digital nerve impulses produce brain. So while the nerve impulses in the brain (and in and out of the brain) process data un-, sub- and pre-consciously, those nerve impulses that are sufficiently synchronized can induce an em-field that is robust enough to produce the phenomenon of consciousness, mind. The Cem-field also provides an alternative explanation of binding. Moreover in turn the Cem-field can affect nerve impulse processing so that a synapse that is poised on the brink of opening (or closing) can be 'pushed over the edge'. Thus mind affects brain, according to the Cem-field theory.[91]

So we can speculate that there may be three systems working in concert in our brain/mind. The most ancient are the aforementioned signal particles communicating between all our body cells, described in Chapter Seven, which in our brain are called neuromodulators, and which prescribe its tone, the emotional subjective feeling. Recall, these neuromodulators do this by affecting the flow of neurotransmitters at the neurons' synapses.[92] Second the nerve impulses through our neurons are analogous to electrons in a futuristic synergistic Darwinian computer, processing and generating signals entirely(?) unconsciously. Third the Cem-field generated around the neurons by the flow of nerve impulses through the neurons would then produce what we experience as consciousness. Thus neuromodulators prescribe emotions, neurons store data and their nerve impulses process data (brain), and the Cem-field produces consciousness (mind). Well, it's an interesting conjecture, maybe even heuristic.

Still another alternative speculation suggests that consciousness is somehow a function of quantum mechanics. The Copenhagen interpretation of quantum mechanics asserts that micro-particle behavior is caused by a mind's conscious intervention, so some speculate that consciousness must also be due to activity in the quantum realm. But I've found little that explains how this might happen,[93] although one theory speculates how consciousness affects volition, which we'll get to shortly.

There are degrees of consciousness as mentioned at the beginning of this chapter. Pursuing our speculation, the synergistic nerve impulses or Cem-field may just barely emerge in-and-out of consciousness only dimly or, at the other end of the spectrum, they may resonate with glowing intensity and clarity. And it's not just *in*tensity that varies but *ex*tensity—extensive areas of the brain can be involved in the experience of consciousness. As said, the basic minimal consciousness is called *core*–consciousness whereas extensive consciousness is called (wouldn't you know) *extended-consciousness*.[94] Accordingly some believe many other animal species experience core-consciousness[95] and probably a few somewhat more, but evidently only we humans experience fully extended-consciousness thanks to our extensive neocortex. Note however, if core-consciousness is lost, all consciousness is lost.[96] (In the next chapter I'll describe how consciousness can be extended even further beyond into even higher levels of intensity which I'll call 'numinous' consciousness.)

Another way of distinguishing conscious levels of discernment that I find useful is as qualia, percepts and concepts. Qualia (singular = quale [long 'e'], same root as quality) are the properties our mind assigns to sensory experiences.[97] For instance a light ray with a wavelength around 600nm or so (depending on the ambient light[98]) is experienced in our mind as having the quale of 'red'. Even though as mentioned in Chapter Four, the visible light spectrum is only a slim band of the electromagnetic radiation range, our mind assigns great importance to 'slight' changes in wavelength, say between red and green. But we can't even imagine 'colors' beyond our visible spectrum such as the ultraviolet and infrared sensed by bees and rattlesnakes. Thus colors are qualia that our mind assigns to visible light rays just as musical tones are the qualia our mind assigns to sensed vibrating air (sounds).[99] Perhaps the most basic quale is 'feeling'.[100] It's argued that nonconscious animals don't have feelings and indeed when we're unconscious we don't.[101] When something creeps into our consciousness, we become aware of a 'vague feeling'.

Percepts are the way our mind integrates various sensory experiences, the qualia of objects, into integrated wholes, gestalts. For instance a round, red, distant object in the sky near the horizon would likely be perceived as the Sun. Whereas, at the next higher level, concepts are the way our mind explains objects (or ideas).[102] For instance the Sun used to be explained as Helios in his chariot driving across the heavens, then as a burning ball circling the Earth, and now (since Copernicus) as a nearby star that our rotating Earth circles. Hence, qualia are how we experience our senses, percepts are how we put our sense experiences together and concepts are how we make sense of them.[103] (But as mentioned above each of us may form our own unique idiosyncratic synthesis from the same data coming into our brain.[104])

But I'm a little mystified when I read that "It is simply impossible to conceive of a conscious state that is not unified."[105] As I sit pondering what that means here in my study on this warm summer evening I'm conscious of the fan blowing on me and my chair pressing against my butt and back. I'm conscious of the string sextet playing on my stereo. As I absently gaze out my study windows I'm conscious of the window curtains and framing, the leaves of the bushes just outside the windows, the trees beyond and the myriad other details many of which could change without disturbing the 'unity' of the scene. But I'm primarily conscious of pondering this question that seems incongruous given these disparate conscious states all seemingly in my mind simultaneously. I conclude either that my consciousness shuttles between these 'states' so rapidly that they merge into a seemingly single state or alternatively that the unity refers to me: I'm always the unit who's experiencing all these states. But then later I'm rescued by reading elsewhere about "... multitasking, the ability to do or think about several things at the same time."[106] And so I struggle on, tossed from one 'expert' to another (maybe you're feeling the same).

By now you're probably getting confused with the three different sets of terms employed to qualify consciousness. I'll try to distinguish among them: As said, most of what goes on in our brain, nervous system and neurotransmission is *un*conscious or *non*conscious. If it's destined to emerge into consciousness it's first processed as *pre*conscious and if it's more-or-less deliberately set aside out of consciousness, it's *sub*conscious. Than there's the degree to which consciousness can emerge, the minimal being *core*–consciousness and higher degrees *extended*–consciousness. And third, there are the levels of discernment, stages data can be processed through from raw feelings, *qualia*, then into gestalts, *percepts*, and perhaps finally into explanations, *concepts*, as described two paragraphs above and elaborated below.

From Percepts to Concepts

We've discussed how our sensory nerve impulses 'evolve' as they migrate forward through our neocortex 'forest' into evermore specialized sensory areas. Now let's look at the routes they travel. Earlier, in discussing how visual nerve impulses travel through the visual areas, I glossed over an important fact. The visual nerve impulses having to do with the object's location, movement, distance etc, the 'where?' nerve impulses, travel from the rear of our brain along the top, from the occipital cortex into the parietal cortex, under our skullcap (if we wore one).[107] Here they associate with touch (haptic) and auditory 'where?' nerve impulses (probably via the limbic system). As the evolving 'where?' nerve impulses continue forward they encounter[108] a frontier that runs across the neocortex from side-to-side. These are the bands of the *somatosensory* (*soma*=body) region followed by the *motor* region with a lateral fissure between (the *central sulcus*). Together these two bands cap the primitive brain components to monitor and control our body, our organism, as discussed earlier in this chapter. This brain frontier divides the 'where?' percepts of our outside world from our body's maps of itself.[109] This somatosensory frontier is where our body orients outside objects relative to itself and thus distinguishes the world from itself, its proto-self.

Meanwhile 'in another part of the forest' the other visual nerve impulses having to do with that same object's color and shape, the 'what?' nerve impulses, travel from the rear of our brain along the sides, from the occipital cortex into the temporal cortex inboard of our ears. Here the 'what?' of vision combines with the 'what?' of sound (again via the limbic system) and, along with smell and taste data, proceeds forward into the frontal cortex, the front 'halves' of our neocortex hemispheres. Indeed the now refined concise 'what?' nerve impulse patterns go 'underground' into the myelin and travel all the way to the very front of the brain, the prefrontal cortex. Similarly the now refined concise 'where?' nerve impulse patterns dive into the myelin and also emerge in the prefrontal cortex.[110]

Whereas the rear part of our neocortex decides 'what?' and 'where?', the front part decides 'now what?'—how to turn those sensations into behavior. After all, our ancestors evolved bigger, energy-voracious brains in order to enhance their potential for action. Contemplation, like sex, didn't evolve just for fun but for results.

Now comes a reversal of direction. The rear neocortex took myriad sense data and as they traveled forward focused them into specific percepts. Then, having resurfaced at the very front of the brain, the prefrontal cortex now takes those percepts and sends them back toward the motor regions looking for and weighing alternative potential courses of action: foresight. And again the 'where?' patterns travel back along the top of the brain (dorsal) and the 'what?' patterns travel back along the outsides (lateral). The insides (medial, where the hemispheres face each other[111]) and bottom (ventromedial) deal with social issues: insight. Along the way to the motor regions, the supplementary and premotor areas create a plan and coordinate its performance (fine-tuned and automated by the cerebellum).[112] The motor region implements the plan by sending signals to the particular muscles in order to carry out the action.[113]

As the result of these encounters it seems at least three things might happen. First and fundamentally, the organism may react to the object defensively, aggressively or however through its motor regions and cerebellum. This is the primary function of the somatosensory and motor regions enabling the organism to deal with its environment as perceived via the perceptual 'maps' generated in the sensory areas. Having gotten an assessment from the rear brain of what and where the object is, the frontal brain then forms alternative plans for dealing with the object. How should it best take flight from the object, or fight with it, or eat it, or join with it or just ignore it? (While deciding it'll probably 'freeze'.) The more complex the frontal brain, the more complex the plans it can evolve.

Second, as the result of the object's percept's encounter with these regions, the organism might possibly experience itself as separate and distinct from the object; its proto-self *may* emerge into consciousness as its self.[114] Consciousness of self may be constructed as object percepts encounter proto-self percepts. (I suspect consciousness of self may have something to do with its Life Urge emerging into consciousness, which we'll pursue in the next chapter.) Recall our previous discussion of the 'theory of mind' wherein our early ancestors learned to infer what others were thinking, others' intentions, (to read their minds) by putting themselves in the other person's place, 'in their shoes' (but back then who wore shoes?).[115] Of course to infer what others are thinking, ideally we should know what we're thinking.[116] To do this requires that the 'maps' in the somatosensory region which represent the proto-self emerge into consciousness as the self, probably by the same intense reverberation of nerve impulses described above. Of course the 'maps' of the self are consistent (we always perceive our right hand even though in different positions) whereas the sensory 'maps' of the panorama around us change as different objects move in-and-out of our surroundings, our self-centered perspective ("Your viewpoint depends on your point of view").

Third, as the object's percept encounters the motor regions, the object's percept may be further processed into a concept. What have our brain's somatosensory and motor regions (sensorimotor system) got to do with concepts? Well here's a clue—Many concepts emanate from metaphors constructed from the body's temporal or spatial activities, or postures. For example in the last paragraph I used the expression '*putting* oneself in the other's shoes'. A few other rudimentary examples (of course the mental metaphors came before the language metaphors cited here[117]): "This will *lead* to trouble." "They *reached* an agreement." "You're *standing in the way* of my plans." "Try to think *straight*." "This *line* of thinking is *taking* you in the wrong *direction*." "Are you *getting ahead* or just *catching up*?"[118] It should come as no surprise that our brain uses perceptual 'maps' to build up concepts; that's how evolution works—it builds on existing structures by adapting and elaborating genes and organs for new functions as described earlier with forelimbs—so why would it not do the same with neurons and nerve impulses?

Our brain builds concepts from percepts mainly by combining unconscious primary metaphors into complex metaphors. As infants we conflated subjective experiences with sensorimotor experiences, such as not distinguishing affection from the warmth of being held. Later as we differentiated the experiences we retained the association so we envisage a 'warm smile' or a 'close friend' as a primary metaphor permanently etched in our neurons. We formed hundreds of these primary metaphors: affection is warmth, important is big (mom and dad), more is up (filling a cup), and so on. Hence we can blend primary metaphors to form a complex metaphor, such as the concept of love as warm, accepting, enduring and important. And complex metaphors can be further blended into even more complex metaphors such as 'love is a journey' fraught with obstacles and requiring perseverance.[119]

Now let's put together some illustrations of how concepts might 'evolve' in the brain. A hair comb is cited as an example.[120] A comb's most important visual category is shape, especially its fine teeth. Its color is not definitive even though commonly black. Sound might be a clue if we bothered to run our thumbnail along the tips of its teeth. But what defines a comb is its function, so its visual 'shape' percept is tested in the premotor regions by unconsciously imagining handling it as we run it through our hair. Does it 'fit' the motor memories of other combs our hand and head have known? So regardless of its exact shape and color, or whether we 'zipped' its teeth, the crucial issue is: Does it handle as a comb? (Whether it's a generic comb or a particular comb, namely ours, depend on its size, color and broken teeth.)

But a comb is a man-made, functional object. An *a*–functional example from nature is our old nemesis 'sunrise'. If our somatosensory neurons are accustomed to "feel the earth beneath our feet" stable and immobile, then our concept says that the huge red ball we call the Sun 'rises' through the clouds above the eastern hills as would a huge bird or airplane. If we've been taught that it's Helios in his chariot just above the clouds (and we know about chariots), we might believe it. If we've been thinking 'heretically' we might conclude that Helios is a myth and that instead the Sun is a ball of fire (like fires we've known) but then takes on another myth of how it melted Icarus' wings when he flew too close. Or with Ptolemy's *Almagest* we might conclude that the Sun is far, far away but still trust our somatosensory instinct that the Earth is stable and immobile. We feel it 'in our bones'. It's a struggle to go against such instincts—'common sense'—in order to think counter-intuitively.

Only when our instincts conflict with other concepts freshly im-planted in our brain—say the image of Earth as a rotating 'moon' circling the Sun—creating perplexing cognitive dissonance, namely competition between conflicting nerve impulse patterns, that our 'evolving' neurons are compelled to 'select the fittest' pattern. The abstract scientific and mathe-matical concepts (formed from other metaphors) in our prefrontal cortex conflict with our somatosensory instincts until we 'rewire' our brain[121] with an exercise such as the Ferris wheel described in Chapter Four.[122] Even after enlarging our conceptual framework we may continue to use 'sunrise' as a shorthand expression even though we 'know better'.

Note again that, in addition to the impediment of our somatosen-sory instincts, the formation of a revised concept can be impeded by an 'authority': Don't *go* there! the Church warned Copernicus, Bruno and Galileo. Our inquisitiveness is counseled and enjoined by our elders, then by teachers, clerics and scientists whether to accept the received 'facts' or pursue some 'heretic's' extraneous line of inquiry. Rebellious youth, trying to disentangle themselves from their elders and find their own Self, quite naturally challenge authority. But as adults we may fall into habitual thinking without questioning old concepts so that it takes constant vigi-lance to intentionally keep an open mind.[123] Just how intentions influence the processing and 'evolution' of nerve impulses as they journey through our brain will be explored after a look at memory storage.

Learning & Memory

Resorting once more to my monkey metaphor, imagine that as the monkeys scamper about in the forest canopy the branches they travel along eventually thicken and grow to reinforce those monkeys' route. Analogously by repeatedly running the same nerve impulse patterns through the neocortex neurons they somehow eventually grow pathways that favor those patterns. Then at a later time when similar nerve impulse patterns travel into those neurons, those patterns fit the pathways and are favored. It's like treading a beaten path through the woods; it's easier going than breaking a new trail. That's why fresh percepts and concepts are harder to discern than familiar ones, as I forewarned in Chapter One when I spoke of 'rewiring' our brain.[124]

Perhaps the most basic way of embedding memories is through repetition. By repeating an experience the same neuronal pathways are re-stimulated causing those synapses and dendrites to strengthen and grow thus forming long-term memories. The first few times the monkeys travel a new route through the forest, they have to search for a way through by trial and error until they find the best trail and clear it; 'breaking trail' is tough going. Similarly when we first try something new, to ride a bike or travel an unfamiliar route, our frontal cortex must sort out how best to deal with it. But after a few trials our frontal cortex finds the best way and no longer has to search; it consigns the pathway to the fewest neurons (in the cerebellum?) that will suffice with the least attention, the 'learning curve', in effect automating it.[125] "Practice makes perfect."

Let's get somewhat more specific. As explained earlier, when electrochemical nerve impulses pass from one neuron's synapse to another's dendrite, they invigorate that synapse at least temporarily in effect leaving a memory trace in the pathway. But recall that as sensory nerve impulse patterns travel into the prefrontal regions only a concise encapsulation, the gist of their meaning, is sent invigorating those prefrontal synapses. If more detail is needed, the prefrontal neurons refer back to the antecedent sensory neurons where the traces of the pattern can be restimulated to recall details. However the invigoration doesn't last and the short-term memory fades if no nerve impulses cross the synapse for a few minutes to a few hours at most; longest in the prefrontal neurons to hold onto a thought (working memory), shortest in the sensory neurons to clear the way for the next wave of inputs.[126]

But our brain has a trick for embedding memories through internal repetition. As mentioned, if the synapse is kept active with repeated impulses the downstream dendrites will thicken and grow forming a more permanent long-term memory trace. This is accomplished by the hippocampus, an expanded component of the primitive brain's limbic system. The hippocampus is a miniature, rolled-up scroll of simple three-layer cortex next to our entorhinal six-layer cortex—a 'woodland' next to the 'forest'—inboard the temporal lobes between our ears. Like the prefrontal cortex the hippocampus receives only the gist of relevant memories—perhaps the way hypertext links to other computer files and websites—but the hippocampus can keep them active perhaps even longer than the prefrontal synapses. Most importantly the hippocampus can continue to reinforce the sensory and frontal memory traces with repeated impulses until the traces become embedded in those neocortex neurons' dendrites as permanent long-term memories. In effect the hippocampus may exercise the new neuronal pathway the same way actual repetition does as described above.[127] There's some evidence that this goes on during sleep.[128]

In the rapidly growing brains of infants and children the young 'sapling' neurons haven't yet taken on shapes and are furiously sprouting dendrites in search of nerve impulse patterns. Thus their young brains learn at an astonishing rate mapping their bodies and how their torso, limbs and little parts move, and assimilating touch, taste, sound and sight data flowing in through their developing senses. Indeed the way their neocortex develops depends on these early experiences in order to model their world: "As the twig is bent, so is the tree ..." formed or deformed. "The cortex is what it eats." The various regions are genetically disposed to 'eat' their own 'special diets', but if they don't 'eat' they don't grow. For instance the visual regions in their neocortex' occipital lobes must receive nerve impulse patterns from the eyes to develop. Unstimulated neurons that don't receive patterns to shape them shrivel and may die. If a child is deprived of sight in one eye, even though that eye is normal, its brain's visual regions for that eye wouldn't develop.[129]

However even though everything in a young person's brain and sense organs may be normal, there still will be differences in the way each person's brain assimilates the data it encounters. This is due not only to the influence of earlier assimilations but to the random nerve impulses generated in their neurons. So even though two individuals encounter the same data, each dendrite 'twig is bent' a little differently. And rarely do they encounter exactly the same data. So each person's brain is formed a little differently and thus is unique. For instance my quale of 'red' may be a little different from yours so our memories of a red rose we both saw will be slightly different.[130]

The tricky part is to recall learning and memories.[131] Memories are stored and accessed via their 'links', the gist of the memory, so if we don't know its 'link' or 'hypertext', we have a tough time recalling the memory. For instance, think of how much easier it is to recognize a little used word than to recall it when we want to use it. If our conscious mind can't find it we may be able to enlist our sub- or unconscious to help.[132] I mentioned earlier how my subconscious sometimes relinquishes a memory if I consciously admit defeat—'stand out of my own way'—more humbling evidence that our unconscious knows a lot more than our conscious. However there's evidence that even our unconscious efficiently only stores the gists of memories and that to fill in details our conscious fabricates them.[133] Language—words and phrases—provides symbols for gists which we'll discuss shortly in the section on Symbols, Music and Language.

Memory processes have traditionally been classified either as short-term working memory—vivid, conscious and active—or as long-term memory—unconscious and inactive. More recently 'long-term working memory' or 'intermediate-term awareness' has been used to describe those memories that can be quickly brought in-and-out of consciousness and updated as needed in performing a task, carrying on a conversation or what have you (analogous to our PC's RAM).[134] A related issue of long-term memory is intentional or volitional recall, known as autobiographical or episodic memory (analogous to our PC's hard-drive). This is the ability to more or less deliberately recall episodes from our recent or distant past, our 'autobiography'. There's some debate as to what extent non-human animals have episodic memory but certainly we do.[135]

Volition

If most of what goes on in our brains is un- or pre-conscious, where does freewill come in? Who's minding the store? Who's flying the plane or is it on autopilot? How are we in charge—or aren't we? Let's approach this question by considering intentions. (In earlier times young men were asked by their girlfriends' fathers if their intentions were honorable—which of course they weren't, as fathers knew.)

Volition—freewill—comes down to whether we're free to choose and carry out our intentions. A definition of intent that I find cogent is, "An intent is the directing of an action toward some future goal that is defined and chosen by the actor. It differs from a motive, which is the reason and explanation of the action, and from a desire, which is the awareness and experience stemming from the intent. A man shoots another with the intent to kill, which is separate from why he does it and with what feeling."[136] Courts assess culpability based on intentions but of course the judge is looking for the accused's conscious intent ("knowingly, willingly and deliberately"). However we humans are not always consciously aware of our intentions (we're sometimes most effective when we're not) and other animals even less so. So let's start with a reductionist approach to get down to basics.

An organism's basic intention is to live, the Urge to Life; everything else is an elaboration of that basic intent. This may seem rather farfetched. Indeed, most of the urges we experience seem a long way from any basic Life Urge but with some effort they can be traced back to that origin. For example an urge to have a treat that's not on our diet may not arise directly from hunger but indirectly from a reward that evolved to sustain Life, what's now sometimes called a sugar- or fat-rush. Other frivolous urges may be the result of displaced basic needs. Even our quest for knowledge and wisdom evolved out of our species' way of understanding how nature and history work in order to optimize our ability to predict and prosper. (Some male science writers argue that the basic urge is to perpetuate one's genes—so the reason they write their books is to get women?!! And does it work?)

Thus because there are alternative ways of expressing the Life Urge an organism must make choices. By running alternatives through its upper brain before acting, a higher organism can try them out, test them, in its virtual 'inside world' before trying them in its real 'outside world', thereby improving its odds of success in the real world. Thus in order to be an effective 'tool' the upper brain had to evolve to model, to be analogous to, to somehow make itself similar to (assimilate), the outside world; it had to somehow be able to represent the outside world's operations and processes. Perhaps since nature in the outside world uses the Darwinian process to evolve and grow, the upper brain models the same process in both the sensory and motor regions for nerve impulse patterns to evolve and grow, but at a much faster rate. Hence the term 'neural Darwinism'.[137]

Just as an organism must be active in pursuing its Life Urge, its brain too must be active (except when asleep, maybe). In the above description of sensory nerve impulses traveling through the neocortex, the neuron 'forest' was portrayed as reactive, but it's rarely so, more likely it's proactive.[138] An animal's means of staying in touch with its environment is through its senses feeding nerve impulses into the neurons of its sensory cortices. Unless it's just idling (meditating?) its Life Urge will compel it to constantly be searching its environment, as represented in its sensory cortices, for opportunities or threats. Its surveillance at times may be general but more often is attuned for signs of specific objects. In effect the brain can bias select patches of its neocortex to favor some nerve impulse patterns over others. How?

Resorting yet again to my monkey metaphor, recall I mentioned how the roots of the trees in the rainforest reach down below the forest floor to bring up nutrients which, along with the rain and sunshine, affect the growth of the trees in that patch of the forest. Growth of fresh foliage and fruit will attract monkeys to that patch, creating a 'basin of attraction' where the itinerant monkeys can prosper. Alternatively a malnourished patch will cause the monkeys to eschew it or languish.

Similarly neurons' 'roots' reach down not only to other areas of the neocortex but to primitive brain components such as the limbic system. We've surmised that an organism's Life Urge somehow percolates from its cells and their organs on up into the primitive components of the brain atop the spinal column. It's in these primitive brain components that vertebrates internally express their Life Urge in more specific wants and needs such as hunger, thirst, warmth and shelter. And as we saw in earlier chapters, as vertebrates evolved they evolved ever more elaborate and varied appendages and organs to pursue those needs and wants including ever more complex brains to imagine and evaluate alternative actions.

A couple comparisons may encourage plausibility. A spider's "eensy-weensy" brain can weave an elegant web to catch flying insects. And a bird's tiny brain can build a secure nest to hold fragile eggs. Analogously our relatively massive primitive brain should readily be able to fashion 'webs' in our neocortex to catch fleeting nerve impulse patterns and 'nests' to hold fragile thoughts. How?

Our primitive brain components have at least two methods of influencing brain activity in our neocortex. Analogous to the nutrients up through tree roots, nerve impulses from the primitive components can somehow affect a targeted patch of neocortex neurons, perhaps by invigorating their synapses, thus generating a basin of attraction that 'tilts the playing field' favoring some patterns of sensory nerve impulses over others, in effect choosing which emerging percepts are given preferential treatment. An example might be an animal averting overheating by searching for water rather than shade, that is, favoring sense data that represent water. Similarly basins of attraction can be generated in the frontal neocortex predisposing the brain to some behavior or concept. On a broader scale several basins of attraction can be linked together into an 'attractor landscape'.[139] (In the same time frame this can also be a dynamic, recursive process wherein the brain repositions the body to better sense the object of interest; for example when we turn an object over in our hand, our brain spontaneously turns our head and focuses our eyes.)

The other method is analogous to the rain and sunshine that have a broader affect on areas of the forest. The primitive brain can disperse various neuro*modulators* throughout the whole brain which affect the neuro*transmitters* of any synapses that are trying to fire either enhancing or inhibiting their flow across the gaps. For example *oxytocin* disposes neurons to favor nerve impulse patterns for bonding and nurturing whereas *vasopressin* favors patterns of aggression.[140]

Just as the monkeys' evolution is influenced by their environment, say the trees in the forest, the nerve impulses' 'evolution' is affected by their 'environment', the neurons in the neocortex. However the primitive brain, in service to the organism's proto-self and its Life Urge, can rapidly affect the neocortex neurons, the nerve impulses' 'environment', by shifting the 'basin of attraction' and by dispersing neuromodulators as described above.

Thus the primitive brain can manipulate the newer brain's neurons through their synapses in order to focus attention on preferred nerve impulse patterns (*preafference*). These include newly incoming data from the senses (environment or body), restimulation of older embedded patterns (memories), random generation of chaotic patterns[141] (creative thoughts), or combinations thereof. The primitive brain has varying intensities of its focus. At one extreme an animal can be intensely involved in an activity and be oblivious to other happenings including severe injury. At the other extreme it can have a detached awareness of everything going on around it (a kind of meditative state) or be daydreaming (lost in thought). We'll explore what happens in the brain when a mammal's asleep in the next chapter.

Another issue needs to be clarified. I've used the analogy of monkeys migrating through the forest as though nerve impulses only flow in the forward direction. This is only generally true—just as monkeys scamper back and forth in the forest, nerve impulses do too which some call 'reentrance'.[142] There's nerve impulse backward flow, feedback, not only for prefrontal regions to retrieve detail from earlier areas, but prefrontal regions, just like the primitive brain, can somehow prime the upstream areas to anticipate nerve impulse patterns so they're searching for something, they're tuned. When the anticipated nerve impulse patterns show up in the sensory areas, they're attuned and ready to recursively sharpen those incoming patterns and suppress others. If those nerve impulse patterns don't show up, the sensory areas may be so primed that they react to spurious patterns or generate them spontaneously anyway in effect imagining them.[143] This is what happens when our mind 'completes the gestalt' as mentioned above at the end of the section on Binding as well as when our mind 'projects' as described in Chapter Two. The trick is to be able to discriminate between patterns that are incoming from the outside reality and those that are imagined, that are a reflection of what's already in oneself, a projection.

Now we can get back to the question of volition. If intentions, one way or another, flow up from an organism's Life Urge, that implies most intentions are un- or pre-conscious even in us humans. Moreover even when we're aware of our intentions it's about a half-second after our brain initiated action[144] (this is in the neocortex aside from the amygdala's unconscious 'quick-draw'). Perhaps it's like the lightbulb filament analogy of consciousness cited earlier: just as there's a delay between the start of current flow in the filament and its glow of light, perhaps there's a delay between the start of nerve impulse flow in the neurons and the build-up to a threshold of intensity for consciousness to emerge. Have you experienced lying in bed in the morning thinking about getting up and the next thing you know you're doing it?

So if we're always playing catch-up where's freewill come in? As best I've been able to ascertain it seems there are four ways that consciousness can control the unconscious brain's activities: Even though the brain has a half-second head-start, if we're vigilant it still gives us time to consciously intervene and abort inappropriate actions or impulses,[145] somewhat as described earlier with the amygdala. For instance 'biting our tongue' as we start to blurt-out something we'll regret. Secondly, if we're attentive we can anticipate some events and shorten our reaction time by priming our 'autopilot'.[146] Thirdly, when our brain presents alternatives, such as the vase-vs-faces mentioned above, or ambiguous words or situations, it usually hesitates so we can weigh them before 'authorizing' action. Finally when no action is called for immediately we can just imagine, variously called fantasizing, contemplation, discursive thinking, planning, science or mathematics. Then subsequently we take whatever action or inaction we've imagined is appropriate. As we'll see, the mind's function is not to micromanage the brain but to provide executive guidance.[147] So rather than see the delay as disconcerting, it turns out to be an asset.

One way of understanding how consciousness might guide the workings of the unconscious brain, is to envision consciousness as a sequence of movie frames. Recall that a movie is made up of a sequence of frames of still pictures' transparencies which, when rapidly flashed on the screen, appear as a smooth flow of action. Even so when the film was shot most of the action actually happened between the frames; the camera captured only brief moments in snapshots. But because of the way our brain works (saccades?) we experience the flashing snapshots as an unbroken flow. Similarly it may be that, interspersed in the unconscious processing in our brain, there are lingering flashes of consciousness when we can adjust or choose the next step. It's as if, with each frame of the movie film, we could somehow influence the subsequent action so that over the sequence of frames we could guide how the action would proceed. The 'action' in our brain is the cacophony of nerve impulse patterns coursing through our billions of neurons as described above. We can augment some patterns and suppress others just as evolution selects some mutations and culls others.[148] This is neural Darwinism described above.

Two other ways of explaining how consciousness guides the unconscious were mentioned above in the section on Emerging Consciousness—how the mind guides the brain. The Cem-field induced by nerve impulses can in turn affect nerve impulse processing (I accept that the neurons' synchronized electromagnetic field can be experienced as consciousness—a Cem-field—but I don't see how that Cem-field can become 'free will' subject to control by our mind).[149] The third way invokes quantum mechanics wherein the release of ions at the synapses is held in superposition until 'questioned' by the mind. Through the Quantum Zeno Effect, repeatedly and rapidly posing the 'question' affects the behavior of the brain.[150] Which of these three ways our brain/mind uses awaits further research— maybe all three.

There's a venerable metaphor for how we knowingly and deliberately direct our attention and our actions. When we're awake our 'stream of consciousness' continuously roams around like William James' spotlight analogy, making a flitting spot of light with a penumbra of fringe awareness. The spot of light is a patch in the neocortex 'forest' where the nerve impulses' synergistic intensity momentarily raises to the level of consciousness, like the monkeys raising a ruckus in their patch of the forest. But what in our brain functions as James' lamp to shine the beam of light? The usual suspects are primitive brain components, the thalamus and the limbic system,[151] and the prefrontal cortex's executive function to be described shortly.

Another metaphor you may have heard is of a horse and rider wherein the horse is the unconscious and the rider the conscious. A wise rider guides a powerful spirited horse with a light rein letting it 'have its head'. Too much control will break a horse's spirit. There's a fine line between rigid control and relaxed natural spontaneity. We need fairly tight control to learn a new routine or skill until we've automated it, consigning it to our subconscious where it can be called up at will. It seems we can then stand outside ourselves in what's been called *metacognition* observing the flow of our behavior with minimal intervention—"go with the flow." This is the executive function of our prefrontal lobes which uses intermediate-term awareness to maintain a broad perspective and keep several things in mind.[152]

Our human brain, then, evolved to afford us the best of both worlds: The modules of our primitive brain together with the older regions of our rear neocortex and cerebellum enabled the instantaneous unconscious reflexes that were necessary for survival in a hostile competitive world and still today enable us to operate subconsciously on autopilot much of the time. The newer general purpose regions of our neocortex, such as the prefrontal, function more slowly but enable us to cogitate and oversee our physical and mental activities, the executive function we call volition.[153]

What I've described above is undoubtedly an overly optimistic view of volition. Our un-/pre-/sub-conscious continuously presents clamoring or whispering thoughts that our executive function must somehow choose among. So just as a corporate executive can't control or even know (or want to know) all that goes on at the lower echelons, our brain's executive function can't constantly be in charge. Sometimes we may inappropriately operate on 'autopilot' and conditioned reflexes, or on basic instincts which I'll discuss next. And just as the corporate executive relies on his or her training and experience, and on the information s/he receives, our executive function is held sway by the information and concepts that were fed to our neocortex in our formative years which shaped our thought processes. Of necessity we learned to interpret our world based on that information and those concepts, some of which are undoubtedly wrong. So our executive judgment is handicapped. The examples I've harped on range from the prosaic to the profound—'sunrise' to belief in God. As children we were taught to believe in Santa Claus, the Easter Bunny, our guardian angel ... and God. We soon saw through the first two but may only now be deprogramming the others.

Instincts

Before hominids attained consciousness their minds probably worked much like other animals' minds. Animals from the simplest, on through insects and on up to 'higher' animals, mostly operate by evolved inherited programs 'hard wired' in their cells, nerves and brains. Those programs that control behavior are called 'instincts.' Instincts of spiders to fashion webs and birds to build nests and defend their territories; instincts to mate and raise young, and so on. We too have many unconscious instincts[154] but with a crucial difference: We can pretty much learn to be aware of them so that they come under the scrutiny of our conscious mind where we can judge their appropriateness. For example xenophobia—fear and hatred of strangers or foreigners—probably evolved in animals as an instinct to guard a territory that they had claimed. This instinct was useful to control resources needed to survive and propagate. But there are circumstances where it's inappropriate and can cause trouble if unconsciously triggered, like road-rage, turf battles and wars.[155] Another instinct our ancestors may have evolved from their long association with, and dependence on 'tools'—carefully crafting and toting them around—is our obsession with our 'material world' which we'll explore in Chapter Eleven: Tools. (In addition to instincts we also have learned behaviors, conditioned reflexes, which are also unconsciously triggered.)

Archetype is the term Jung applied to instincts or drives that are more flexible and can be expressed through a variety of behaviors, both unconscious and conscious.[156] Xenophobia might be such. Jung used the term 'shadow' for an instinct/archetype that operates unconsciously, is regarded as 'evil' and thus can bring on 'guilt'.[157] But we humans are masters of rationalization, denial, blaming ("The devil made me do it.") or whatever to avoid acknowledging our shadow. Most of it's just irritating to our family, friends and coworkers but it can become exasperating. In a tyrant or psychopath it becomes dangerous.

All instincts/archetypes are 'good' in that they evolved to facilitate survival and reproduction, else they probably wouldn't have been retained. But that was then and this in now—now some may be obsolete. As humans we can learn to be aware (mostly) of when our drives, moods and emotions are rooted in our instincts/archetypes. Then we may be able to judge whether they're appropriate and behave accordingly. In order to do this it's helpful to understand the origins of instinctive traits to see if they're still valid and if so, when. Flexibility is our species' trump card, but only if we're aware of our choices. Of course there's a danger here that we lose our spontaneity, our 'naturalness', through too much control. We need to be able to 'get emotional' without getting 'too emotional'. After all remember, Life's energy flows up through our emotions (e+motion).

The trick is to disentangle awareness from behavior. Like a wise parent watching their child at play, 'true restraint is to let a child venture'.[158] Moreover observing our feelings and reactions to emotions as they're arising can provide a window to increased self-knowledge. Repressing our body's needs leads to either obsessing on them or having them expressed in subversive ways. Overindulging our body's needs, of course, also has its consequences. More in Chapter Ten.

Creativity & Reason

Now that we have an inkling of how the un- and pre-conscious mind 'evolves' nerve impulse patterns in the neocortex' 'forest' of neurons, we can began to understand how and why creativity works or doesn't work.

Even when idling our neurons are spontaneously generating impulses[159] in a chaotic cacophony similar to the way organisms continuously produce mutations but on a greatly accelerated and pervasive scale. And just as their natural environment selects which, if any, of the mutated organisms 'fit' an available niche, and thus will survive and reproduce, the brain's 'environment'—namely basins of attraction in patches of the neocortex—selects which spontaneous nerve patterns 'fit', survive and are augmented, or are culled. In other words just as mutations in organisms generate a variety for their environment to select from, chaotic patterns in the brain generate variety for its basins of attraction to select from. And in both, the process is recursive so with each new generation the selection is refined into an ever better fit until a pattern evolves which is preferred by the natural environment or the brain's 'environment', and temporarily stabilizes.

But the 'evolution' of nerve impulse patterns doesn't start only with randomly generated impulses. Impulse patterns from the outside world or from inside the brain's memory can be modified and elaborated by chaotic manipulation most of which produces useless garbage. But because the patterns are manipulated so fast, like nature's evolution, occasionally something interesting or worthwhile might turn up. These too can 'fit' a basin of attraction and be augmented.

The basins of attraction for a creative process are most likely in our prefrontal cortex in conjunction with our association (parietal) cortex.[160] In effect they're formed by the criteria for a problem's solution or the specifications for a creative work. The process, as said, is most likely recursive coming up with patterns that don't quite fit the criteria but provide grist for further elaboration until something clicks and is presented to consciousness. Even then it may be sent back into the unconscious for further elaboration. This recursive process can also modify the basins of attraction in effect refining the selection criteria. How much deliberation depends on the issue. If we're just arranging flowers in a vase we probably shouldn't agonize too long. But other issues may involve much longer rumination. There's often a dilemma of when to push through for an answer (which is often counterproductive), accept the less than ideal or let it germinate in our unconscious a while longer. Sometimes we need to stoke the mental fires and then just let it cook awhile on the back burner of our mind—sleep on it.[161] Nor can we predict how, when or where our unconscious will present the answer—in whole or just in part—to our conscious; anecdotes abound from Archimedes on.[162]

Cultivating creativity can be likened to cultivating a garden: a garden grows by itself in its own time but the garden's layout provides a structure to cultivate the growth we want. We need to start with a gardening culture (a supportive or at least permissive milieu) and fertile site for the work (read 'fertile mind'[163]), then prepare the work area (office, studio, shop ...), weed out distractions, plant some ideas, and feed and water them (bagels & coffee?). But then we just have to let the ideas grow undisturbed—we can't make them grow faster by pulling on them or we might tear their roots out of our brain, nor can we let others trample on them—like seedlings, new ideas are very fragile. Nor do we want to be too neat or we'll grow a monoculture—maybe we've got to allow some weeds, some wild ideas, to emerge so we can see if they're useful. And we need just enough structure to dare working on 'the edge of chaos' without falling off and losing it.[164] All this has been said many times before, of course, but try envisioning the 'garden patch' as a patch in your neocortex 'forest'.

It seems we humans have a need to express ourselves—at times a compulsive need. It's as though our vigorous brain is continuously generating thoughts, images, music or whatever, and needs to get them out of itself. (With some it seems this compulsive need is expressed in a kind of verbal diarrhea either to an unfortunate companion or peripatetically into a cell-phone.) The creative approach is to get the material out of our brain where we can look at it, listen to it or whatever, and begin to study it with an eye to refining what's of value and discarding the rest. Even discarding material is useful as a kind of defecation to get it out of one's system. Whether working at a canvas, drawing-board, chalk-board, word-processor, piano or whatever, it becomes a recursive process between what's emerging in the brain and what's expressed on the medium.[165] And I find no matter how 'obvious' the new idea is, if I don't jot it down it can disappear as easily as it came, maybe never to return.

Reason is the flip-side of creativity—wild, free-flowing ideas must be tested against some criteria, a reality check.[166] We've mentioned association formation in vertebrates as well as how our pre-conscious mind tests the plausibility of candidate percepts before presenting them to our conscious (non-dreaming) mind.[167] And how our brain evolved to model the outside world in order to test alternative concepts. Reasoning is the consciously deliberative application of our pre-conscious mind's processes. Rationalizing is the misapplication of these processes to justify proposed or past actions.[168] Some even believe we have an 'interpreter' in our left brain that compulsively 'explains' our own actions and that attempts to interpret others' actions as well as our world.[169] But while creativity must ultimately be subjected to the cold light of reason (and testing), premature criticism can have a chilling effect stunting, 'throwing cold water on' the creative process. A marriage of creativity and reasoning has been called 'paradigmatic thinking' wherein the creative process operates from a theoretical understanding, a paradigm, of the subject such as with invention—more on this in Chapter Eleven.[170]

Of course, reason assumes causality, that effects have causes. And even though, like the weather, the causes may be so complex and chaotic that the best we can hope for are statistical correlations, still most of us believe in underlying causality as an article of faith. That's why Einstein never accepted quantum mechanics as mentioned in Chapter Four's note 30. However instead of linear causality some invoke circular causality and relational thinking, and propose that "Causality is in the minds of humans ..." that it's a quale, the feeling of necessity.[171] Why do we ask 'why?'? Undoubtedly it evolved because it enabled our ancestors to make better predictions about relationships in their world. Given their 'flat-earth' world, initially their causal explanations were limited and naïve, but as their conceptual framework enlarged they conceived ever more comprehensive explanations—and we still are today, that's what science is all about. But as our explanations become more sweeping and penetrating, we're learning to be more tentative, appreciating that there's still very much we don't know.

Symbols, Music & Language

If the most fundamental part of our human brain is the sub-cortical primitive brain while our neocortex is a massive cauliflower-like growth overlaying it inside our swollen skull, what was the neocortex' benefit to our species' evolution that tolerated the persistence of such an energy-squandering protuberance? Other mammals have more modest neocortices which enable them to model their world and alternatives well enough. Why did our ancestors evolve such an extravagant neocortex? The short answer is culture—our neocortex enables culture.

Broadly, culture is all the tangible and intangible extensions of our mind, body and group. We humans have evolved extensions of our minds in the form of symbols, music and language which we'll explore in the remainder of this chapter. Extensions of our bodies started with the 'sticks', hand-axes and other rudimentary 'tools' described in Chapter Eight, then gathered ever accelerating momentum until now our runaway material culture is both empowering and entrancing, as we'll discuss in Chapter Eleven. Extension of our group or society includes all our institutions, both religious and secular, which we'll discuss as applicable in the next three chapters. Of course there are many distinct local cultures which had adapted to their isolated niche pretty much well enough until contacted by other cultures. Here though we're dealing with culture in general; for instance, not with English, Swahili or Japanese as much as with language in general.

Also, in this chapter we've been focusing on the individual, but 'culture' is the property of a society even though it resides in the individuals who compose that society. We could quibble whether, say a book embodies an aspect of culture, but until an individual reads that book, it's meaningless. It's analogous to 'species' which is the property of a larger society, a population, but without individual members that species goes extinct.

Language is "... an abstract property of a group, related to its speakers somewhat as a species is to its members."[172]

How does the neocortex enable culture? Briefly, our neocortex enables us to interact with our culture, to understand and utilize these extensions and to invent new ones. Mammals in general use their neocortex to perceive, categorize and respond to natural phenomena as described early in this chapter. But our neocortex is three- or four-times larger than that of even our nearest living relative species, the chimpanzees and bonobos, and proportionately many times larger than the other mammals' neocortices. The expansion of hominids' brain was mostly in the neocortex and cerebellum[173] concurrent with culture's emergence. Early on there was a reciprocal development of the neocortex and culture, each augmenting the other, *pari passu*, but now culture has raced ahead.

Ours has been called a 'hybrid mind'.[174] Like other mammals our animal mind resides within our body, primarily in our brain. But unlike other mammals our mind makes extensive use of symbols both inside and outside our brain. And like other mammals our neocortex assimilates data from natural phenomena outside the brain. Unlike most other mammals our neocortex also assimilates data from manmade symbols originating mostly outside an individual brain. A symbol of course is something that stands for or suggests something else. When a dog sprinkles on a tree as a sign to other dogs we could quibble whether that's a symbol, but let's not.[175] And a few chimps have been meticulously taught to understand a number of symbols. But we humans have evolved such a vast wealth of symbols in our world that our mind is largely dependent on them to function. On this page you're reading I've arrayed symbols in the hope that in decoding them you'll catch my meaning. And the many other things we read and write use such symbols.[176] We talk in sound symbols—in person, over the phone, radio, TV and so on. And we often use symbols when we think—forming thoughts and turning them over in our mind and on paper, doing calculations and on and on. The human mind evolved as a blend of symbolic thinking and basic animal analog thinking—a hybrid mind.

Of course we could go further and recognize that we're hybrid organisms. Not only is our mind dependent on symbols but our body is dependent on our invented manmade culture—our clothing, buildings, vehicles, computers and so on—our 'tools', the 'extensions' of our body. We have a pervasive and long-standing symbiosis with culture. Thus as a hybrid species, since our culture is 'evolving' it could be said that we are evolving right along with it at an accelerating rate. More on this thought in Chapter Eleven: Tools.

Early Development

So how does it all get started? As an infant cloistered in our mother's womb, our neocortex undergoes prodigious growth producing far more elemental 'seedling' neurons than will survive.[177] Infants are endowed with unbounded curiosity and a voracious appetite for learning about their own bodies and about their surroundings, especially their culture. Unlike other mammals, human infants have a culture rich in symbols, and all the artifacts and information our culture generates. So they have far more to learn at the beginning of their life-long quest to feed their growing, extravagant and insatiable neocortex (humans have been called 'informavores'[178]). We've noted how their nascent 'seedling' neurons frantically sprout dendrites and synapses in search of nerve impulse patterns to assimilate (become similar to).[179] Many that find none atrophy, crowded out by those that do, like seedling plants that don't find sunlight.[180] The traces of all the nerve impulse patterns that ever crossed the neocortex, from even before birth while sequestered in the womb, may unconsciously shape that person's thinking and behavior throughout their lifetime.

As noted already, our minds are fundamentally solipsistic.[181] For instance my internal experience of 'red', my quale, may be different from yours even though we're both viewing the same light rays with the 'red' cones in our retinas. Aside from any differences between our respective cones, our visual cortices may have learned to assimilate the experience differently, we have no way of knowing. We can partially escape our isolation by comparing notes—if we're both pointing to the same red flower, we can easily confirm our comparable meanings. But if what we're referring to is more remote, say a distant flower each saw, then it's more problematical. That's when language comes to the rescue.

Other animals must experience the same isolation. If they're mostly solitary like bears it may not be much of a problem. But if they're social animals like us they need to bond and communicate with one another. Birds and whales sing,[182] and other animals have their cries, howls, barks and so on. Why did our species alone evolve language? In the previous chapter we explored how prolonged childhood mandated parental tutoring, but many animals train their young through mimicking without language. What was it that enabled our ancestors to evolve such a complex communication system? One answer is mothering, another answer seems to be tools, indirectly.

First though recall from Chapter Seven's section on Evolution's Ways the two step iterative process of variation and selection. Unless there were some variations in hominid organisms, there'd be no choices for the environment to select among—of mothering practices, tools or anything else—to favor some variations over others. Recall also that variations continuously come about through sex and mutations. The variations that were favored promoted such physiological changes as lengthening of the pharynx, lateralization (specialization of right/left brain) causing right-handedness and left-brain speech areas (such as Broca's),[183] and other changes discussed earlier. Such variations were favored by mothering practices and tool making.

Mothering practices shifted from the tree-climbing hominid's clinging infant's tactile communication to ground-dwelling hominid's use of facial and vocal expression, and imitation for communication between mother and detached infant. This difference is seen today in chimps versus humans. It's suggested that the use of vocal and visual signaling led to symbols as childcare and training were prolonged due to evolving ever enlarging brains and lengthening childhood.[184] Moreover it's thought that gossip concurrently evolved as an extension of grooming. Non-lingual primates such as monkeys and chimps spend a lot of time grooming one another to maintain relationships. Humans gossip, schmooze, in pairs and in groups, thereby spending less time on each person and so enabling maintaining a much larger circle of relationships and thus a larger troop.[185]

On the rôle of tools: For more than a million years our ancestors made and used virtually the same simple style hand-axe not only unchanged over that time but unchanged across *Homos'* range.[186] Other now perished wood and fiber tools may have gone unchanged too. During that time what was changing was our ancestor's brain. If you've been reading the notes [oh sure] you'll recall how making hand-axes favored brains with the left hemisphere specialized for detail and the right for overview, and how sexual selection was keyed to hand-axe skill. This evolved brains pre-adapted for the left selecting words and the right guiding thoughts. Namely, just as to form a hand-axe the right brain envisions the overall shape while the left plans the sequence of chips to produce that shape, in order to describe a scene the right brain envisions the scene while the left breaks the holistic scene into a lineal sequence of words to describe it.[187]

Moreover fabricating materials with hands and fingers (and mouth parts?) perhaps prepared fine-motor brain regions needed for rapid manipulation of vocal sounds.[188] Breaking-up and pulverizing coarse foods with tools relieved teeth and jaws so the mouth and throat could also evolve vocalizations. And holding their breath to steady their tools developed breath control necessary for speech. These and perhaps other changes[189] pre-adapted (some say 'exapted') their 'hardware' so they were equipped to evolve language.

The 'software' for language, as mentioned just above and in the previous chapter, evolved[190] from what we now call body language: gestures, postures, facial expressions and (non-word) vocalizations. Because our ancestors were a social species they communicated, probably by miming—like two people trying to talk who don't speak the same language—called mimesis.[191] For some vocalizations that went with the miming—the grunts, moans, murmurs, sighs, whines, wails, yells or what have you—to become words, phrases and crude sentences, namely to become symbols, those vocalizations not only had to be somewhat standardized into common usage but had to tie into internal symbols in the brain. How?

How does an abstract sound become linked to a representation of a specific memory in the brain? The same way a concrete sound does, by simple association as Pavlov's bell did with dog-food. To elaborate, you'll recall that both the hippocampus and frontal cortex don't store composite traces of nerve impulse patterns as do the rear cortices but only their gists, like links to web pages. Perhaps these gists somehow became associated with the abstract sounds so the sounds became links to links. (This was long before writing.[192]) Of course initially the sounds probably were minimally abstract, not only accompanied by miming but associated with a sound of the object or action, like 'snake' or 'gallop'. So they probably used such stepping-stones rather than a broad blind leap to evolve symbolic minds.[193]

And initially speech was probably laconic but embellished with mimetic gestures. They must have encountered the same difficulty we do when we try to converse in a foreign language: not only is it difficult to remember and assemble the words in order to speak but also in listening to try to decode the unfamiliar sounds. To speak did they just blurt out the sounds spontaneously or did they first rehearse them in their mind subvocally? We may never know or even care except ...

This raises the issue mentioned in Chapters Two and Eight about their internal dialog. Did they realize that the spontaneous voices in their head were theirs or did they believe someone was somehow talking to them? (It's perhaps analogous to an animal seeing itself in a mirror but thinking it's another animal.) Today troubled minds believe they hear voices but as recently as two- or three-millennia ago it was common to believe the gods spoke directly to privileged persons such as the heroes in Homer's *Iliad* and the many oracles, prophets and saints.[194]

Words and sentences, semantics and syntax, namely language, evolved from mimesis along one path.[195] Another path led to music when prosody was combined with the rhythm of dance. Prosody is the intonation and timing of speech, absent in writing like this.[196] Rhythm, cadence, was used to entrain troop members to act in concert. Prosody and rhythm produced chant or song which evolved into music, especially with musical instruments. Words are generally believed to be a function of the left brain while music is the right's.[197] More on music's 'charms', its emotional content in the next chapter.

Here though let's take a closer look at music's origins. Some believe that language and music evolved together from our distant ancestor's vocalizations which contained both referential and emotive meanings, dubbed 'musilanguage'.[198] Musilanguage bifurcated to emphasize either propositions or emotions thus evolving toward language or music.[199] Perhaps our distant ancestors went from imitating animals to imitating each other.[200] It seems likely that each generation went through a cycle of various uses of music, improving on what they learned from the previous generation to pass on to the next. Begin the cycle with an infant in its mother's womb, then in her arms or sling rocked to the rhythm of her walk and attuned to the reverberations of her humming.[201] As a child, it joined in other kids' ditties and maybe improvised.[202] As it grew it joined in the dancing and chanting around the fire until wearied, then collapsed into sleep. But each year it grew stronger until it lasted long enough to become entranced as did the adults.[203] Probably she or he learned the women's or men's work songs, even war chants. There's conjecture that guys' choruses proclaimed their territory thus luring roaming gals,[204] and that the gals 'sang' responses. Dancing and chanting around the fire, guys and gals could assess each other's fitness—stamina, coordination, creativity or whatever caught their eye—and single out a prospective mate. Perhaps serenading was used in courting, seducing and coupling resulting in a new generation to begin the cycle all over. Each generation could improve on the repertoire but the next generation selected what would be carried forward—a co-evolution of music by Lamarckian means and of individuals by Darwinian—that is, the evolving music and dance subjected individuals to ever more demanding tests by which the genes for the next generation were selected by prospective partners/parents.

Consider a few of music's evolutionary benefits. Music attuned and bonded couples for prolonged parenting. Lullabying quieted babies so they attracted fewer predators and were less disruptive. Singing and dancing prompted aerobic development, displayed talents, entrained troop members into a cohesive group united in their beliefs and formidable to outsiders,[205] and enhanced brain development for other applications. Music's evolutionary roots go wide and deep.

Now back to language—in addition to employing their evolving language in everyday activities and gossip, we surmise that they must have told and retold stories dredged from their episodic memories. The words mostly told the facts but the mimesis conveyed the emotions[206] and reinforced remembering the words. Think of the way rhyme and music help us recall the words of a poem or song. Prosody, music and dance heighten emotions and entrain listeners. Even still today a few oral cultures have their minstrels dedicated to preserving their stories, idylls, legends and myths by memorizing long and complex ballads, and reciting them at gatherings as well as training apprentices to carry on after them. As populations evolved in isolation they each evolved their own cultures[207] and utilized their minstrels with their legends, fables and myths, as well as priests with their rituals, to enculturate that population. This stage of human cognition and culture is referred to as 'episodic' or 'mythic'.[208] It still prevails throughout the world today augmented not only by writing (novels, histories, biographies, children's books ...) but by all the other technologies today's culture provides (movies, television ...).

The next and current stage is referred to as 'theoretic'. It includes and builds on the earlier stages but adds cognition and culture based on theories or paradigms (hence it's also called 'paradigmatic'). A rough example of the distinction between episodic and paradigmatic thinking is getting route directions ("Go two miles then turn right at the gas station, then left at the next light ...") versus using a map. Scientific thought and invention exemplify paradigmatic thinking.[209] This book is replete with examples of humans' understanding of natural phenomena graduating from mythic stage cognition to ever deepening levels of paradigmatic cognition. Indeed the purpose of this book is to facilitate one's graduating fully into this stage; seeing through the myths without diminishing the rich emotional affect of the earlier stages. It's likely that this stage is the most recently evolved which explains why reading theoretic material (like this) is more demanding[210] than episodic materials like novels, biographies and histories—our evolving brain likely only recently acquired this paradigmatic style of thinking. Can paradigmatic thinking be overlaid on episodic thinking? Sure. When we try to explain history that's probably what we're doing.

Yet it seems a lot of people are not predisposed to paradigmatic thinking—not inclined to ask 'why?' Why? Certainly it's only in the past century or so that science has begun to provide answers that get down to fundamentals—that don't raise more questions than they answer, wild-goose chases that discourage futile chasing. Or fed us myths that were 'beyond human comprehension'. So perhaps our culture only recently acquired inquisitiveness for other than just the elite. We'll delve into this further in the final chapter.

Language, and more broadly, culture shapes the neurons of our neocortex and thus influences the way we perceive our world and conceptualize it. And as mentioned in Chapter Four's Recap, our words describing our world are often based on misleading, obsolete concepts which have to be unlearned and discarded in order to grasp a better understanding of our world. In a way it's fortunate many words' original meanings have been lost and replaced with new meanings—how many know what a 'backlog' was or when they say 'the phone's ringing off the hook' that phones haven't had bells or hooks for decades? And I've repeatedly described how the term 'sunrise' can mislead to an obsolete concept of the Earth as stable and the Sun as moving, but lamented the seeming futility of trying to replace 'sunrise' with a more cogent term. Still we should keep trying— changing 'trivial' words and behavior *can* induce changes in thinking and attitudes. Reducing initial misconceptions facilitates a better conceptualization of our world.

Nonetheless we humans need our culture to shape our neurons, especially in our early years, in order to understand our world. This suggests an explanation for why—even though by a hundred-thousand years ago our species had evolved the basic anatomical body and brain we have today—it's only in the last thirty-odd-thousand years that there's archaeological evidence of significant cultural development. But again, culture is the property of society not the individual. At best the individual can acquire the culture they're immersed in and maybe add a little to it. Still it's a slow reciprocal process, each generation hopefully building on their predecessors' accomplishments (if their society's not opposed to progress, as traditionalists are). So for our early ancestors, with a meager culture, progress must have been agonizingly slow, only gathering momentum once they began to have a rich cultural base to build on.[211] But our culture is now evolving so rapidly that we're in danger of initially being taught obsolete concepts and, even if they were up-to-date at the time, of having to unlearn them as new concepts and culture come along. Whereas in earlier times a person was educated in their youth and applied that education during their lifetime, now we must continually re-educate ourselves (it's fun once you get the knack).

Some Musings

Throughout this long chapter I've presented what impress me as the most plausible theories, admittedly filtered through my own personal biases to support my thesis. There are of course other theories of the evolution and operation of consciousness besides the ones I'm advocating here.[212] The oldest of record—at least twenty-five hundred years—are the 'dualist' theories of mind/body separation, of a discontinuity between mind and body, Cartesian.[213] Most dualists see the mind as unique to humans and one way or another as originating from God, endowed to man by God. With the possible exception of Platonist,[214] only steadfast religious believers still cling to *explicit* dualism—to whom this book is not addressed per its subtitle and opening sentence of the second paragraph—so I'll not pursue it further here. No doubt most of my target audience were educated by dualists and were taught to view consciousness, the 'soul', as distinct from the body, and so may be susceptible to *implicit* dualism subtly creeping into allegedly non-dualist theories.[215] While I don't intend to pursue any of those either we should stay mindful of dualism's pervasive influence.

However even though this chapter's getting overly long, there's an area of speculation that I should touch on since it'll pertain to the issue of prayer in the next chapter. In Chapter Seven under Speciation, I mentioned the 'morphic resonance' concept wherein each organism is believed to emit and receive information between their own kind via 'morphogenetic fields' which enable communication among them and influences their development.[216] To understand this concept think of the 'mental radio' metaphor used since the early 1900s to explain mental telepathy.[217] Radio transmitters/receivers tuned to the same detectable frequency in the electromagnetic field can all 'talk' to one another like people talking face-to-face in a group.[218] Similarly if all the members of a species were on their assigned 'frequency' in the 'morphogenetic field' they might all unconsciously be tuned into one another. Presumably the mature members would influence younger members' development.[219] Trouble is, what's the medium for such fields?

As mentioned, our brains operate at a nominal frequency of 40Hz, much below radio frequencies (but within a range that includes 60Hz electric power current). Moreover lower frequencies not only use less energy but are less repelled than higher frequencies like radar.[220] So maybe the low energy, low frequency electromagnetic field in our head can get into other heads. Might it be that people who're attuned to one another—kindred souls, on the same frequency/vibes—literally tune into each other's electromagnetic fields in their brains, which is to say, read their minds to some extent? As mentioned, many have had the experience of thinking of someone, the phone rings and it's they. If other's 'brain waves' can affect our thoughts, and our own thoughts can affect our own brain's development (neuroplasticity), then more robust minds might influence pliable minds this way.[221] 'Sounds far out?

There's enough evidence[222] of psychic phenomena—generally called 'psi' (as the Greek letter Ψ) including telepathy, clairvoyance, ESP (extrasensory perception) and so on—that a few reputable scientists are researching and speculating about it, and generally looking to quantum mechanics for explanations. Recall from Chapter Four some of quantum mechanics' and light's weirdness: its 'wave-particle duality', uncertainty principle and especially nonlocality (separated particles' coherence or entanglement). Since quantum physics and consciousness are both mysterious, even though a long shot, might there be some connection?[223] For example, as mentioned above, the cytoskeleton of animal cells, including neurons, are arrays of microtubules—microscopic hollow tubes. It's speculated that not only might the interior of a single microtubule be involved in a quantum-coherent state but that this quantum coherence might extend to other microtubules not only within that neuron but in other neurons across an appreciable part of that entire brain to produce comprehensive consciousness.[224] With a further stupendous leap, other remote but attuned brains' microtubules might be entangled in that same quantum coherence which would explain telepathy. Some go even further and posit a 'hidden domain'[225] which sounds like dualism.

Now we can get back to the question parenthetically raised in the last chapter: What were Neanderthals using their big brains for? From their sloping foreheads it's inferred that their prefrontal cortex was less evolved than ours which implies poorer planning ability as reflected in their lifestyle and tools. But their extended rear skull 'bun' suggests a larger visual cortex and/or cerebellum. And recall that their language capabilities were less evolved than our ancestors'. So—in the spirit of the foregoing—did they rely more on psychic abilities for intra-group communication which was less explicit and proved less effective in competition with our ancestors? And might their vision include seeing electromagnetic frequencies beyond 'visible light' such as auras? I know of no reputable scientist who's pursued these questions, only fiction.[226]

One other prevalent theory should be touched on, memes, which is an outgrowth of the selfish-gene theory proposed a quarter century ago. It was proposed that genes have a life of their own and simply use animals to replicate and perpetuate themselves. Similarly it's proposed that ideas, memes, have a life of their own and use human brains to replicate and perpetuate themselves. Memes only exist in brains but can be transmitted among humans via speech, writing, visuals and similar media. While the concept of memes has caught on, not only doesn't there appear to be any particular virtue in invoking memes to explain information transmission, but their existence remains speculative.[227]

Recap & Trend

In Chapters Six, Seven and Eight we traced how the Life Urge emerged early in Earth's development and evolved ever more complex ways of expressing itself, from simple single-celled organisms on up to elaborate multicelled organisms like us. In this chapter we've traced how those organisms evolved controls to select among the alternative opportunities and challenges presented by their environments. Single cells expanded their limited repertoire by joining with other cells and then evolving specialized cells, neurons, initially programmed with stereotypic re/actions in ganglia and in primitive brain components. Then some vertebrates evolved an auxiliary brain, the neocortex in mammals, which greatly expands the primitive brain's options as well as enhances mammal's ability to learn and form memories.

The marvel of the neocortex is that it uses the evolutionary process in its 'forest' of neurons to grow networks, to assess incoming data and to generate new data. The neurons are first shaped by the nerve impulses presented to them through the primitive brain from the senses, both internal and external. Thus the neocortex assimilates its mammal's inner and outer worlds. Moreover it then uses those networks of neurons to assess new nerve impulses, trying to contrive gestalts—complex synergistic patterns—through ultrafast evolutionary processes. It also uses the neuron networks to generate 'mutated' impulse patterns through chaotic activity in the neocortex thus generating alternatives for the neocortex 'environment' to select from.

Somehow at some point along the way consciousness arises apparently from the intensity of nerve impulses coursing through extensive areas of the primitive brain and neocortex and/or from the synchronized electromagnetic field they induce. Most activity that goes on in brains, ours included, is unconscious but we humans at least are both privileged and burdened to be aware of a little of it. Evolution gave us awareness of alternatives and their consequences, and as an ancillary 'perk' it also gave us the 'agony and ecstasy' of that awareness. Even so like all organisms I believe we're primarily motivated by our elementary drives often misleadingly lumped together as 'emotions'. They're probably how our basic Urge to Life is felt.

How Life finds a way is through blind evolution, not only in the outer world outside our body but in the inner world in our brain. But because of our consciousness, we aren't just the pawns of evolution—we can glimpse where evolution might lead and try to steer it. Our era is seeing 'evolution' accelerated in our hybrid organism's extensions as described above—our runaway material culture—which perspicaciously we might 'steer' as we'll explore in the final two chapters.[228]

Thus we can express our Urge to Life in informed deliberate ways—provided we're in touch with it. A central theme of this long essay is to trace our detection of that Urge to Life. It must be 'sensed' in our somatic cells and on up into our brains where somehow it's subconsciously perceived, probably in conjunction with perceiving our Self distinct from our environment. Perhaps like air pressure described in Chapter Four, we're so accustomed to it that we're unaware of it—we don't consciously realize it's there. Unlike light, sound, heat and the others, there doesn't seem to be any sensor for detecting Life—it preexisted the evolution of the senses—so we don't seem to have an explicit experience of the Life Urge (although we can feel exuberant or debilitated, up or down, full of Life or empty). Yet all organisms somehow implicitly sense Life even without brains or even nerves—it must be the most basic 'sense'.[229] We somehow sense death—when something lacks Life—so we must somehow sense its inverse, Life. You must have had the shock of discovering some person or animal you thought was alive, was actually dead; or the opposite, some supposed inanimate object turns out to be alive (the stuff of horror stories). Such reactions suggest that our reflex to discriminate the live/dead dichotomy must have deep roots in our Life Urge.

Let me conclude this chapter with what may turn out to be a really dumb idea but at least it'll help flesh out how the Life Urge may find expression. Suppose there's some structure in our primitive brain which reacts to the Life Urge akin to the way our amygdala reacts to perceived threats. Recall that when we're startled, it's our amygdala reacting to signals which it instantaneously interprets as a threat and increases heart rate, blood pressure, stress hormones and so forth which we experience as a start or even fear. Our neocortex receives the same signals and interprets them at a more deliberate rate and so may override the reaction. Similarly this supposed 'Life Urge brain structure' might receive Life Urge signals or whatever from throughout our body with which it generates our urges, our active emotions. But it might also attune our senses to signs of Life so that our first reaction is to assume an object is alive until our neocortex tells us otherwise. Just as with experience the neocortex learns to override the amygdala's tendency to see threats everywhere, it might override the supposed 'Life Urge brain structure's' tendency to see Life in everything, as did our early ancestors until they learned better. And just as an overactive amygdala can cause anxiety or panic, an overactive supposed 'Life Urge brain structure' might presumably cause a person to have religious experiences, and see and hear spirits including God.[230]

In the next chapter we'll look at some of the methods that we humans have employed throughout history to experience and interpret (or misinterpret) this basic of the Urge to Life, and at how we might get in touch with and foster rapport with our authentic Life Urge unique to our own individual Self. (The distinction I'm making between self and Self will become clearer then.) The hunch I'm following is that Life's evolution has a trend, maybe even a trajectory, and that consciousness enables us humans to not only discern that trajectory but to augment it.

In case you feel you're getting lost in all this brain/mind talk, here's an overly-simplified 'pocket-guide' to carry with you for the next three chapters. Envision your primitive brain as the 'heart' of your mind. Indeed it's where you experience your heartfelt emotions, your innermost feelings, where you 'know in your heart' and probably where your Life Urge emanates as we'll see in the next chapter. Than envision your newer brain that overlays and enshrouds your primitive brain, namely your neocortex, not only as your intellect but as your passport both to the natural world and to the invented 'cultural world'. (Again by 'cultural world' I mean all the tangible and intangible extensions of our mind, body and group described above—language, tools and institutions.) Our innermost primitive brain crowned and augmented by our neocortex.

Chapters Five through Nine have been a description of how Earth, Life, animals and mind evolved as I can best determine from my perspective. Along the way I've speculated about the roots of religion, not only as a pre-scientific method for dealing with the world, but as an expression of what I believe is our Life Urge. As you've tagged along, more or less, I presume you've been forming your own opinions—Was what I've been saying credible and/or plausible, and is it convincing, both intellectually and viscerally? If not, hopefully it's useful in forming your own tentative opinions. So let's press-on to consider in the next three chapters how my ideas might apply in our 'spiritual', material and social worlds, and you can continue to develop and formulate your own thoughts.

Part III

Culture Concepts

Chapter Ten

'Religion'

Maybe in the thin air at this high altitude we're hallucinating, but it seems the cloud briefly parts and we think we glimpse the Mountain's magnificent glaciated summit glowing brilliant white with sunlight—but for only that briefest moment. If only we could dispel the cloud . . .

Note that I've put this chapter's title in quotation marks. While most contemporary religions center on a belief in God, the premise of this book is that an experience of a god 'out there'—whether in a formal worship service or spontaneously—is a projection from 'in here' of our unconscious Life Urge. Hence I'm using the term 'religion' very broadly to include not just organized religion but any activity that involves the same access to our unconscious that I believe is sought unwittingly by traditional religions.[1] The purpose of this chapter is not only to recognize as one's own and take back those unconscious projections which religions encourage, but also to utilize such practices and other means to connect us to more of our unconscious and thus to our fuller Self, to our Life Urge and to Life's meaning—'the meaning of life' sought in religion. Accordingly in addition to traditional religions we'll explore meditation, psychotherapy, art, music, nature and other activities and techniques which try to connect us to our unconscious mind in order to bring some of its richness into consciousness, to foster a rapport with one's unconscious. Of course organized religions encompass other societal functions as well—social, educational, beneficent, governmental—which we'll consider in the final chapter.

Fathoming the depths of one's unconscious so that it emerges into consciousness, however, should be very selective—heck, most of our unconscious we don't need or want to be aware of. For instance as you read this page your unconscious goes through a complex process to decipher the ink marks on the paper so they become thoughts in your mind, perhaps not even conscious of some of the words you read. Why clutter up your consciousness with such details? Even less so, our autonomic system unconsciously controls our blood pressure, heart rate, body temperature and so on, usually quite well without 'us', so 'stay out of the kitchen'. But certainly what we do want to be aware of is any of our unconscious projections, unlike the joke about the salacious man shown all the 'dirty pictures' on a Rorschach inkblot test. And there are other aspects of our unconscious it'd be nice to have better access to such as memory and creativity but these are outside this book's intent. What I intend to explore is how we might connect with and raise our Life Urge a little bit more into awareness.

A major impediment in attempting to explore 'religion' objectively is the enculturation most of us were subjected to as children. As our voracious nascent neocortex developed it likely was fed a diet of stories about little Jesus, guardian angels, child saints, the Blessed Virgin Mother, our Father in Heaven and so on. We've had to learn to see them for what they are—only 'stories'—and view them the same way we learned to see the stories of Santa Claus and the Easter Bunny. Moreover our culture is so replete with blatant theistic assumptions—"In God We Trust" on all our currency—so that holding an opposite view takes constant vigilance. And even when we think we're free of such programming, it can subtly influence us—my expletives are often profane. Deprogramming, 'rewiring', our neocortex takes time, patience and persistence.

First another brief review of where we are so far in trying to probe prototheism, asking Where does the belief in gods/God come from? Our early ancestors' way of dealing with capricious nature was to infer mental abilities in natural entities—trees, brooks, clouds—called animism[2] and deal with them just as they dealt with people. But because, unlike people, natural entities didn't actually talk, they had to imagine those entities were talking to them, in effect guess what those entities were 'thinking'. This meant unconsciously projecting their own thoughts and expectations out of themselves and onto those entities based on then popular myths. Myths were pre-scientific explanations and stories mostly of nature. Then as explanations improved, natural entities were demythologized and our later ancestors began projecting their thoughts out onto ever more ethereal spirits or 'gods'—angels, devils, saints … and God. As earthly fire was explained as a natural phenomenon, the fire-god was promoted to the Sun-god just above the clouds. And of course before the Sun was better explained,[3] the Sun-god was promoted to God ever higher in the firmament, namely in Heaven. Humans have long explained the unexplainable as gods/God.

Even as more and more phenomena are explained, the 'need' for a God may still persist.[4] What remains that's beyond explanation? If we accept that 'God' is a projection 'out' from 'within' us, what's within us that we project out which is as yet unexplained? Even though these 'gods' may not have been real, whatever was being projected out *felt* real, not only back then but still does now. Maybe there's a need to have faith in something—if not God, than what? So now we're trying to invert the concept of an unexplainable God and discover whatever it is in ourselves—the as yet unexplained fundamental 'something'—that we project out onto 'God' which we then sometimes experience as unexplainably wondrous, awe-inspiring and numinous.

But more often than not, experiences of 'God'—or lesser 'gods', spirits like angels, devils and saints—are more prosaic, most likely a parent-figure, the superego of our conscience, critically monitoring our every action and even our thoughts. This personal 'God' can dispense love, protection, acceptance, justice, or alternatively can demand obedience, obeisance and inflict punishment, here or hereafter. It's the image of God/Christ as shepherd and of us as sheep. Usually these reactions were programmed into us in our youth—they may not be real but they *feel* real. They need to be discarded or exorcised in order that we become mature, self-reliant adults. It can be useful though when they're consciously experienced to see them for what they are in order to work them through and out—more on this later. However a parent image is not the fundamental 'something' that I'm referring to that's projected out onto 'God' and experienced as wondrous, awe-inspiring and numinous.

The notion we're pursuing is that the fundamental 'something' in us that we projected out is our sub/pre-consciousness of our own Urge to Life. Recall that what I'm calling the Life Urge is not the *élan vital* of a century ago that then was thought God infused to give us Life. Rather my 'Life Urge' is what emerges naturally when complex matter organizes critically, synergistically, and spontaneously comes alive. It's our Life Urge that enlivens each and every cell in our body and that's channeled on up into our primitive brain. There it may be *per*ceived by our mind as our own emotions or it may be disowned and projected out where it's *con*ceived as a 'god'.[5] Whenever we conjure a 'god'—an angel, devil, saint or God—we imbue that 'god' with Life and Mind. If there's no 'god' 'out there', it seems to me that its Life and Mind must come from within us.

Yet maybe the Life Urge is so fundamental within ourselves that we're not usually aware of it. (Again, like we're unaware of the nearly fifteen pounds of atmospheric pressure on every square inch of our body.) Are we only aware of our Life Urge if we project it out of ourselves? We are acutely sensitive to Life outside ourselves, namely whether an object is alive, whether it's animate or inanimate. So we're obviously aware of Life, both outside of and in ourselves.

But what about Urge? Well certainly we're often aware (though not always) of our many urges, physical and psychological (e-motions) which are sometimes quite *urge*nt. These must all stem from our Life Urge—without Life (if we're dead) there are no urges. And the more lively we are, the stronger our urges, our zest for Life. Our urges are experienced in our primitive brain and monitored by our executive brain in our prefrontal cortex (recall the example in the previous chapter of the amygdala versus the cortex). Our neocortex endows us with the ability to delay an urge's expression while we assess the best way to express it, or to curtail or sublimate that urge. As a bonus, our ability to delay expression enables us to roll the urge around in our conscious mind and savor it in anticipation. But not all our urges raise into consciousness. Maybe the Life Urge is one that's normally deep in our unconscious.

So if our Life Urge is the unexplained fundamental 'something' that's sometimes projected out onto 'God', yet if the Life Urge is so intrinsic that it's often taken for granted and normally not noticed—if we're oblivious of it—that would explain why the projection of it as 'God' is 'unexplainable'. In other words if we're unaware of our amazing Life Urge until we project it out onto 'God' no wonder 'God' seems so mysterious and totally 'other'. Or if our intuition of our Life Urge is so intrinsic maybe it's what's felt as 'faith' and misattributed to God.[6] But then why would our projection of the Life Urge sometimes become numinous? In searching out the Life Urge, are we so intently attuned that our anticipation can intensify— like being 'in love'—to a numinous level? Hence is our Life Urge the prototheistic basis of our numinous experiences, of the phenomenon that's called God?

Numinous Consciousness

What seems to be a cardinal aspiration of all religions is the experience, to some degree, of the numinous[7], of going beyond oneself to heights out of the ordinary, which most religions interpret as contact with God or a saint (Buddhism being a possible exception). Instead an alternate interpretation based on recent research is that numinous experience is a further intensification of consciousness. In the preceding chapter, recall that consciousness was described as a continuum from minimal 'core' consciousness intensifying to 'extended' consciousness—and sometimes going beyond, intensifying to 'numinous' consciousness. (These aren't discrete but rather are degrees within the continuum.) It's inferred that numinous consciousness is the further intensification of nerve impulses reverberating in our brain like an incandescent lightbulb filament glowing with ever more electric current and flaring (hopefully our brain doesn't burn out as the filament usually does).

Inducing a level of numinous consciousness requires sustaining a single thought or sensation in mind indefinitely rather than letting it pass through into action. Our brain's a little like our mouth—rather than bolt down food and drink we can hold a flavorful morsel or sip in our mouth savoring it. Or like sex—we can just get off or we can prolong foreplay and delay orgasm heightening sensations. While nutritional, reproductive and mental activities evolved in order to improve results, evolution favored activities that were pleasurable, and with consciousness these activities can be protracted to increase awareness of them in anticipation. Thus prolonging awareness of what's going on in our mind can lead to heightened levels of awareness.

[The next few paragraphs build on the detailed explanations of the previous chapter. So if that wasn't to your liking, you may want to just peruse the next five paragraphs. I won't be offended and there's no quiz at the end of this chapter.]

Here's an idea of how it seems to work: Recall from the previous chapter that the 'where?' nerve impulses, mostly from the visual and auditory cortices, join up in the posterior parietal (association) cortex mapping the outside world. There they encounter the somatosensory band's map of the body thus orienting the self in its outside world. The gists of the mapping are forwarded (via primitive brain components) to the prefrontal cortex (along with their percepts described below) where normally the executive brain decides 'what to do' and relays instructions to the motor cortices to take action. Instead the action is blocked, as we'll see, and the prefrontal bounces the mapping back (again through primitive brain components) to the parietal so that it's bounced back and forth between them setting up the intensifying reverberation loop mentioned. Hence the inverted admonition "Don't just do something, stand there!"[8]

Also recall how a million years of making hand-axes favored brains with the left hemisphere specialized for detail and the right for overview which for language became words versus syntax. For body orientation the left hemisphere concentrates on the body and the right on its surroundings, the self vis-à-vis its world.[9] So as the reverberations intensify between the parietal and prefrontal cortices (as well as between the hemispheres?) it's believed the demarcation between the self and its world softens and blurs. It's said either that the self dissolves to become one with the world (Buddhism)[10] or that the self expands into the Self embracing its world (but not megalomaniacally). Either way the narrow I-me-mine selfish self gains empathy for the world around it. The Self transcends the self.[11]

Meanwhile the 'what?' nerve impulses from vision, auditory, olfactory and gustatory (taste) in the temporal cortex proceed into the prefrontal cortex and, instead of leading to action, are similarly blocked, bouncing back and forth between the temporal and prefrontal cortices also setting up reverberations. Consciousness of the emerging percepts and their qualia intensifies to an ever brightening blinding glow. These qualia and percepts combining with their merging Self/world become at once wondrous, transcendent and peaceful, in short, numinous.[12]

While numinous consciousness culminates in our neocortex, it likely emanates from primitive brain components[13] and from the autonomic nervous system in our body's viscera, and perhaps even from signal particles flowing through our vascular system (our Life Urge?). Some believe the autonomic nervous system—which controls functions like heart rate, blood pressure, breathing and sweating, and is believed connected with the limbic system—is fundamental to numinous experience either through deep relaxation (quiescence) or acute arousal, or both by one 'spilling over' into the other.[14] Signal particles from the body and brain stem, such as testosterone/estrogen and beta-endorphin (of the alleged 'runner's high'),[15] affect our moods. These can focus attention by blocking other incoming sensations.

Now let's rephrase the above description in the previous chapter's neural Darwinism terms. Resorting yet again to my monkey metaphor for our neocortex, imagine one species of monkey so richly nourished by their niche in the forest they proliferate displacing other monkeys from that area. Moreover those that earlier migrated out of that area of the forest were turned back reinforcing their population in the area and further displacing other monkeys. Similarly if a pattern of nerve impulses in an area of our neocortex is favored by its basin of attraction and displaces all other patterns, they too will proliferate and also will be reinforced as their predecessors return. Thus these synergistic nerve impulse patterns prosper escalating the intensity of their reverberations to the exclusion of competing nerve impulse patterns. We experience such intensity as heightened consciousness of that percept.[16]

Three broad routes have been described for inducing numinous consciousness which overlap each other and can be implemented by a great variety of practices. Meditation, such as sitting zazen, attempts to empty the mind of all thoughts and distractions—the 'fruitful void'—by say concentrating on one's breathing—the passive approach. Alternatively in contemplation one concentrates on say a candle or a *mantra* (the Rosary?) excluding all other thoughts and distractions—the active approach.[17] The third route, ritual, is less cerebral, more physical, and engages one's body in music, singing, chanting, dancing, twirling or whatever, alone or in a group.[18] While such practices attempt to induce numinous consciousness, its onset is often unpredictable, spontaneous, seemingly coming not *from* us but *through* us 'out of nowhere' when least expected, misconstrued as 'a gift from God' or a glimpse of God, Christ, Mother Mary...

But why would evolution select for such abilities? What benefit were they to the evolution of our species? One notion is they were an outgrowth of the ecstasy of orgasm[19]—good sex can bond partners for the rigors of extended parenting crucial to our species. Another is that it was an outgrowth of group dancing and chanting which enlarged each individual's self to encompass the troop thereby inducing solidarity and altruism.[20] Thirdly, intently concentrating on an object in nature to discern what a presumed god is saying could 'reveal' myths (from one's unconscious) explaining the world and human's place in it, useful in unifying the troop under common convictions for their mutual survival and prosperity.[21] A fourth is that it may have lead to symbolic thinking.[22] All of these and other benefits could accrue to our species' success. After all we evolved as a social species, not solitarily.

Prototheism and Life Urge

Now back to the search for the phenomenon that's called God. The hunch I've been pursuing is that the phenomenon we call 'God' is somehow our amazing under-appreciated Life Urge which we humans have more or less comprehended but misconstrued as God. We've traced the operation of evolution's iterative variation/selection through the Earth's formation, Life's emergence, mammal's and human's evolution, and consciousness' emergence. Finally we've considered how consciousness can go critical to attain numinous consciousness. But is numinous consciousness necessarily consciousness of our Life Urge?

I've had experiences, while perhaps not full fledged numinous consciousness, that certainly were marvelously breathtaking. For instance brilliant red poppies against the green of my front lawn on a bright summer day burning their redness into my brain. Or in a canoe at dawn on a placid wilderness lake, the sunlight shimmering off the water luminescing a rocky cedar-lined island through the patchy mist. But should I attribute these and other mesmerizing moments to the Life Urge? True-believers would attribute them to God. These entrancing experiences help me appreciate the beauty of Life and feel privileged that I'm in our world.[23] But

I question whether the intensification of such percepts and their qualia, in themselves, are the Life Urge emerging into consciousness.

Rather it seems to me, as suggested in the previous chapter, that as the proto-self emerges into consciousness as the self, it's somehow propelled by its Life Urge. Perhaps it's in the guise of the narrow self-centered ego so vital to an individual's survival (at least minimally). The Life Urge is not quite the same as the self but rather is the basic urge that sustains and motivates the self. The self is a conscious organism's sense of itself and it's where in our mind the Life Urge is experienced even though it's probably not recognized as such. (Lacking a better explanation some true-believers may simply call the Life Urge 'faith'.) Then as the narrow self expands to a more enlightened holistic Self through enlightening experiences, the Self becomes aware of its Life Urge as something wondrous, transcendent and immensely precious.[24] (The 'faith-full' call it being born-again.)

If the Life Urge is so elemental why's it so obscure? As suggested already perhaps the 'problem' is that it *is* so elementary, so general and so pervasive. Beautiful experiences like my two described above have specific inputs producing unique percepts that intensify in our brain until they glow, whereas the Life Urge doesn't produce unique percepts, it's nonspecific. True, it may get expressed in specific urges—emotions and physical drives—but it seems the Life Urge itself is so pervasive that it doesn't produce specific percepts, which explains its obscurity. Rather it infuses our whole self so inexplicably that when it's intensified it seems ineffable, like 'God'. Also when the Life Urge intensifies it's so overwhelming that it seems omnipotent, omniscient, like 'God'. It becomes too grand and wondrous for our narrow self, so that the self must either expand into the Self in order to embrace it or the self will deflect it out onto a 'god', and probably not just any god but onto 'the one and only God'.

Let's put this in synergistic complexity terms. The Life Urge may be acting as what I'll call a 'pre-gestalt' in search of a percept or concept on which to form. If the only percept/concept it knows about that fits is of 'God', then the Life Urge is experienced as faith in God, it emerges into consciousness as 'God'. What I'm advocating is that the Life Urge instead should be prompted to coalesce as a gestalt of one's Self, to enkindle the self with the glow of the Urge to Life so that it's experienced as the Self. By this explanation my two near-numinous experiences described above required an active outgoing Life Urge to notice and revere them—with a depressed Life Urge they'd go unnoticed. Did I project my Life Urge onto those scenes expanding my Self?

As I see it there are four paths the narrow self can traverse as it expands with the awareness of its Life Urge. The self might puff up, filled with its own importance, egotistical, even megalomaniacal. Alternatively the self might broaden its perspective to see its Self as part of the World, as a participant in Life's evolution, as a courier or executor in evolution's long trajectory (more on this shortly). A third route is the Buddhist way, *Tao*, wherein the self dissolves into the Great Self[25] of the World, loosing its identity as it merges with the Whole. Finally, as I've described, the self can refuse to acknowledge and accept its Life Urge, instead projecting it out onto some likely target. On this fourth path the Life Urge is often deemed too much for a measly human to identify with and claim as their own, and so, in my view, it's mistakenly attributed to God.[26]

As you might expect, I favor the second path—the Self as a courier or executor in evolution's long trajectory.[27] Since all organisms are an expression of the Life Urge—from the simplest single cells on up to the most complex multicelled organisms (arguably we humans, at least so far anyway)—we should see ourselves as kin to all living beings,[28] participating in Life's evolution. But we have a unique privilege and therefore a singular responsibility. We have consciousness so we can conjecture where evolution optimally might be leading—we can be evolution's 'eyes'[29]—and thus we humans can be its leading exponents, its executors. You may shrink from the audacity of claiming to be evolution's executors, but with our run-away technology, we are anyway, for better or worse.[30] Indeed as its leading exponents we should shun hubris and instead humbly embrace opportunities to advance Life's evolution each in our own fashion using whatever are our own unique capabilities.[31] We are 'standing on the shoulders' of all the organisms that came before, just halfway through Earth's term, owing our great-good-fortune to our many precursors and hence obligated to all who will come after—a debt to the past owed to the future.[32] Viewed this way our expanded Self sees each individual Self as a contributing-member, a citizen of our World charged to not squander our inheritance but to do the best with it that we each can thus giving profound meaning to our lives. (There's still the danger the Self may see itself as a member of an elite chosen group, sect or nation rather than of all living beings—past, present and future.[33])

More on this in the final two chapters. First we need to look at the various ways of getting in touch with our unique Self by discarding the inauthentic personas and traits, and by mining the depths of our unconscious to uncover our genuine and complete Self, and hopefully our own Life Urge. But rather than hope to achieve numinousness, we perhaps should have more modest expectations—to nudge the threshold of consciousness, our liminal state,[34] farther down into our unconscious.

Know Thyself

Earlier I rephrased "As the twig is bent, so is the tree ..." formed or deformed. Our childhood not only formed each of us in invaluable ways but probably deformed us some too. Growing up we not only learned myths but we learned to behave in ways that were effective or acceptable for various situations—we learned unscripted parts to play in the dramas of Life. We learned rôles to act out at home, at church, at school ... To do this we had to suppress natural urges in order to play our part, to take on the required personas. And so the rôles became habitual. At home we learned how to act with our parents, our siblings, and our relatives to get what we wanted or at least to avoid unpleasantness. At school we learned how to act to get the grades we (or others) wanted. With our peers we probably tried out several rôles until we found the ones that suited us for various situations. And so on, in gender rôles,[35] at work, with our spouse and children ... and we may have lost touch with who we really are.[36] Oh we played our parts well and fooled most everyone including ourselves until it began not quite working. We may have been 'successful' in the eyes of others but eventually their acceptance wasn't enough, something was missing in our lives and hopefully we set about finding it. (I'll draw on my own experience to suggest ways of finding it.)

One way is to talk with a confidant whom we can trust—maybe even a stranger we'll never meet again. They need to be a good listener which means they're not injecting their advice. Rather they're helping us get our feelings and thoughts out where we can examine them but our listener's not accepting any of our self-deceptions. A pioneering approach was called the 'nondirective method' wherein a professional psychotherapist just listened with complete attention and acceptance.[37] A nonprofessional adaptation of this approach was called 'RC' (Re-evaluation Counseling) which trained participants in counseling techniques (such as how to mine nonverbal cues), then paired them up to co-counsel each other—it proved quite effective for a while.[38] A similar approach was used in encounter groups meeting continuously for say a weekend or week with a skilled facilitator but with no agenda so that interpersonal dynamics were laid bare.[39] The power of these approaches is in providing a non-threatening environment in which our behavior patterns are exposed where we can see them objectively and non-defensively, and ideally feel them drain away.

As we learn to accept ourselves we can become adept at observing our own behavior intermittently and see it change gradually without much deliberate effort—our subconscious does most of the work. An attitude I heard of, somewhere long ago and have occasionally tried to adopt, is to avoid identifying too closely with our ego, even though 'ego' means 'I'. Instead try at times to identify with our whole Self observing our ego, perhaps amusingly if we don't take ourself too seriously. For example, as we're going about our routine activities or having a casual conversation, kind of 'rise above' and watch what's going on. This may sound a little schizy—our detached 'voyeur' Self is observing our emotional, spontaneous self—but we're not really splitting our personality.[40] We're just expanding our awareness while continuing our usual behavior, what in the previous chapter was called 'metacognition'.

But then we may decide we need something stronger. An approach I tried for a while with professional therapists was then called 'bioenergetics'.[41] Their belief is that feelings originate in the body and normally flow on up into the head. But unacceptable feelings can be blocked by spasticities along the way which are compensated by other muscles and organs. For example if a young child's genital behavior is suppressed he may block those feeling with a spastic groin which throws off his leg muscles and thus his balance requiring overuse of his eyes, straining them (yes I wear glasses). The therapist first works to 'ground' the body by strengthening the legs and by stretching, so for instance the groin can safely be relaxed. The therapist only deals with any repressed sexual feelings if and when they come up. It may be combined with therapeutic massage. The overall objective is to help the person get connected with their body, not just centered up in their head. Other approaches using pure 'talk therapy' include Freud's and Jung's but I've had no formal experience with them. Whatever approaches a psychotherapist may employ are not as important as the competence and growth of that person themselves, and our own perseverance and self-acceptance—'This is who I am'.

A *caveat*: Just as when a crustacean sheds its old shell so the new one can grow, when we abandon obsolescent behaviors and attitudes, and try out new ones, we too may be awkward and vulnerable. So go easy until you and others become accustomed to the 'new you'. Like the crustacean we may want a safe haven to assimilate our growth. Remember, we're 'rewiring' our brain. "Make haste slowly." Another *caveat*: don't be too open about what you're up to. In our society whereas religion is accepted as a way into our unconscious (albeit unwittingly) psychotherapy has been seen as a stigma (to the undoing of a vice-presidential candidate and myself[42]). Hopefully this is now changing, but don't bet on it—'the road less traveled' has potholes.

Poly- to Mono-Theism

But just maybe, society's acceptance of religion can be used to advantage in delving into our unconscious. As said, communicating with gods/God is in fact communicating with a projected unconscious part of ourself. For example if we pray to the Virgin Mother, we're projecting our mother archetype and/or our anima out onto a mental image or onto Her statue or whatever. If we acknowledge that it's not really Her 'out there' but a projection of part of ourself, then we can begin to take back that part of ourself and integrate it into our Self. If all these 'gods'—the angels and saints we pray to, and the devils that tempt us—don't really exist, than they're in our unacknowledged unconscious. By acknowledging that they are us, we can reclaim those parts of our disowned Self.

Perhaps this is kind of what happened as religions evolved from polytheism to monotheism. Perhaps it was a failed attempt to integrate the many diverse parts of the personality into a composite whole. But the attempt was betrayed both by the inability to recognize the parts as belonging to the individual and by religious leaders who—albeit with the best intentions—instead integrated the many gods into one God. Or rather thought they did, but the many gods were instead retained as lesser gods, namely angels, saints and devils. If the projection onto a god is not owned but stays 'out there', it can't be integrated into the Self and so polytheism continues under the guise of nominal monotheism.

To Sleep, To Dream . . .

Freud's and Jung's contention that dreams are the royal road to the unconscious, its 'Rosetta stone', is lately being challenged. They believed dreams were, for instance, disguised (Freud) repressed childhood sexual wishes or (Jung) socially-unacceptable primitive drives.[43] They encouraged their patients to recall and record their dreams, and attempted to decipher them and thereby bring the dreams' disguised contents into consciousness. Now with an improved understanding of how our brain functions, rather than see the unconscious as scrambling the dreams' contents in order to disguise them, it's proposed that during sleep our brain is handicapped in its attempt to unscramble its normally scrambled contents. During sleep both the inputs to the brain and its executive function are minimized or even shutdown so internally generated bizarre scenarios are subjected to less scrutiny by external reality or by internal logic and censoring.

Specifically, recent sleep research shows that mammalian wake/ sleep cycles are mostly controlled by the brain's circadian clock atop the optic chiasm (where the two eyes' nerve pathways cross and split right/ left views) which sends nerve impulses to the brainstem.[44] In the brainstem are specialized nuclei which can synthesize and disperse neuromodulators up their long axons into select brain areas to modulate the flow of neurotransmitters from synapses to adjacent dendrites, and thereby affect neurons' activity. Two such brainstem nuclei dispense norepinephrine and serotonin which enhance brain operation, keep sensory-input and motor-output circuits open, and the mammal awake.

It's proposed that the circadian clock can order a reduction of norepinephrine and serotonin which reduces brain activity, disables input/output circuits, and induces sleep. As norepinephrine and serotonin decline to near zero they no longer inhibit dispersal of a third neuromodulator, acetylcholine, which excites some parts of the brain but not its dorsolateral prefrontal cortex[45] (executive and working-memory) or the brainstem's input/output circuits.[46] A level of consciousness[47] returns but sleep continues with twitching face, fingers and especially eyes, but the eyelids remain closed—hence this rapid eye movement stage is called REM sleep.[48] There are four stages in a full sleep cycle—each full cycle lasts ninety minutes or so in humans. Most vivid dreams occur primarily in REM sleep, whereas ones that come as we're falling asleep are fragmentary and those in deep non-REM sleep are bland. If our sleep is uninterrupted we progress through several cycles each night but the later cycles may skip the deep non-REM sleep stage in favor of lengthened REM sleep.[49]

This theory explains several characteristics of dreams when put with a couple ideas from the previous chapter—namely that neurons spontaneously generate random nerve impulses and that the hippocampus can generate periodic 'reminder' impulses to reinforce memory traces in the neocortex embedding them as permanent memories, most likely during sleep.[50] The eye movement of REM sleep is likely initiated by an ancient component (the superior colliculus on the brainstem[51]) scanning for threats with barely opened eyes, but since the eyelids are closed the eyes see only specks and so send virtually nothing to the primary visual cortex (V1&2).[52] But as in projection, the activated down-stream visual areas use any meager inputs along with both the random and the reinforcing nerve impulses in trying to form percepts. With the prefrontal shut down and no external input, the handicapped brain forms percepts as best it can—hence the weird vivid images and plots of dreams.[53] Moreover working memory is stored in the prefrontal so since it's disabled most dreams aren't remembered on waking.[54] The acetylcholine excites the amygdala but without prefrontal plausibility restraint, it can run wild—hence the high anxiety of some dreams.[55]

Thus some believe dreams reveal the dreamer's emotional state but contain little if any disguised meanings.[56] But how about a few obscure meanings? After all, our unconscious has much information which isn't accepted by our conscious because our prefrontal cortex' executive function censors and won't allow it. Our prefrontal has learned biases—denial of behaviors (our 'shadow' side) that conflict with our self-image or received 'truths' (like the 'sunrise' example)—which it unconsciously uses in assessing data generated by the rest of our neocortex and primitive brain. But in sleep our prefrontal is enfeebled which is both good-news and bad-news. The good-news is that the rest of our brain is then free to conjure percepts as best it can from whatever's available. The bad-news is that most of it's probably garbage and would take an awful lot of skilled rummaging to glean a few treasures. Putting it in the previous chapter's neural Darwinian terms, the prefrontal can generate basins of attraction favoring some patterns of nerve impulses over others, in effect prejudicing which percepts are allowed to form. But when the prefrontal is enfeebled in sleep, presumably the basins of attraction are not formed[57] so percepts form as best they can thus allowing uncensored thoughts free reign. Some of those thoughts must somehow be meaningful. Whether it's worthwhile pursuing them depends on our priorities.

So I'm not convinced to jettison dreamwork altogether. Sure, much of the canned approaches and pat interpretations are hokum. Yet still there's much responsible and intriguing literature about dreams—for example Jung's fascinating reports of his own dreams[58] and Perls' gestalt work with his patients' dreams.[59] What's more, it's creditably argued by Jung, Campbell and others that there are universal symbols appearing in dreams which express primordial ideas.[60] At minimum some believe dreams 'contextualize' emotions, that is, a dream provides an image or metaphor picturing the context of the salient emotion.[61] While I've had little success deciphering my own dreams (with no outside help), over the years (especially since I retired and can sleep in) I've become more conscious of my dreams both while sleeping and while waking up—"On The Threshold Of A Dream"[62]—and if nothing else at least they're entertaining. When people believed in gods, angels and devils, they believed they came to them in their sleep[63] (examples are found in the Bible and Shakespeare) but just because we don't believe in spirits doesn't mean our dreams can't be insightful.[64]

Of course some believe they rarely dream, but sleep-lab work suggests that we all do.[65] With diligence we can learn to become more conscious of our dreams, called lucid dreaming.[66] It's said that dream intensity can be increased by first creating a REM sleep deficit—by several nights of sleep deprivation curtailing REM sleep—followed by prolonged sleep wherein missed REM sleep is made up along with intense dreaming, perhaps including numinous visions.[67]

Windows of Perception

I'm altering Huxley's[68] *Doors of Perception* because of the concern that if we go through psychedelic 'doors' we may find them closed behind, impeding our return or our long-term mental capacity.[69] So we'll just peek through the 'windows'.

It's been suggested that there's a strong analogy between dreaming and the mind-altering effects induced by some psychedelic drugs. Specifically it's suggested "... that LSD psychosis is a dreamlike state that occurs in waking and that dreaming is an LSD-like state that occurs in sleep."[70] LSD has the advantage of preserving many of the waking aspects of cognition and memory allowing self-observation and insight. But lucid dreaming can have the same advantages with the further advantage of being legal and free.[71] Drug laws hamper research on psychedelic drugs but the limited (biased?) studies on the hazard of various drugs run the gamut from pernicious to benign.[72]

In the late '60s I too briefly dabbled with marijuana under the tutelage of a younger, more venturesome brother-in-law. After a few uneventful tries, one night sitting on the carpet before our fireplace I was suddenly reduced to tears by the astounding beauty of the simplest things—my wine mug, the carpet, the snot running from my nose, the fire—and I then understood what it meant to 'stop the world'.[73] That experience opened my eyes to what can be seen by just looking with a truly open mind. Long after I'd stopped dabbling, we attended a banquet put on by our old parish in the hope of seeing people we were once chummy with. To my chagrin we were seated at a table with people we'd never seen before—'fat, vacuous, social climbers'. In a snit, instead of making conversation I just stared at the cheap candles on the center of the round table and got caught up in the way the light shown through them and the wax dribbled down. Then feeling guilty I looked back at those people. They were still the same but now it was ok. Regardless of what they weren't, what they were was more than enough—each in their own way, they were quite beautiful. I resolved to learn how to bring on such visions naturally but only rarely succeeded.

Nonetheless just knowing such beauty lies hidden in every living thing and in many natural and manmade objects is a precious revelation which, lacking the marijuana experience, I might never have discovered.

So based on my very limited experience, psychedelic drugs can open doors of perception. Of course, Huxley and many others have opened those 'doors' far wider than I'm willing to try.[74] Moreover based on some of their descriptions of what's beyond those 'doors', I'm not sure I care to know anyway. That is, if it's just more jumbled images and stories like my dreams, why should I want or need to know them? The answer is that just maybe I might be able to extract something from all that jumble that might tell me something of great value. And that 'something' might be what we're searching for as discussed early in this chapter—the as yet unexplained fundamental 'something' in us that we project out onto 'God' which we then sometimes experience as unexplainably wondrous, awe-inspiring and numinous—an inkling of our own Life Urge. At least that's my notion.

Is there another way? Maybe—artists, composers, writers—whether they were 'high' on drugs, nature or whatever—have endeavored to express in their art, music and literature what they 'saw' in their dreams, daydreams and reveries. True, they're not *my* dreams from *my* unconscious, but maybe I can connect vicariously. Maybe my very limited experience has opened my eyes to the possibilities of seeing with a more open mind so I can glimpse what they 'saw'.

Art & Architecture

For centuries the Church built lofty cathedrals; decorated them with paintings, stained glass, statues and tapestries; permeated them with candle light and incense, instrumental and choral music; staged pageants in splendid vestments and tolled the mighty bells high above, summoning the faithful to gather and be uplifted by the sacred wonder of God, the saints and the marvels of heaven depicted on the ceiling. The Church was increasingly a major employer of artists[75] and artisans which led to extravagances, such as the sale of indulgences to pay for it all. The backlash came with the Protestant Reformation and it's emphasis on relating to the people, say with services in their vernacular rather than Latin. There are still uplifting elegant churches being designed and built but most focus more on the congregation. Even the Catholic Church belatedly joined the trend with Vatican II, dropping the use of Latin in the mass and renovating older churches to reverse the altars and commune with the people. But most services are still centered on God 'out there' albeit maybe not as far out there. Yet there are those who lament that the mystical nature of religion has been sold out for the cognitive and communal.

Perhaps our early ancestors crawled deep into the bowels of the Earth in caves at Altamira, Chauvet, Lascaux or Niaux to witness shamans wave smoking torchlights making the beasts painted on the cave walls and ceiling seem to charge and lunge, along with archaic music, and thus initiate youths to the terrors of the hunt.[76] Today we file into a dark movie-theater to watch an absent shaman/director's histrionics flash on the screen, along with surround-sound, vicariously experiencing the thrill of a chase or the pathos of a tragedy, while we nibble popcorn. Or we can rent the video and watch it on our wide-screen TV from our couch.

Or we wander an art gallery or museum viewing painters' and sculptors' interpretations of their dreams and musings. We can also sometimes purchase copies of their works to hang on our walls so we can contemplate at leisure what they're trying to tell us.[77] VanGogh's *Starry Night*, his fields and portraits; Dali's warped watches and crucifixes; and Magritte, Escher, Picasso and many others were either trying to tell us something or perhaps just telling themselves. Maybe we should instead do our own drawings, doodling or whatever as uninhibited as we can manage,[78] then try to contemplate what our unconscious is trying to tell our conscious. While the quality may be far less, the relevance may be far more.[79]

A high quality painting, drawing or photograph at minimum can 'stop the world' and force us to just look, to see with the artist's eyes. For instance the power of Ansel Adams' work to show the marvel of some rather prosaic scenes we might otherwise pass unnoticed. I remember when first learning photography years ago how it caused me to look with fresh eyes[80] and see what I'd previously overlooked.

Music & Dance

Undoubtedly a leading candidate for the emergence of the Life Urge into consciousness is music, "... the language of the emotions."[81] I've suggested that the Urge to Life is felt in our active emotions,[82] our urges. Urges are normally expressed in actions. But alternatively, instead or in advance of action, emotions can be revealed in prosody and gesture, which can be further elaborated in song and dance. Conversely emotions—instead of arising from within—can be stimulated from without, evoked and even manipulated by music and dance. Recall toward the end of Chapter Nine, how our hominid ancestors evolved song[83] and dance to elevate and entrain their emotions, and thereby unify their troop.[84] And ever since, from the chants of monks,[85] to martial music, school songs, hymns, operas, musicals and so on, all have been used to call forth emotions for benign or malign motives.

While its name implies that our brain processes music just in the auditory cortex of the upper temporal lobe, recent research shows that many areas in both hemispheres and in our primitive brain are involved even when just hearing music.[86] Even more areas get progressively involved when we sing or whistle, play an instrument, or dance. Our species evolved the same brain architecture shared by our primate relatives but to a far advanced degree. Yet music's roots go even farther back in our ancestry, down into our reptilian brain, which "... could explain why we find so much meaning and emotion in music ... "[87] Perhaps it's the tap-root to our Life Urge. But the theistically inclined attribute music's ineffable qualities to the supernatural.[88]

Often I've a tune or song playing in my head, over and over. Sometimes I'll try to find out what I'm trying to tell myself—What's the music's hidden message my unconscious is trying to convey? I can let the music out by singing or whistling (my mother said I began whistling while crawling around before learning to walk) and then listen to myself analytically. Conversely a single bell or wind-chimes can pull us out of ourselves to meditate on the pure sound reverberating in the air—Buddhists use pure tones this way. Contrarily, huge bells in church belfries would call the faithful to Mass while tiny bells announced the Eucharist. Before the advent of recorded music the educated read sheet-music, played an instrument and attended concerts; now we have our CDs, stereos and radios. Music permeates our lives.

While most of us don't enjoy being sad, nonetheless we can 'enjoy' sad music.[89] The 'hillbilly' musician Hank Williams even managed to put a humorous twist on some of his laments (♪"... I got to the river so lonesome I wanted to die, oh lord! And then I jumped in the river, but the dog-gone river was dry."[90]) The abundance of genuinely sad music attests to its appeal—consider "Londonderry Air" (♪"Oh Danny Boy ..."), "The Red River Valley" (♪"From this valley they say you are leaving ..."), Chopin's Piano Sonata #2's (op.35) 3rd movement (*funèbre*), Mozart's Requiem's (K.165) "*Lacrimosa*" and Bach's St.Matthew Passion's (BWV 244) "*Erbarme dich*"[91]—to mention just a few. Perhaps they resonate with a deeply felt despair of the human condition, the 'existential angst', the solipsistic feeling that we're each utterly alone, that 'we each die alone'. As suggested above, we can use the pain of these feelings as a window to our unconscious when our latent or repressed emotions reveal themselves.

But the negative feelings can also lead to a catharsis so that deep sad-ness can be a prelude to great joy[92] as Beethoven showed in his Ninth Sym-phony.[93] Sometimes we've got to scrape bottom before we can rise up. Music can ofttimes provide a vehicle that can help transport us out of the doldrums to a more hopeful view of life.[94] Some Protestant hymns can have marvelous power this way, for example ♪"Softly and tenderly Jesus is calling ..." and of course "Amazing Grace."[95] While I reject the theistic message that's wrapped in the music, if we can get past that and just feel the emotions, we can use it to learn about ourself and work through those emotions. (If we can't get past it, that tells us something too.) As said, the feelings are real even though I'm convinced they've been projected out and misattributed to God. Better they be owned as our Life Urge and nur-tured within. Dory Previn's "Mythical Kings and Iguanas"/"Going Home (is such a ride)" recounts her travails in her quest to exhume her Urge to Life. Another secular song celebrating the Life Urge is Joan Baez' *"Gracias a la Vida."*

Nature

The most fundamental access to the Life Urge is the most obvious—nature! Nature has been eulogized by untold writers, most notably Henry David Thoreau.[96] Most of us have an attraction to nature (dubbed 'bio-philia'[97]) although the more macho disguise it as fishing, hunting, golf and SUVs. Even New York City's cement canyons have their Central Park. House plants, office shrubbery and landscape paintings decorate our spaces. When our kids were small we built a home in exurbia on a wooded pond near an undeveloped half-square-mile of woods, meadows, bogs, streams and lakes so they could grow up 'grounded in nature'.[98] Then I only intuited what I now understand.

So music may be the language of our emotions and thus a route to the Life Urge in us, but in Nature the Life Urge is instantiated in every liv-ing thing. If we're out in Nature[99] in its growing seasons, life is happening all around us. But because we're so accustomed to it, so jaded, we often fail to notice.[100] Stop and marvel at the wonder of it all. Every tree, bush, vine and grass is answering its Urge to reach for the Sun. Pick out one tree and try to commune with it, to envisage its Life Urge permeating its every cell, coursing up from its roots through its trunk and branches, and into every quivering leaf. It and every plant are expressing their Urge to Life (but don't get carried away or you'll be conflicted about mowing your lawn[101]). Envisaging the Life Urge in every living thing is not the same as our early ancestors or primitives seeing gods everywhere, but in a way it could be said that we're honoring each living thing's 'soul', that we're 'worshiping' their Life Urge.

Digging down in the ground a little (depending where) we'll unearth innumerable, mostly microscopic organisms: We'll see worms, sow bugs, ants and lots of tiny critters. And there're many more we can't see without a microscope. We may have trouble relating to some of them like centipedes, although I kind of like toadstools. But don't just look at them scientifically—marvel at the profusion and wonder of Life. Above the surface, on the plants and in the air are all sorts of other critters: insects, beetles, spiders ... briefly alluded to in Chapter Seven. They're all marvelous if we can get past any fear or revulsion we may feel initially. And they're each and every one expressing their Urge to Life in their own inimitable fashion.

Finally we come to "... the paragon of animals!"[102] although at times I have trouble relating to some of them too, as I described above. Yet we're also part of Nature though we've so ensconced ourselves in our cultural artifacts—clothes, jewelry, gadgets, media, vehicles, structures and so on, as well as mannerisms—that it's difficult to see that we *are* part of Nature. When we can cut through all that stuff and nonsense, and begin to experience each other unadorned, for who we really are, we encounter each other's 'soul'. Not the same immortal soul we were told about in catechism that was placed in us at conception by the Holy Spirit and survives after death—that concept is outmoded (although considering what the Church's theologians knew back then, a 'soul' was a good attempt to explain what I'm here proposing is the Life Urge). The crucial difference is that, whereas the concept of a 'soul'[103] posits a supernatural origin and so is separate *from* nature, the concept of a Life Urge doesn't require a supernatural origin because the Life Urge originates *in* nature, it's *part of* nature. All that poetry about looking deep into one another's 'souls' still applies but absent the theology. Or maybe with proto-theology, to perceive another person's Life Urge is to see 'God' in them.[104]

Undoubtedly there are other avenues to numinousness and liminal states, good sex[105] can be one and 'near death experience'[106] another (generally not recommended), but the ones I've described are representative. Given the unparalleled freedom from the demands of eking out a living that today's material culture provides most of us, we should have the leisure to regularly indulge in the pursuit of liminal states, the threshold of our sub/unconscious. Instead it seems we're entranced by our runaway material culture, addicted to ever increasing 'doses' of gadgets and stuff, futilely pursuing satisfaction at escalating thresholds of satiation. Maybe like the Sorcerer's Apprentice,[107] we don't know how to stop it. Yet maybe if we're more in touch with our expanded Self, we're less needful of ego-props to prop-up our fragile self.[108] I suspect that most traditional salvation religions—Christianity and Islam, and perhaps rabbinic Judaism—leave their adherents unfulfilled, the faithful project their deepest Self out of themselves, leaving their Self empty. To fill the void they may indulge in self-aggrandizing behavior and possessions trying to fill their gnawing emptiness. And it may work as long as they keep busy and don't let it get to them. Sometimes though we need to stop and smell the roses. More on runaway materialism in the next chapter.

Still there are people who feel they're not religious nor do they want to be. They certainly don't believe in God, Christ, Virgin Mother ... spirits or fairies, nor much less have a 'warm glow of faith'. But they have a 'warm glow of Life'—generally an enthusiastic positive attitude—which to me says they're experiencing and owning their Life Urge, they're just not projecting it out of themselves onto some imaginary being. Should they try to get more in touch with their Life Urge? Maybe if they can without losing their spontaneity—why not? But if they find their Life too busy, frantically seeking new adventures, even extreme dangerous experiences, unable to 'mellow out', maybe they need to delve into their Self.

Non-Theistic Religions

Wait a minute! Before delving into the non-theistic, what about all the many theistic religions we've known and loved? I'm not going to just ignore them, am I? Well, to my way of thinking they're stages in the long progression religions have followed in humans' short history (evolutionarily speaking). Religions evolved from animism and ancestor worship into polytheistic paganism, then into monotheism and now I'm suggesting into prototheism. Recall how Abraham purportedly superseded the Sumerian gods and how Jesus' followers superseded Judaism and the Greco-Roman gods. Now I'm suggesting we take the next step and supersede the very concept of gods. But I recognize there are many scientifically minded faithful who believe in evolution and science, yet don't want to abandon their theistic beliefs. If you're of such a mind there are objective theistic science writers you might like.[109] I respect their choice and would defend their right to make that choice, just as I hope they'd defend my choice—that's a cornerstone of our free society. But as for me, I've moved on.

Buddhism has flourished for twenty-five-hundred years without belief in God, although the various sects venerate statues of Buddha and employ prayer wheels and flags, and they believe in incarnation.[110] Zen Buddhism "... emphasizes meditation as a way to enlightenment" and eschews intellectualizing. "Zen values the simple, concrete, living facts of ... direct personal experience ... is intensely pragmatic ... stresses self-reliance, self-discipline, and personal effort ..." believing that the "... inner journey is but a prelude to going out."[111] While I find much to admire in reading about Zen, I'm not persuaded to pursue it. It seems to emphasize putting major effort into developing one's inner self in order to abandon striving and merge with the "Great Self"[112] rather than in developing an enlarged Self which encompasses one's world. Yes, it emphasizes compassion for all living things but it sees life as cyclical rather than evolving and the world as stagnant rather than progressing. Somehow, it seems to me, we need to find a way of combining the intuitive powers of Zen with the intellectual powers of science.[113] A step in that direction might be Transcendental Meditation (TM)[114] which, along with yoga, is based on Hindu practices as was Buddhism long ago. TM uses personalized mantras to induce alternative states as described above. The Beatles reportedly used it to their creative advantage.

Unitarian Universalism has an interesting appeal even though it has some contradictions. Though its name represents the consolidation of two doctrines,[115] they don't hold to any one doctrine. Instead they encompass a wide range of persuasions—Christian, Jewish, Muslim and Buddhist; pagan, pantheist, agnostic and atheist[116]—postmodern? A long-held tenet is "deeds not creeds."[117] They do hold what they call a 'common faith': "inherent worth and dignity of every person; justice, equity and compassion ... acceptance of one another and encouragement to spiritual growth ... free and responsible search for truth and meaning; rights of conscience and the use of democratic process ... goal of world community ... respect for the interdependent web of all existence."[118] Their theism sounds a little like non-theism: "... 'God' is not God's name, but our name for that which is greater than all and yet present in each ..."[119] "'Whom should I adore: the Creator or the Creation?' ... 'The Creation, surely, for whatever there be of the Creator will be made manifest in Her handiwork.'"[120] "Part of being born again ... lies in waking up to the fact that all of *life* is a gift ... redemption has little to do with death ... it involves discovering and acting upon *life*'s hidden yet abundant richness ... By remaining open to experiencing the mystery of *life* anew, we are born again and again."[121](my italics) My exposure to Unitarian Universalism is limited to a few adherents I've esteemed over the years, to reading one short book and to attending a few events at a local church.[122] It certainly has a positive flavor but it seems to me that without an overarching doctrine it runs the risk of lapsing into righteous do-goodism. But maybe I'm too steeped in the old Catholic mass where we focused on 'God' and dare not look around. Still, I think it's better to try to focus on the Life Urge however it expresses itself through each person. Maybe they do but I missed it (see above my italics of *life*).

Humanism[123] is more a philosophy than a 'religion' as defined at the beginning of this chapter. However I'm sure many religious people see it as 'anti-religious', atheistic, which indeed it usually is. One of Humanists' principal concerns seems to be freedom of religion, religious liberty—including the right to *not* believe in God—even though their Statement of Principles[124] is much broader. They don't hold services nor have churches; rather they have seminars, courses and local groups. My principal exposure to Humanism is through two periodicals: "The Humanist" and "free inquiry: Celebrating Reason and Humanity" which feature thoughtful and pertinent articles on current issues especially those that infringe or threaten our rights and liberties. Reason is their prime weapon and they seem to give scant credit to intuition's rôle in reasoning and in generating ideas.[125] Moreover I'm not alone in sensing a belligerent, dour attitude running through much of their writings rather than a 'joy of Life', *joie de vivre*. Yet in face-to-face social situations the humanists I've met are quite personable.[126] I agree with and applaud most of their issues and activities yet it seems to me their ideals don't go far enough—they're anthropocentric rather than seeing humans as evolution's latest accomplishment, as evolution's 'eyes' responsible for steering Life's trajectory at an ever accelerating rate, as extolled in these pages.

So 'non-theistic religion' is not an oxymoron[127] and it's entirely reasonable to conceive of a prototheistic religion that would honor, even exalt our Life Urge, if you agree with my notion of what the root of religion really is. I can envision several ways that such a religion might come about— 'Religion' not necessarily in its formal institutionalized meaning but more importantly in men's and women's hearts, in the way they conceptualize and in how they live their lives and raise their children. I'd like to think this book will be a key step that will engender thoughtful discussions, articles and forums including on television and online[128]—maybe even lead to further research and books. If it also generates controversy that's fine too—controversy generates publicity through word-of-mouth and the media—as long as it doesn't degenerate into just thoughtless reactionary protests (although that's probably inevitable if it's successful). Early Christianity as described in Chapter Three provides an outdated model. Perhaps a more recent and relevant model is the gay movement[129] where a long suppressed 'abomination' has 'come out' and is slowly being accepted in spite of the AIDS epidemic. Atheism has also long been an abomination to many and even implicated with plagues. Hopefully a prototheistic 'religion' will fare better if it can be seen as a progressive outgrowth of theism just as Christianity was an outgrowth of Judaism and paganism. Another model that might be adapted is the modern Quakers, the Society of Friends whose belief is that divine revelation is immediate and individual as the 'inner light' or 'Christ within'[130]—read the 'Life Urge' to adapt it to prototheism. In the final chapter we'll explore further how a prototheistic 'religion' might be institutionalized in society.

However there are at least a couple open questions. A Christian woman I occasionally hook up with on morning runs, when I explained some of my ideas, asked "But how do you pray?"[131] In my view when one prays to God, a saint or dead person, they're projecting from their conscious mind out onto a figment of their imagination. Any answers they get back come from their own unconscious mind.[132] It's a kind of Rogers' nondirective method of psychotherapy so it's good if it helps get stuff out but not if they don't own it.[133] Traditional prayer postures, like kneeling, palms together or turned up, are those of a lowly suppliant[134] which may induce emotions but I'd think contradict Self-hood ('stand on your own two feet'). If we tell a person we'll pray for them,[135] it's not only a way of saying we care but perhaps it has the placebo effect[136]—if they think it works, it just might.[137]

Still sometimes life can be lonely. Our 'friends' and relatives may not be responsive, are too busy with their own priorities ... It can be comforting to have an imaginary friend such as Jesus, Mother Mary[138] ... who's always there (at least in our imagination). But rather than turn to an imaginary 'Jesus' figure, it's better to first reclaim that part of our Self that we're projecting onto 'Jesus' (maybe that's what it means to "take Jesus into your heart")—become our own best friend.[139] Once we've refilled the emptiness and aren't so needful, we can relate to friends reciprocally, even expecting to get less than we give—if our Self is full, we can afford to. Truly "It's more blessed to give than receive."

Another woman runner, a mother, a high-school science teacher and an ex-Catholic, asked "What do we teach the children?" We teach them the truth! Sure, children pretend both in play and in stories—that's how they develop their imagination[140]—yet soon they learn to discriminate truth from fiction. But let's not fill their heads with the religious fiction we were taught as if it were true. About death and afterlife: it's sad when a loved pet, friend or relative dies but if we as a parent-figure and adult-model can handle it, they'll likely follow our example in spite of others' religiosity.[141] About God: as discussed in Chapter Two, belief in God—"Our Father Who art in Heaven"—may simply be looking to the ultimate parent-figure who's in charge rather than facing the unknown. If the child's real parent is comfortable not believing in God, then the child may be too until old enough to decide for themselves. If we as adults don't pretend to have all the answers, yet can tolerate uncertainty they'll eventually learn to too. "What we do speaks louder than what we say."[142] Of course as young children they look to us to deal with the world. But as they get older they should gradually learn to take more and more responsibility in making their own decisions, and to seek appropriate information before they proceed. If we're open and encourage their incrementally escalating decision-making, they'll have less to rebel against and may even come to value our guidance—it does happen once in a while.

But like a niece of mine who says she's a 'disenchanted Catholic' and 'skeptical Christian', perhaps many parents don't feel qualified to teach their children about God (well then don't!) so are searching for some religion that's at least close to what they believe ... and has a children's program. Hopefully they're not simply looking to salve their conscience, feeling their kids *should* get *some* spiritual training. But is the formal teacher more qualified than the informal parent? Ideally parents would find qualified teachers to augment what their kids are learning from their parents' example, impromptu lessons and answers to a child's many questions. If the parents have done their 'homework'—thinking through their own beliefs with the help of books like this so they're not conflicted—they'll feel more comfortable and confident guiding their children. Hopefully books will be published for various ages that will help adults teach children about prototheism. Already there are books and videos to teach them about nature, science, history, and so forth which are a good start. Today's parents are on the cusp, the turning point, of many changes in technology and society— theism to prototheism is just one of them, which requires helping their children discover the source of their religious feelings. Just as we wouldn't stagnate our children technologically—like the Amish do in a misguided attempt to shield their children from materialism—so we shouldn't stagnate ours theologically with outdated worldviews and values.

Perhaps a restatement of the Life Urge tenets is in order here: Life initially emerged from Earth's matter nearly four-billion years ago as molecules randomly rearranged themselves to better withstand some adversity. Other molecules adopted the practice and elaborated on it, passing their ever more complex and elegant arrangements on to other macromolecules—they replicated. What was a *re*action became a *pro*action, a way-of-life, a Life Urge. At first Life was housed in simple cells—archaea and prokaryotes. But as this Urge to Life experienced ever greater adversity, it randomly found ever more elegant solutions—synergistic arrangements of complex structures. By building on earlier arrangements in nested hierarchies, they evolved. Some prokaryotes merged with archaea into single cell eukaryotes, then some eukaryotes combined into multicell organisms by dedicating differentiated cells to specialized functions and somehow coordinating them. As coordination became more elaborate it enabled movement—animals with nervous systems. As nervous systems became more elaborate they became brains and finally brains became reflexive—consciousness emerged. All Life is innately aware of its Life Urge else it wouldn't be alive. Consciousness not only is intuitively aware of this Life Urge (faith?) which can be experienced as numinous and transcendent, but consciousness can also infer Life's evolutionary trajectory—where Life's evolution might be heading. Hence we conscious humans can not only revel in Life but can be evolution's executors, we can choose to help carry Life's evolution forward each in our own way. This can be our calling, our mission in Life, our 'religion'. Not to honor and serve a projection of some imaginary God but to honor and serve Life, and to be part of evolution's long trajectory in advancing Life. I believe this is the Meaning of Life.

Paradox Resolved?

Singly or in combinations, meditation, art, music, dance and drugs[143] can induce numinous experiences which Western religions have traditionally interpreted as contact with God or spirits. But why? Why not now interpret them as one's Life Urge? Admittedly I haven't presented conclusive, incontrovertible proof that the numinous is consciousness of the Life Urge, but it's far more credible and conclusive than what's presented as proof of God. Why resort to a two millennia old 'supernatural' interpretation of a natural phenomenon when the past two centuries have produced a far better understanding of nature? Two millennia ago most thought that the Earth was flat, that each day and night the 'heavens' passed by overhead, and that it was all the domain of mostly invisible gods who controlled everything including men's fates. We don't rely on two millennia-old maps, communication, vehicles, medicine, and so on. Why rely on two millennia-old religion? Virtually all readily accept the fruits of today's science, yet many hesitate to apply today's science to theology[144] and so cling to theism. Why? As suggested at the beginning of the book, perhaps for some it's because there hasn't been a creditable alternative. Now I think there is.

Yet it seems there are many who haven't even began to look for an alternative. Until there's a glaring inconsistency or discord in the Church's teachings or practices that produces cognitive dissonance, we don't begin any serious questioning ('I-don't-want-to-talk-about-it'). We're too busy with our daily lives so 'if it works don't fix it'. For my wife and me it came when the Church's teachings proved patently absurd. We'd been married only eight-and-a-half years when we had our sixth child (the first was born when we'd been married fourteen months and all were single births)—"Six kids in seven years" my wife used to say. Serious soul searching ensued (as mentioned in Chapter One's note). Thus I suspect until there's some cognitive dissonance that 'pulls the rug out from under' the Church's teachings, they're unassailable. Put another way, those teachings may be so firmly 'wired' into our brain that only a short-circuit can blow or burn them out.[145] Perhaps only then can we begin arduously 'rewiring' our brain perhaps along the lines described in these pages.

Still I realize I'm naïve. There are Catholic couples I know, my contemporaries, who somehow managed not to have 'six kids in seven years' by picking and choosing what they believed and practiced, somehow salving their conscience (that's what confession's for?![146]). Yet to this day they consider themselves to be good practicing Catholics. Theirs is a more flexible faith. Maybe they're conflicted too and won't admit it, even to themselves. I envy today's generation of Catholics, they seem to somehow rationalize their premarital sex and cohabitation, and low birth rate.[147] Pope JohnPaul II still preaches against contraception but apparently he's being ignored by many nominal Catholics. Hopefully it's creating cognitive dissonance between the Church's teaching and Catholics' practices which will lead to a search for a creditable alternative. We'll see. "When the pupil is ready the teacher will come."

Undoubtedly there are some, maybe many, who don't want to know of a creditable alternative! As mentioned at the end of Chapter Four, the realization that there is no "Father in Heaven" overturns and uproots entrenched lifelong beliefs. It can be very upsetting[148] as was the thought that the Earth wasn't the immovable center of the Universe back in Copernicus' and Galileo's day. Like then, it not only can bring on denial as mentioned, but anger and rage against whoever is advocating such 'outrageous' ideas. They're not burning heretics at the stake these days but we should still try to go softly, eschewing strident advocacy. Put the ideas out, not dogmatically, but simply as our own, and in the true spirit of religious freedom, respect others' beliefs even if we think they're naïve and outdated. It's their choice! But I do try to put my ideas out where they can be noticed, understood and ferment cognitive dissonance. And I try to remain open to any who're ready to begin exploring creditable alternatives. But I watch my back![149]

Another impediment to openly exploring creditable alternatives is vested interest. A bishop, say who's invested his whole life in his career, it seems to me, would encounter great difficulty in objectively considering this alternative. He'd probably think like an attorney (which in French is *avocat* = advocate) to whom we turn to advocate our case by selecting only facts favoring our position and exploiting any weakness in the opposition's position. The objective is not to discover truth but to prevail. Vested interest can trap us in our mind-set.

In short as I see it there are three overlapping phases a person must want to go through: First comes cognitive dissonance—until there's dissatisfaction with, and inconsistencies in the belief system based on a God 'out there', a person won't be open to alternative explanations. Second, the person needs to 'deprogram' their brain/mind—to 'unplug and melt-down' the old concepts 'wired' into their neocortex—often an anguishingly slow process. Third, the person needs to 'reprogram', to 'rewire' their brain/mind circuits with alternative concepts or paradigms which can also be a slow faltering process. Putting it in Chapter Nine's language, the pre-conscious brain/mind must be retrained to form different gestalts from the sensory data reaching it in order to interpret those data differently. This sounds like brain-washing, something totalitarian regimes and cults do! But if ethical psychotherapeutic practices are upheld wherein the person is in charge and the change-agent is a supportive consultant, such dangers are mitigated. But don't expect overnight results, it may take the rest of one's Life to undo the programming of our formative years.

In this chapter we've looked at extending our conscious mind *down* into our pre/sub/unconscious mind. In the next chapter we'll look at how we're extending our conscious mind *up* ever higher through the use of logic, literacy, mathematics, computers, communication, science and so on. We'll also look at how we're empowering the actualization of our minds by extending our bodies *out* through the use of tools, vehicles, energy, shelter and so forth. Then in the final chapter we'll look at how we extend our society, our institutions.

Chapter Eleven

Tools

The mountaineer guides who have led our party so well now want to go off on their own in a try for the summit of the Mountain somewhere up there in that cloud. We're happy for the break while they carefully inspect the climbing equipment they brought along: ropes, carabiners, pitons, crampons, ice axes ... the tools of their trade. Before dawn the next morning they're off... Hours later as the light fades they're finally back, exhausted but exhilarated even though they'd failed. They'd discovered how not to, so the next time . . .

Evolution's trajectory has produced ever greater complexity of form, not just in the integral body form but in extensions of the human body—not just a hand but a hand-axe, not just fur/hair but hide-clothing. To cite just one example, take the hand-axe's 'evolution'. Perhaps after a couple million years of hand-held hand-axes, someone got the bright idea of somehow attaching the hand-axe to the end of a club—the hand-axe was hafted, a breakthrough. Much later its head became bronze, then iron and now steel, and in the last couple centuries it became a power jackhammer, and so on. Whereas the biological evolution of body forms 'til now has been a tortuously slow Darwinian process, the extra-biological evolution of human body extensions can be faster and more flexible, somewhat like a Lamarckian[1] process. These extensions I'm including under the broad category of 'tools' and in this chapter examining how tools 'evolve'. Now if you accept the concept proposed in Chapter Nine's 'Symbols, Music & Language', that we humans are hybrid organisms—dependent on our invented manmade culture, our tools, the extensions of our minds and bodies in a symbiotic relationship—then the 'evolution' of tools is tantamount to the evolution of us humans. In effect we humans are evolving at an ever accelerating rate. But is this evolution advancing Life?

In addition to addressing the 'evolution' of the *extensions* of our bodies and minds, this chapter will explore the impending evolution of our bodies and brains *themselves*. Just as scientific discoveries enable the 'evolution' of our tools, other scientific discoveries are beginning to enable the enhancement of performance and longevity, and the genetic engineering of our biology. But will it advance Life either?

When we view the three-million year sweep of *Homo* evolution we see an interesting pattern of tool innovation matched with body innovation: *Homo rudolfensis* developed their Oldowan stone culture some two million years ago, then stagnated in their body form and tools. *Homo erectus* initially adapted Oldowan, but then invented the more advanced Acheulean technology and stayed with it until the end of their time. *Homo neanderthalensis* initially adopted Acheulean, but then invented Mousterian culture and stayed with it pretty much until their end when some started using the Upper Paleolithic stone implements of *Homo sapiens*. Not until *Homo sapiens* did this pattern of cultural innovation followed by stagnation begin to change.[2]

This pre-*Homo sapiens* pattern we also see in 'lower' animals: For example each species of bird evolves its own nest style and pretty much stays with it until extinction. Each species of spider does the same with their webs. The phenotype (body style) and extended phenotype (nest, web or whatever) evolve together, then stagnate. And we humans have done pretty much the same throughout our history until very recently: A society of people evolves its own culture (tools and everything) and stays with it until almost forced to change, usually by an environmental change or by contact with a more advanced society, for instance, aboriginals exposed to western tools (arguably a mixed blessing). Even today there are many people in modern society, not necessarily neo-Luddites, who are slow to embrace change such as computers. But there are others who are almost addicted to change—if it's new it must be better ... or more fashionable.[3]

A related human trait probably also has its roots in our early ancestors—the accumulation of stuff. As described in Chapter Eight, tools were key in hominid evolution. For two million years migrating hominids' survival depended on their hand-axes, spears, and all kinds of other stuff which they had carefully crafted from often distant sources of raw materials. So they evolved an affinity for their stuff and it seems we've inherited that trait. Hence we can blame our material culture on our distant ancestors!

Extensions

Let's take a closer look at what's meant by 'extensions' which extend our physical and mental capabilities. Some writers use the term 'prostheses' in a broadened definition. Clothing—hats, gloves, clothes and shoes—are extensions of our skin and hair as is shelter—tents, houses and other buildings. Extensions of our eyes[4] would be a magnifying glass, microscope, X-ray imager and telescope, including the orbiting Hubble Space Telescope and space probes. Extensions of our hand would include a hammer, pliers, knife, saw, power-saw, shovel, tweezers, spoon, brush, broom and so on. Extensions of our feet would be shoes, roller-skates, skis, bicycle, car, airplane, space-shuttle and whatever. But let's not get hung-up on classifications—for instance whether writing and print are extensions of our voice or memory—they're both, as are our myriad electronic devices like telephone, radio, television and computer. You get the idea. These extensions extend our personal body and mind enabling us to function finer, faster, farther and/or stronger, and maybe even better depending on our criteria.[5]

These extensions of our physical body have a marked limitation though. Whereas we can feel our hand and finger tips, and we can feel a pencil held by our fingers, we can't feel the pencil the same way we feel our finger—the pencil's numb, it's devoid of sensation. As mentioned in Chapter Nine we can project the feel of the pencil's tip pressing on paper, a kind of virtual feel, but our feelings are not in the pencil per se. The same goes for the feel we have of a hammer, tennis-racket, bicycle, car and so on, but it's a virtual feel—the sense is in us and not in the numb tool. The same can be said of all our other extensions—we risk becoming desensitized (though who knows, maybe someday technology will extend our feelings into our tools). But this limitation does have its advantages—most of us wouldn't reach with our fingers to turn the meat barbequing on a grill, we'd use a fork or tongs to avoid getting burned.

Another major advantage of bodily extensions—as mentioned in Chapter Eight's 'Internal Factors' regarding our distant ancestors using stones to break-up coarse food rather than evolving massive teeth and jaws—is that tools can be 'evolved' and adopted or abandoned much more readily than bodies thus conferring flexibility to deal with changing circumstances. Flexibility in their extensions enabled our distant ancestors to survive and prosper in varying environments. Since the last fifty thousand years or less our species' evolution has apparently been negligible in our integral bodies and brains but has accelerated astonishingly in our extensions. This acceleration has been uneven[6]—sometimes less than other times—but right now it seems to be going asymptotic. And soon the evolution of our bodies and brains may also.

The 'evolution' of extensions isn't a Darwinian process—they don't mutate on their own and pass those mutations on to the next generation of that extension. Rather there are human innovators who design improve-ments of the extension or invent a radically new extension. Yet even so there are many similarities to the evolutionary process. For instance just as an organism may occasionally have a mutation in its germ cells which it passes on to its progeny, an inventor may 'mutate' an extension, that is, change its design. But just as the organism's mutated offspring may not be viable, the inventor's idea may not be workable either. Even if the organ-ism's mutated offspring lives, can it successfully compete with the other organisms in its environment? Similarly even if the inventor's idea works, and his invention can be produced and marketed, can it successfully com-pete in its market? Just as there are many mutations that never become successful species, there are many inventions that don't make it either, per-haps only one in a hundred, who knows. "Many are called but few are cho-sen." And even if a new species or product does get established in its en-vironment or market for a while, they both have limited life-cycles and eventually will be displaced by upstarts or bad luck, and go extinct.

Even though there are many similarities in the 'evolution' of species and extensions, there's a very important difference—natural evolution comes from blind-chance mutations whereas innovative human exten-sions come from the mind of the inventor—evolution is 'blind', we're not. In the previous chapter under Life Urge, I described how our conscious-ness enables us to 'see' where evolution's trajectory might be leading and do what we can to advance Life. There are a couple ways we can do this—as suppliers and as consumers. Think of it as an evolutionary process where the suppliers provide the variations and the consumers select which will succeed in the market environment.

In our modern world we alternate between being suppliers and being consumers. Because most of us are somehow involved in supplying products and/or services, we should have a sense whether they're ad-vancing or impeding Life's evolution. Even if buried deep in a large or-ganization, hopefully we know what it does. If it's an auto company, for example, certainly cars and trucks enable people to get around, but we can't be expected to know what each customer's up to, whether they're ad-vancing Life. Yet if the cars and trucks are pitched on the basis of power, prestige or sex-appeal it compromises their utility. Secondly we're all con-sumers and can choose to support products and services that advance Life or at least don't diminish it. There's nothing wrong with enjoying what we're doing as supplier or consumer—it probably makes us more effective at what we do—but we need to take responsibility for the consequences of our actions however remote or trivial those consequences may seem.

'Hunter-Gatherers'

Perhaps it's a question of attitude. Like most other animals our early ancestors initially had an eat-as-you-go attitude which later evolved into the
hunter-gatherer attitude. They opportunistically took what they found—
perhaps with little thought of how it came to be there or maybe they gave
the gods credit for providing it—and ate it then-and-there, or toted it back
to the troop's encampment to be divided and consumed with others. After
a few million years of this, around ten millennia ago it must have dawned
on a few of our ancestors that they might improve the supply by somehow
fostering growth, either as herders guiding goats or as farmers cultivating
crops—the original entrepreneurs. They still had to deal with hunter-
gathers—human and other animals, free loaders—that raided their herd[7]
and stole their crops. And this hunter-gatherer attitude has persisted on
down through the millennia—whether out of ignorance (they don't understand how value is produced) or out of arrogance (they don't care, they
just want it)—from the ancient conquerors like Alexander the Great, to the
Spanish conquistadors, to tyrants like Hitler and Stalin.[8]

The hunter-gatherer attitude still persists today all around us. We can
point to the classic corporate raider who corners the stock of a conservative,
cash-rich firm in order to loot it.[9] Or as I write, the 'captains of industry'
who 'cooked the books' of their corporations (aided and abetted by ac-
countants and securities analysts) in order to inflate the price of their op-
tioned stock, then 'abandoned ship' in the process effectively stealing their
employees' pensions. But the person who hires a predatory contingent-fee
lawyer to sue an insurance company on an inflated claim is also a hunter-
gatherer (as is the lawyer), just on a less audacious scale. It seems to me anyone who tries to take more than their share, who doesn't reinvest at least
part of their take for 'seed', who tries to get something for nothing, or who
trashes the environment, displays the basic hunter-gatherer attitude—the
'tragedy of the commons'. The Sun's energy graces our Earth with a rich
bounty we all benefit from beyond our own merits, why get greedy?

I suppose I shouldn't be so judgmental. I've known people who seem
not to have a clue to how value is created and think if they want something
they must somehow get it from someone else, or get lucky with the lottery.
Though employed they seem to not see the connection between what they
contribute and what they're paid. I don't have much patience because of
my long exposure to a 'there's no free lunch' ethic. But I've also been fortunate in my exposure to innovative climates—from my parents, education and work. Years ago I heard that in creative endeavors, "It's far worse
to have to steal than to be stolen from"[10] so I try not to be judgmental.

And I suppose there still are conservative cultures where the work ethic is upheld but innovation is frowned on as an affront to traditional values—'It was good enough for your grandfather so don't get uppity'. It's a wonder with all the innovation of the past century—telephones, radios, televisions, cars, planes—that such an atavistic attitude could still persist. But maybe they think of these innovations as 'gifts from the gods' never dreaming they too could innovate. Maybe that helps explain why the hunter-gatherer attitude prevails, though hopefully in decline.

Innovators

On the other hand few are blessed with the talent and tenacity to be a successful innovative entrepreneur.[11] It's not only overwhelming but fraught with hazards—you're all alone or with a few fellow venturers having to do everything yourselves with a hundred things that can go wrong, any one of which can doom your project.[12] If you have the patronage of a venture capitalist, even the reputable[13] ones are often nervously looking over your shoulder—too many 'coaches and referees', and too few 'players'. To further ask the entrepreneur if their innovation advances Life's evolution seems ludicrous—a potentially successful idea is hard enough to come up with without imposing additional criteria. But it's best to ask early on before investing time and energy—Is this something you'll be proud of having done or is it just to get rich?[14]

As said, we humans are privileged to be evolution's 'eyes', its executors, thus *noblesse oblige*. We've a noble calling, all of us, but especially the entrepreneurs who can not only create the products and services, but put together the organizations of people to produce and distribute them. Whether a product will advance Life's evolution can be a difficult question to assess—easier in retrospect than in prospect.[15]

In my experience the innovative entrepreneur plays the key rôle in putting together all the elements essential to a successful enterprise and shepherding them through the perils of start-up. There are many elements that must be identified, assessed, recruited and organized synergistically— all the pieces of the puzzle that must either be developed or be acquired, and fit together. Scientists discover and verify some new knowledge, a breakthrough, that may be key to the innovation, but that's only the beginning. Technicians and engineers work out the practical how-to elements, and lawyers the agreements, the deals. Production plant and equipment must be acquired and installed after securing financing from lenders or more likely from angel investors.[16] Workers must be recruited and trained. Marketing and distribution must be set up. All those involved in the enterprise should be dedicated to the vision, but the entrepreneur is the one who must first see the overall vision, the big picture, and motivate all the others.

There are pseudo-entrepreneurs, those who put together deals without a conscious vision of how it all fits together synergistically—it seems to me they're basically 'hunter-gatherers'. They may acquire a business because it's a 'bargain' or take over a struggling entrepreneur's endeavor. Hopefully their unconscious has keener and nobler instincts, and they may unwittingly accomplish some good rather than let an endeavor die, but don't bet on it—more likely they'll ruin it. "A greedy man never knows What he's done."[17]

Of course as said there's another class of innovators whose work often proceeds, indeed inspires and enables the entrepreneurs'—namely the scientists. Whereas entrepreneurs work to produce and market new products and services, many scientists instead work to discover and disseminate new knowledge—and have fun and excitement doing it.[18] The knowledge these scientist seek may have no obvious practical application and so it's usually sponsored by an academic or government institution, or a philanthropic foundation. Still other scientists work for enterprises endeavoring to apply new knowledge. Engineers then take the scientists' new knowledge and translate it into practicable applications. Some scientists or engineers attempt to launch a new venture themselves, but then they're functioning as entrepreneurs.

Innovations

The rest of this chapter will survey some of the innovations that are emerging but in no way attempt to be comprehensive. Rather I'll identify some major extensions, review their past 'evolution' and their likely future developments in order to gauge their trajectory. Then I'll consider how we might affect their trajectory in order to influence Life's evolution. To have some semblance of order, I'll start with our bodies and brains themselves, then the extensions of our senses, our minds (singly and jointly), our extremities (vehicles and robots) and our skin (clothing and shelter plus infrastructure). But in using these I'll not be overly rigorous since there's much overlapping. Institutions will be covered in the next chapter.

Bodies & Brains

In the past couple centuries we've seen profound improvement in human health and longevity in the developed world. This was due initially to non-biological improvements such as sanitation, working con-

ditions, nutrition, education and hospital conditions, and then to biological and biomechanical innovations such as vaccinations, antibiotics, con-
tra- and *in vitro* conception, pre- and postnatal care, internal imaging,
blood and organ transfer, corrective surgery, prostheses (like hip replace-
ments, pacemakers and now mechanical hearts) and many others. Some
folks have used the knowledge and innovations to improve their lives
through exercise, nutrition and consultation. Others assume medical-mir-
acles and insurance will save them and so are overweight and smoke, and
don't exercise.[19] It's true, the improvements we've seen in the past century
will pale next to those we can expect in this new century. The Human
Genome Project coupled with proteomics—the protein complement encoded by the genome—will be medicine's Rosetta stone.[20] "Humanity is
moving out of its childhood and into a gawky, stumbling adolescence in
which it must learn not only to acknowledge its immense new powers, but
to figure out how to use them wisely. The choices we face are daunting, but
putting our heads in the sand is not the solution."[21]

The successful cloning of 'lower' animals has raised the specter of
cloning humans. Cloning is abhorrent to many Christians even though we
were taught that God cloned Eve from Adam (maybe that's why some
guys are apprehensive!). Moreover a clone is basically an identical twin albeit born decades later. Third, all somatic cells in our body multiply by
cloning. Closely related to cloning is stem cell research which shows promise of repairing specific organs as nature does. Both have been denounced
as a 'slippery-slope' but the metaphor can be expanded to assert that adept
'skiers' know how to safely negotiate slippery-slopes and won't shrink
from the challenge of potentially beneficial and inevitable science. It's far
better to have cloning and stem cell research legitimate and in the open
where they can be monitored rather than drive them underground or
offshore.[22]

Even though Hollywood depicts a future of cyborgs—bionic humans
with implanted electronics—it seems unlikely that very many people will
elect invasive hardware for some time unless it's to correct their ailing natural organs. But the acceptance of performance enhancing drugs and supplements, and cosmetic embellishments like laser eye surgery and breast
implants suggests that acceptance may be sooner rather than later. Certainly wearable 'symbiotic' devices like eyeglasses and hearing aids as
well as Walkmans and cell-phones are well accepted. Interfacing with electronic extensions through our senses (maybe even telepathy?) is more feasible and acceptable than interfacing directly with our complex nervous
systems and brains.[23]

But more radical planned evolution of bodies and brains will eventually come about. Enhancement of future generations—designer children—might begin in the next several decades[24] using existing and emerging science as follows: Multiple immature eggs would be retrieved from a woman by ovarian biopsy and banked. When a child is desired, several eggs would be fertilized and nurtured *in vitro*, then genetically tested to eliminate any genetic diseases like cystic fibrosis or hemophilia. Next the remaining eggs would be further screened genetically to select an egg with alleles of the desired traits and that egg implanted in her uterus, and the other eggs disposed.[25] Further enhancement could be achieved when auxiliary chromosomes become available. Recall that humans have twenty-three chromosomes from each parent for a total of forty-six (chimps have a total of forty-eight). Extra artificial chromosomes might be inserted into the human egg's cells. These could carry potentially beneficial genes that remain inactive unless, at some future date, they're selectively activated by non-naturally-occurring triggers.[26]

At first this may sound Orwellian but attitudes change over time. When *in vitro* fertilization was first used in 1978 the pejorative 'test-tube baby' was coined.[27] A century ago few births were even in hospitals.[28] Most couples want what's best for their children so as 'germinal choice technology'[29] improves and becomes affordable, more couples will elect to use it. Indeed it seems inevitable; as more women pursue their educations and careers, and postpone childbearing ever nearer menopause, natural conception becomes problematical as their affluence increases. They can afford to resort to *in vitro* fertilization which opens up opportunities for germinal choice as described above, and given a choice they'll choose to design their children.[30] Coitus will be contraceptive and used for recreation and bonding, as most married couples already know.

Whether our government supports it, others may be more enthusiastic like China's current government.[31] And recall that from 1933 to 1944 Hitler tried to create a master-race through eugenics.[32] But it seems doubtful that germinal choice technology would produce super-humans in the foreseeable future. The alleles there are to choose from are only those already in the current population's gene-pool which occasionally endow gifted persons. Thus germinal choice technology could produce many more gifted people but not people who are more gifted than today's most gifted—in other words technology might regularly do what nature occasionally does, but not more. The danger may be that in a few generations a caste system would emerge—an elite gifted caste versus all the rest of the population whose parents didn't have access to germinal choice technology.[33] It would be comparable to Europe's old caste system—nobility versus commoners—of a little over a century ago. Back then the elites' alleged superiority was due to control of nurture, nutrition and education; in the future it'll be due to control of nature. Thus it'll behoove us to make germinal choice technology as world-widely available as prudently manageable and let robots become the under-caste instead of humans.[34]

If parents have a choice of alleles, what traits might they select for? Sports fans might go for athletic abilities. Scientists for math and analytic aptitudes. You get the idea. The Romans put it succinctly: *mens sana in corpore sano* (a sound mind in a sound body) but than the Romans were proud and ruthless, and practiced infanticide.[35] From the perspective of Life's evolution what traits should be selected for? Health and agility (but not necessarily athletic prowess), openness and sensitivity, intuition and introspection, acuity and acumen would all seem to be desirable.[36] Of course enhanced nature is only half the equation—nurture is just as important: a loving family and a rich culture. But nature and nurture are not destiny—initiative, aspiration and self-determination will continue to assert their influences in spite of the best or worst endowments.[37] And in addition along with all that, the enhanced should have vigorous longevity[38]—after all with so much invested, they should stick around as long as possible to share the wisdom they accumulate. All these attributes would be coupled and augmented by the 'evolving' innovative extensions we'll discuss next. Indeed since our biology evolved largely in prehistoric times, some adaptations, modifications and updating would seem to be in order to better adapt our Stone Age biology to our high-tech culture.[39]

Senses Extensions

Our 'five' senses are not only being extended but broadened to utilize media beyond our natural ranges. Take for example sight, arguably we primates' principal sense. Not only are we using visible light to see both farther and finer, but we're translating non-visible light—such as infrared and ultraviolet wavelengths—into our visible range. Galileo's telescopes of four-hundred years ago extended our vision out into our solar system overturning man's place in the universe. Hubble's Mount Wilson telescope early in the last century extended our vision to long ago, faraway galaxies revealing an expanding universe. Now the Hawaiian and Andean telescopes, the Arecibo and Very Large Array radio-telescopes, the Hubble Space Telescope and space probes, and many more, are extending our vision to the ends of the universe and the beginning of time. Radar doesn't extend sight per se but rather reflects short wavelength 'light' off objects using their 'echo' to locate them.

Looking back through the other end of the telescope, so to speak, over three-hundred years ago it became a microscope extending our vision ever finer to reveal Hooke's cells and microbes. The capabilities of visual light were broadened by X-ray imaging and in the last century by the electron microscope, CAT and PET scans, and MRI imaging which are being refined in this century.[40] The workings of our body and brain are being further revealed.

If sight is our principal sense, hearing is a close second. In the last century hearing was greatly extended by the telephone and radio, by phonographs, magnetic tapes and compact discs, and along with sight by movies and television. Microphones can pick up and translate into our range the calls of bats and the songs of whales, and can 'spy' off distant windows and bug remote conversations. Ultrasonics, like radar, doesn't extend hearing per se but rather translates sound echoes into visual images for medical and engineering uses.

Our other senses have largely been given short shrift. Not only don't we use our sense of smell nearly as extensively as say dogs, but we contaminate it with perfumes, deodorants and sprays. 'Use it of lose it' applies in evolution so rather than extend our sense of smell (except for smoke and carbon-monoxide detectors), we lost much of it in deference to sight and speech as the hominid face became flatter. Our sense of taste we've titillated with salts, spices, condiments, exotic foods and wines, but I'd hardly term that extending it. Our kinesthetic sense probably evolved from our tree-dwelling ancestors' brachiation into our fine sense of balance for walking and running upright, which in recent times we've adapted to equestrian, gliding and vehicular transport, and augmented with instruments like turn-&-bank indicators in airplanes.

Finally our haptic sense of touch and feel—while if anything we may be less sensitive to touch and feel than were our early ancestors because we've clothed and sheltered our bodies to insulate them from the elements—in another way we've further refined our early ancestors' remarkable ability to sense and handle tools. They must have evolved the hand-eye coordination during their couple million years of flaking hand-axes, throwing stones and spears, prying up roots and manipulating all manner of implements and materials. In our youth we develop the skill to handle simple things like a pencil or a fork, to touch a piano (musicians' fingers learn to feel notes) or a computer keyboard, to ride a bike and to drive a car. We not only feel our grip on the tool but we project our sense out onto the action end of the tool—where the pencil touches the paper or the fork the meat, thus the extension becomes virtually part of us. Think of the way experienced drivers have a feel for their car—it's an extension of them.

Today kids manipulate joysticks to play computer games—next they'll remotely control robots.

Mind Extensions

That pencil I just mentioned is also an extension of our mind as is speech both of which enable us to get our thoughts out of our mind where we can share them with other minds. We can hopefully remember what was said in order to refer back to it later. And writing down our thoughts not only allows us to share them near and far but to preserve them so we can return to them at any time. This five-millennia old innovation extends minds to share their thoughts even beyond the grave. Initially writing was preserved on clay or stone, then papyrus or parchment, but in the 1400s with paper and Gutenberg it spread from the preserve of the Church first into the elite educated class and now to virtually everyone in the developed world in the form of letters, books, newspapers and junk mail. And now the advent of the Internet has freed writing even from paper. With automated translations and the amalgamation of languages, writing has gone global taking our minds along with it. Now we're coming full circle—speech recognition, artificial intelligence (AI) and synthetic speech promise to obsolete writing to some extent.[41]

Writing is only one of the extensions of our mind, math is another— yes, mathematics or more broadly, abstract logic systems and devices. Math enables us to count beyond our digits—our fingers and toes. When the West began the switch from Roman to Hindu-Arabic numerals in the 1200s,[42] math took off. Calculating and logic devices followed, from the abacus and slide-rule to mechanical and vacuum-tube computers, and now with the advent of silicon semiconductors to hand-calculators, personal-computers and supercomputers. Indeed with the continued shrinking of computer components' size and cost, and their increasing capabilities, computers are being incorporated into more and more devices—appliances, vehicles, clothing and all manner of gadgets. At the same time they're becoming more 'user friendly' designed for the consumer more than the techie. Computers are becoming ubiquitous and invisible.[43]

Another extension of our mind is graphics. Even before flight and satellites, abstract maps depicted territories, construction plans depicted buildings. Now Cartesian, flow, organization and other charts convey abstract ideas and relationships. Of course drawings and paintings have depicted humans, animals, plants, buildings and scenes for millennia, and now movies and television put them in motion. Still they're two-dimensional images of our three-dimensional world which some try to correct with 3–D or holograms.[44] Computer games give the illusion of depth which is being developed for remote robot control. Ever more powerful computers are modeling complex systems like weather enabling us to visualize and forecast. And just as computers allow translating non-visible light into our visible range, animated caricatures and graphic-metaphors translate the very small—gene-sequences, cell parts and sub-atomic particles—and the very large—the Sun, galaxies and the universe—into the purview of our imagination.

But it seems there are limits to the virtual extension of our mind. E-mail is fast and convenient but it doesn't have the ambience of a handwritten letter, which doesn't have the tone and banter of a person's phone voice, and even adding video still can't compare to face-to-face encounters. In the future virtual encounters may simulate touch and embrace with body-suits, adding smell to voice and vision—virtual reality[45]—which may induce emotional reactions deeper than we get at a movie but we'll still know it's not real.[46] On the other hand maybe because we know it's not real, we'll be more willing to let our emotions flow without feeling embarrassed, as we might do in a dark movie theater or in private with a novel. I understand there are folks, not just the young, who often project their selves into their computer screens—step *Through the Looking-Glass*—not just to chat and play games with 'net-pals but to anonymously indulge their fantasy multiple personalities, expressing parts of themselves they wouldn't show in real-life situations.[47] It's probably fine as long as they bring some of what they learn in 'wonderland' back into their real world.

What about artificial intelligence (AI)? Might computers some day replicate our brain/mind? Certainly there's much already that computers can do better than we—memory storage and retrieval, and computation and modeling are just a couple areas, with much more on the way. But it seems to me there's an important distinction—today's computers are built of silicon chips and magnetic storage, whereas brains are built of neurons. Neurons are living cells each with its own Life Urge that are coordinated in a complex organ, the brain, in a living organism, humans. Silicon chips are also coordinated in a complex 'organ', computers, but they're dead, they're not alive and thus not individually responsive to a Life Urge. If, as explored in Chapter Nine our brain utilizes an ultra-fast evolutionary process called neural Darwinism, is it possible for computers someday to emulate that process? The answer is probably yes.[48] But we needn't just wait to be obsoleted by computers. As computers develop to take over brain functions, computers could free-up capacity in our brains which might adapt to perform more unique human functions, so that in our posthuman future we become ever more human, not less.[49] Moreover perhaps our brains can 'evolve' in tandem with computers' evolution. There are those who see a merging of biology, technology and culture in a merged evolution.[50]

Arm & Leg Extensions

I've already cited examples of extensions of our hands and feet near the beginning of this chapter. Early on, the 'evolution' of the hand-axe, spear, digging stick and other rudimentary tools went *pari passu* with, and was in part the cause of our ancestors' evolution. Whether our biology has evolved much over the past few millennia, certainly the extensions of our arms and legs have 'evolved' at an ever increasing rate. Achilles' horse-drawn chariot in Homer's *Iliad* of 1100BC 'evolved' into the carriage in use until a century ago when horses gave way to internal combustion engines powering horseless carriages—cars, trucks and now SUVs. Indeed the industrial revolutions[51] obsoleted slave labor, both animal and human, in the developed world. Horseback has largely given way to other vehicular modes—motorcycles, bicycles—which spawned other vehicular toys— skateboards, roller-blades, skis, snowmobiles, surfboards, kayaks, jet-skis. Asked which of these are advancing Life, the answer has less to do with the extension itself and more with what the extension is being used for. Is it being used to somehow enable the person to advance Life? If it's being used for recreation, does it help the person become a better person? For example, I know that snowmobiles have their uses but I prefer the quiet of cross-country-skis on an invigorating scenic outing, and the same for jet-skis versus my solo canoe as mentioned in an earlier note 5.

The third socio-economic revolution[52] is upon us as miniature electronics replace mental chores in our cars, appliances, gadgets and production-tools, as alluded to above. Mobile programmed robots will go about mundane tasks with little guidance from us humans.[53] Robots will free educated humans for more human endeavors but will they displace less educated humans, condemning them to sub-human tasks, an under-caste alluded to above? This becomes a social issue addressed in the next chapter.

Skin Extensions

I've also cited examples of extensions of our skin as clothing—hats, gloves, shirts, pants, coats, shoes—and shelter—tents, houses and other buildings. Skin, our largest organ, seals our insides from outside light, gases, liquids, non-piercing solids and infections, and from moderate temperature differences while allowing dissipation of internal heat via convection and evaporation. Most other mammals have fur hides which our early cold-climate ancestors appropriated as hide clothing for themselves. Not only has our clothing become more effective and efficient (and fashionable), but our shelter has 'evolved' from the stereotypical damp drafty cave with a blazing smoky fire, into spacious windowed houses and multistoried offices equipped with heating/air-conditioning, lighting, security, kitchens and bathrooms, posh furnishings and Muzak. Our cars may be even more posh than our homes. And even more conveniences and comforts are on the way.

Infrastructure

We could quibble whether shelter—a building with all its utilities bringing us water, air/heating/cooling, electricity, electronic media—is an extension of our skin or is infrastructure, but let's not. Our early ancestor took hollow gourds to the stream to fetch water, now we bring the stream to us in plumbing. Our early ancestors cleared a path through the woods, now we build roads. We change our environment, but is it for the better? Paving more and more land for roads and parking-lots hardly seems like it.

Life's Trajectory

Before looking ahead let's quickly glance back. As evolution's 'eyes' we can look back in time to see how it all began and what patterns or paradigms seem to be operating. We've looked back nearly to the beginning of our Universe and surmised a Big Bang that started it all off. We've traced how some of that energy congealed into quarks and gluons, which congealed into protons and neutrons, then into simple molecules of mostly hydrogen and helium. We've seen how these molecules congealed into ever larger bodies until some grew so large and dense they initiated nuclear reactions which fused ever larger molecules of oxygen, carbon, silicon, sulfur and iron, then blew apart fusing still larger molecules of all the other elements. Their cosmic dust again congealed into stars one of which became our Sun with smaller bodies in tow, one of which is our Earth.

We've looked back at how our Earth cooled and formed a crust, at how various elements combined into complex molecules to deal with their environments and at how some macromolecules found a way of converting their *re*action to a threat into a *pro*action which perhaps emerged into an Urge to Life. This elemental Life Urge opened up a whole spectrum of possibilities which through trial-and-error evolved all the Life forms we see today. Lately a few of these Life forms have become reflexive—they *know* that they know, they're conscious. At least one of these, we humans, evolved extended consciousness so we can not only see where we came from but also where we might be going. Not only where Life might be going but where Life could be going and how we might steer it there. The possibilities seem unlimited. But even responsible projections of the future are too often off the mark and science-fiction writers conger up outlandish scenarios more to titillate audiences than to project realistic futures.

Now let's try to infer Life's trajectory by once more succinctly reviewing Life's trends—where Life has come from for clues about where it might be going—how Life's progressing. Yet the idea of *progress* in evolution has been refuted by pointing to the success of the simplest organisms. Bacteria have thrived for nearly four-billion years and even today can out-evolve our most potent antibiotics—moreover there are far more of them than any other mode of organisms.[54] But by that last criterion we'd have to call non-living molecules—from hydrogen, nitrogen, oxygen and water, and on to extremely complex mega-atom minerals—the most successful since they've been around even longer (before Earth!) and there are far more non-living molecules than there are living molecules. The base of a pyramid is much broader than its peak. So that anti-progress argument seems pointless.

However there's no disagreement about increasing complexity. Non-living molecules increase in complexity up to mega-molecules, but their crystals repeat the same basic structure without further increase in complexity. Bacteria are more complex than any non-living molecules I know of. Chapter Six described symbiosis, how archaea took in bacteria, co-opting their capabilities as organelles, thus becoming more complex and versatile single-cell eukaryotes through *synergistic* organization. Then Chapter Seven describes how less than a billion years ago some eukaryotes joined together into multicell organisms by differentiating cells to specialize, evolving into ever more complex synergistic organisms. Both plants and fungi coordinate their specialized cells with chemical signals flowing among their cells. Additionally, animals evolved nervous systems to transmit the signals more rapidly enabling movement. Then nerve clusters formed into brains to direct the organism's movements and other functions. Thus the evolutionary trajectory has been toward increasing synergistic complexity, as we've previously noted.

Mammals' big break came from the demise of the dinosaurs, and from their abilities to regulate body temperature and nurture their young. Mammals also evolved a neocortex, a kind of auxiliary brain. Among the mammals the primates' social life in the trees favored the further evolution of brains especially the neocortex. But as the climate thinned the trees, one line of primates came down to live by their wits. The hominids succeeded on the ground by reciprocally evolving larger brains in tandem with culture—language, tools and social forms.

Over a couple million years their increasing mental capacity came in part from inventing tools as they progressed from working them out externally by trial-and-error to figuring them out internally in their mind's imagination. Tool's 'evolution' shifted from their hands more and more into their heads, literally—that is, the trial-and-error of evolution went on in their neocortex, as described in Chapter Nine. Their neocortex preconsciously generated nerve impulse patterns from which 'basins of attraction' patches in their prefrontal cortex 'selected the best fit' for the tool they 'had in mind'. When their prefrontal cortex preconsciously found a good fit, it'd present it to their conscious mind. This creative capability not only expanded their holistic imagination and intuition but also their memory and judgment. In turn these capabilities were applied to other functions both in nature like mapping, and in their culture like language and other social activities. And as their culture 'evolved' ever more efficacious 'tools' it had a compounding effect—they were able to 'evolve' still even more efficacious 'tools' at an accelerating rate in nested hierarchies, just as does nature—except they 'evolved' *extensions of* their body not just their body.

So it seems Life's trajectory has been toward more imaginative, creative, holistic minds augmented both by our body extensions to free-up time and energy, and by our mental extensions to increase our mental capacity with aids such as writing, graphics, computers—extending our thinking and off-loading data to free-up memory for internal mental use. Am I being anthropocentric? Perhaps, but I don't know of any other species here on Earth as advanced as ours—maybe more beautiful, mellower, kinder ... but not more advanced. Might there be more advanced beings somewhere out in space? Perhaps, but then wouldn't they be an advancement of Life's trajectory? Until we encounter them (not in fiction but in fact) we won't know if they're on our trajectory or some other. Are we only evolving in our extensions or in our brains too, that is, are we smarter than our ancestors putatively thirty-thousand years ago who painted deep in caves? That's hard to tell—probably not much if any—they didn't have the advantage of all the culture that's come since then that we build on for our advanced civilization.[55] Until about ten-thousand years ago there were selective pressures for 'smarts', but not lately—now smarter folks usually don't raise more kids to adulthood than prosaic folks, usually fewer. Perhaps with the advent of designer children we'll again select for smarts.[56] Does Life's trajectory verify the anthropic principle—that our universe is fine-tuned to evolve us humans? Since we're only half way through our Earth's life-span, as described at the beginning of Chapter Eight, it seems highly unlikely—and hubristic—to presume that we humans are the culmination of evolution's long trajectory, its 'purpose'.[57]

Motivations

So far anyway, that seems to be the evolutionary trajectory of organisms, particularly ours. We've already surveyed the innovative trends of our various extremities' extensions but we haven't considered what motivated those innovations. It's said "Necessity is the mother of invention" (I suspect indolence is the father). What were the needs that prompted the innovations and thus the types of extensions that were produced? I envision three broad categories. First for sustenance such as food and water, clothing and shelter: A spear extended the arm to bring down prey which 'evolved' into a bow-&-arrow, then into a gun. A digging stick for roots perhaps evolved into a hoe, then a plow drawn by a horse and now by a thousand-horsepower tractor. Gourds for carrying water evolved into goatskin water bags, then wells, aqueducts and water mains. A buffalo hide ultimately became a fur coat. Fire for cooking and warmth went onto a hearth and eventually into a stove and furnace with a chimney. A tepee became a log-cabin, then a high-rise.

Second, pursuing the 'hierarchy of needs', once you had sustenance you'd want security so the spear or bow-&-arrow or gun could be used to fend-off predators or marauding tribes. And the log-cabin could be fortified into a castle. But if we can fend-off marauders we can use the same weapons to become marauders ourself and capture livestock, slaves and lands. The horse can be unhitched from the plow and its collar exchanged for a saddle with stirrups to go raid our neighbor.[58] After generations of reciprocal animosity some may realize it's better to have your neighbor as your trading partner rather than your enemy.

Third, once you have sustenance and security, you might enjoy some luxury and leisure to feed your other needs and wants—your ego-needs (fancier clothes, bigger house, more slaves), your cultural needs (acquire art and bring in a poet and musicians), your creative bent (build an alchemist's or inventor's workshop), your religious aspirations (study under a shaman or build a cathedral) or indulge in play (outfit the horse with armor for jousting or buy a motorcycle).[59]

How a person approaches all the extensions we've created—and continue to create at an accelerating rate—depends on their attitudes. To illustrate I'll draw two opposite extremes: today's compulsive 'hunter-gatherer' versus a compulsive innovator. A person who's an insatiable 'hunter-gatherer' may strive to get as much as they can not knowing or caring where all the wealth comes from, only about how they can get more. They buy and sell in the stock market—not as an investor (although that's what they call themselves) who's studied a company and its market, and wants to support its mission and growth as well as earn a good return on their investment—but more as a speculator who buys the stock thinking its price is about to rise and will sell it tomorrow if the price is right,[60] what's been termed "infectious greed".[61] (They make the term 'publicly traded corporation' a pejorative.) What they buy with their profits may be more about form than function—prestige house, cars, clothes, vacations—conspicuous consumption more to prop up a fragile ego it seems, than for inner gratification.[62] They're acquisitive to a fault, it seems they "know the price of everything and the value of nothing."[63] Not knowing value, they'll squander resources on frivolous acquisitions and so are preyed on by hucksters. (See the final chapter's 'Money'.)

An opposite extreme is a person who's more of a compulsive innovator constantly wanting to know how something works and why, and how it might be made to work better. They're less interested in money per se than in what they might accomplish with money. They understand that 'profit' is not just what they can cajole from others but is society's reward for producing a surplus of value over cost.[64] But they might get caught up in innovating, missing out on other aspects of Life. Even if not compulsive, innovation can demand much concentration. They're agents of change, but change to what?

These two extreme caricatures might also be distinguished by their mode of thinking. Hunter-gathering uses mostly 'episodic' thinking while innovating uses more 'paradigmatic' thinking. Recall from Chapter Nine's 'Early Development' the episodic or mythic stage relied on stories, either past or future scripts, while the paradigmatic stage began relying more on concepts of how things work. But there's an earlier, more fundamental 'intuitive' mode of thinking elaborated in Chapter Ten. All three modes of thinking should work together, it seems to me. Intuitive thinking should form the base yet be informed by episodic thinking—history and one's experience—and by paradigmatic thinking—does it make sense? Both episodic and paradigmatic thinking can be directly augmented by extensions such as external memory and graphics whereas intuition can be indirectly aided by extensions that free-up time and energy. In other words we should strive to be continuously in touch with an intuition of our Self while utilizing and appreciating extensions' power and limitations. We should view extensions, not as integral parts of our Self, but as separate auxiliaries of our Self. We own our extensions rather than are 'owned' by them. We might even view our neocortex as an extension of our core brain—a marvelous, powerful and invaluable extension—but only the latest part of our brain/mind.

Whither?

Let's now see if we can get some sense of direction from all this as to where the trajectory of tools' evolution may be leading, or rather where it should be leading if it's to advance Life's evolution. Certainly consciousness is a major, if not the preeminent, advancement evolution has produced so far. In the previous chapter we surveyed some of the ways 'religion' can bring more of our unconscious into consciousness. And earlier in this chapter we surveyed some of the ways medicine is improving the health of human minds and soon may be selecting genes to produce the best minds available from our gene pool. Computers facilitate getting thoughts out of our mind and onto paper—and onto the Internet—where those thoughts can be shared with other minds as I'm doing now. Modeling and graphic imaging facilitate visualizing relationships to grasp more of the 'big picture' and the consequences of actions. Memory storage and access continues to be enhanced. The interface between computers and humans will further enhance these trends enlarging consciousness. Scientific advances are broadening and deepening our understanding, gradually replacing episodic, mystical explanations with paradigms.

On the other hand biological enhancements that enable elite athletes to run a little faster (like thoroughbreds) or overachievers to win spelling bees has little to do with advancing Life's evolution—these feats can more easily be accomplished with tools. Nor does a bigger, more elegant SUV seem to have anything to do with advancing Life's evolution. Nor so many of the other luxuries we seem to waste our lives acquiring. What if we resisted the hucksters' hype and spent our earnings (or credit) only on tools that truly enriched Life, we'd have more time and energy to enjoy them. It seems unlikely it'd suddenly become such a mass movement that'd throw our economy into a tailspin and crash. Maybe we could shift from producing more and more stuff for our frivolous *wants* to producing more goods for the rest of the world's basic *needs*—help the rest of the world to become self-sustainingly productive. Of course if the rest of the world had our current standard of living the world would soon drown in junk. So why not lead the world in innovating a progressive and sustainable lifestyle—now that's a truly noble pursuit.

Should we in the developed world feel guilty about what we have? I think we should be moderately proud of our accomplishments humbly acknowledging that they're built on advantages others in this world don't enjoy. Suppose instead of being born into a nurturing family and an affluent society, we'd been born almost anywhere else in the world—what would we be today? So to what do we owe our great good fortune? You or I didn't choose our parents, or our time or place of birth—we just got lucky. So why not a two-pronged approach? Continue to innovate tools that truly advance Life but eschew the superfluous in favor of providing basic tools to afford the disadvantaged humans of this world a chance for a decent life.[65] That was the rôle of theistic missionaries with their agenda of 'saving souls' for the *next* world. It could just as well be the rôle of prototheistic 'missionaries' with the agenda of advancing Life in *this* world. Yet the acquisitive 'missionaries' we've been sending the underdeveloped world peddle fast-foods, cigarettes and soft drinks—no wonder Islamic militants see us as evil![66] In addition to the goal of advancing Life, a prototheistic frame of mind might help overcome a couple excuses for terrorism—poverty and religious war.

Evolution's trajectory appears to be headed toward increasing materialism. Rather than use the time and energy our tools free-up to nurture our humanness, we seem to expend ever more time and energy to acquire even more stuff. Instead of becoming more human, we're becoming more like our tools. And the more tools we own, the more they 'own' us as their caretakers. If we extrapolate this trend, science-fiction fantasies could easily become reality in just a few generations—artificial intelligence robots and computers like HAL in the 1968 movie "2001: A Space Odyssey" patronizing humans, scheming to replace us. If we try to compete with machines on their terms, they'll win—they can outperform us. I believe theistic religions inadvertently exacerbate the trend—even though they preach against it—by exhorting the faithful to project their Selves out onto illusory spirits leaving their selves depleted and impoverished, to be vainly stuffed with stuff, attempting to fill their insatiable emptiness.

It needn't be so. We can use tools as effective extensions of our Self to facilitate our search for and enhancement of our humanness, our inmost Self wherever it comes to us—in nature or music or love, in dreams or art or literature, or even in science or mathematics, wherever and whenever it calls. Tools advance Life if they somehow enhance humanness, not if humans become addicted to and servants of tools. Tools don't have Life, we do. Life's trajectory it seems to me is toward increased synergy through complexity, cooperation and enhanced consciousness. We can each nurture Life every day in our own small and big ways, alone and in concert with others as we'll explore in the next, final chapter. Like it or not, the choice is ours, we mustn't shrink from it—we're evolution's executors, let's remember. When Darwin wrote "There is grandeur in this view of life."[67] he may not have been thinking this far ahead, but why not extend his vision?

Yes, we have indeed become evolution's executors with the advent of advanced tools—science and technology. We've inherited the wealth our predecessors generated. But unlike an executor of a will, we don't have a written will to execute, only our best judgment to guide us. And extrapolating Life's trajectory from trends is problematical for at least three reasons: disagreement over the trends' meaning, difficulty in foreseeing synergy and unreliability of extended extrapolations. Nonetheless we must try. Like prudent executors we should use some of our inheritance to generate more wealth by supporting the sensible advancement of science and technology. And like beneficent executors we should also expend some of our wealth for the benefit of humanity in order to broaden and deepen our consciousness, our innate humanness.

A couple billion years from now our Sun may begin expanding into a red giant as described in Chapter Five. Earth will be blasted with the strong 'winds' of our Sun's debris, shedding its mass and losing its gravitational grip so that the planets will drift out into longer orbits. Perhaps as Earth moves farther away from the Sun and our 'year' lengthens, it'll postpone Earth's destruction until our Sun's inevitable explosion. But instead of a couple billion years we may only have a hundred million years before Earth no longer supports plant life.[68] Long before, will we have destroyed ourselves and our fellow species? Or will 'we' as our descendent posthuman species, still be around? If we're in charge of evolution's trajectory, unless we screw up badly we should be able to extend our species' lineage indefinitely. I believe the best stance is cautious optimism. Just a few generations back our forefathers couldn't have envisioned the improvements we have today. If only a hundred years ago they couldn't predict today's innovations, why despair over future innovations a hundred million years hence? Maybe some of our descendants will have abandoned this doomed Earth-ship and migrated to other habitable planets. I'd like to think that a future 'humanity' will have matured from our species' current 'adolescence' into exemplary citizens of our Universe. Just as adolescents often don't realize that their youthful choices affect their Life's course, we may not yet fully realize that we're now determining the trajectory of Life's evolution.

Looking back over my writing I see it's been getting pretty heavy lately so I'll try to lighten-up a little. Still we need to slog on one more chapter and consider how all this applies to our social world today, to today's and tomorrow's history. We enjoy watching historically based movies and TV documentaries or reading historic novels, yet we're making history right now! It's messy and hard to see, since we're in the confused midst of it. Even so that's where we are, that's where the action is. So let's not just study history but help make it. In the next chapter we'll look at some of today's issues to see how a prototheistic perspective might help guide our actions and maybe make some history. You can then decide what, if any, part you want to play in it.

Chapter Twelve

Society

Now at last we descend from the Mountain pass toward the lowland be-
yond, toward civilization, and somehow we feel elated and revitalized. Sure,
the oxygen thick air is invigorating after our high altitude conditioning.
But it's something else too, much more. The heights and panoramas we've
beheld of the lands behind and the horizons ahead forevermore will glow in
our memories. We've been to the Mountain! We've gained new perspectives
and insights. Tho' we may each go our separate ways from here on, we'll
never again view our once familiar world quite the same. It's a marvelous
home, this "Sweet Old World,"[1] truly a Promised Land.

This final chapter generally covers societal issues and cultural institutions.
First we'll consider issues that affect individuals due to attitudes in contemporary society such as birth and death control, and education. Next
we'll examine the history and influence of money in our society, and then
some of the institutions we share in our passage through Life such as family, school and work. Finally I'll suggest some ways a prototheistic mentality might be propagated into our society. The issues in society are so
broad and far-reaching that we can only touch on a few and naturally I've
included some of my pet peeves. The issues we'll discuss hopefully will
serve to illustrate how prototheism might be applied in society. And I'll try
not to get too preachy or rant.

Aren't I being rather brash in suggesting that my *unproven* notion of
a Life Urge, prototheism, replace the long established beliefs in gods/God,
theism, as a bedrock of society's institutions? Yet neither has the existence
of gods/God ever been *proven* in spite of the long history of such theistic
beliefs, although certainly many have tried succeeding only in convincing
those who already believed—it's called apologetics. There's growing evidence that beliefs in gods/God are the result of projections from our unconscious. During the past century the workings of our unconscious and
our brain/mind has been increasingly understood—if not 'proven'—described in Chapter Nine, as has our understanding of Life described in

Chapters Six through Eight. Thus it seems to me a logical next step is to take back those projections by using the notion of a Life Urge. Not Bergson's *élan vital* of a century ago *infused* by God[2] but an Urge to Life *emerging spontaneously through synergistic complexity*, percolating up through an organism, described in Chapters Four and Six. So the Life Urge paradigm now seems to me far more plausible than the God paradigm, but can it be proven? I would certainly hope so, yet offhand I don't know how. Furthermore I believe prototheism is the logical successor of monotheism which was the successor of polytheism—from many gods in nature to one God 'out there' and now to my notion of a Life Urge 'in here'. So I'll be brash and present my musings on what I see as some of the implications of applying the Life Urge as the criterion for establishing and justifying our institutions. Then you can decide for yourself.

Antiquated Mind-sets

In order to function effectively societies rely on cooperation among their members—voluntary, programmed or imposed. As noted in Chapter Eight's 'Social Pressures', hunter-gatherers were egalitarian whose leaders were 'first among equals'. But the advent of agriculture required control of land and whoever controlled the land could exercise control over the people inhabiting that land. Indeed for most of the next ten-millennia the primary productive resource was land with its people and animals. Cooperation or compliance was imposed by the strongman who had conquered that land and/or who could defend it against other conquerors. But nobody lives forever so upon his incapacity, either the land was taken over by the next strongman or, if the society's myths decreed, it passed to the first strongman's heirs. If you planned to pass your lifework on to your heirs when you die, you need to know they're *your* heirs and not someone else's. Hence to control land transfer meant birth control which back then meant controlling sex. Thus every society developed their own myths—religious morals—concerning sex and also often concerning the rights of rulers, along with myths about virtually every aspect of life. Religious morals were programmed into the fabric of that society—into folks' conscience as 'guilt' more or less enforced by the clergy and secular authority.

Birth Control

To enforce the feudal system of land control in Europe's stagnant Dark Ages, the Roman Catholic Church developed a hard-line on sex. With a ubiquitous belief that this world is only a tryout for the next and that the Church interprets the rules of that try-out, ruling that the normal human sex urge is sinful gave the Church insidious power. At one time or another (or much of the time) everyone would be guilty and have to come to the Church for forgiveness. Before the Roman Church's split with the Eastern Church around 1050, married clergy were common, but marriage divided priests' loyalty between the Church and their families, and made them empathetic to lay family life. Because sex and conception were inseparably linked back then, the Church could thus control reproduction and maintain the semblance of an orderly stable society here on Earth.

But during the past half-century the technology of reproduction has changed drastically yet the Roman Catholic hierarchy has been slow to adjust to that change. There are several reasons for this. They're reticent to admit that the Church's past pronouncements are not eternally true—it took them almost four-hundred years to admit that Copernicus, Bruno and Galileo were right and even then it was only a half-hearted acknowledgement. Also being celibate there's a disconnect between their sexual fantasies and married life, whereas most non-celibate clergy seem more open-minded. Being male they're hampered in understanding what women go through in pregnancy, birthing, nursing and child-care. Not being parents they have no first-hand understanding of what's involved in raising children—feeding, clothing, nurturing, transporting and so on— for twenty years without a break (having been raised in a family is not the same as raising a family).

Yet above all, their belief in an eternal life-after-death convinces them that the prime purpose of our brief life-before-death is to 'audition' for a place in Heaven, forever-after. Therefore unless a person gets born—gets 'onstage'—they've no opportunity to audition, to tryout for Heaven. Apparently they believe that regardless how unloved and miserable a child's life might be, it's their big break, their only chance for Heaven regardless how slim their chance may be. The Church holds that only God decides who gets born to tryout for Heaven.[3] Hence the Church's opposition to 'unnatural' birth control and deliberate abortion.

But this mind-set betrays an ignorance of our species' evolution, as described in Chapter Eight. Our species succeeded not because our early ancestral fathers procreated more—apes and australopithecines tried that—but because our ancestral mothers, with support from fathers and grandparents, nurtured more of their big-brained off-spring to adulthood. We haven't changed that much! Nurturing is still essential to early child development. Without loving nurturing a child hardly stands a chance to achieve a fulfilling Life. Moreover the fact that those who argue for the opposition are mostly celibate—don't 'play the game'—undermines their credibility, in my view. (It'd be like taking golf lessons from someone who'd never played golf.)

Natural abortion or miscarriage—and premature birth, if alive—usually is the result of the mother's system aborting the fetus because something isn't right. Just as the mother's physical system can abort the fetus if it's not viable, the mother's 'mental system' should be allowed to abort the fetus if she can't (without the father's support) or won't provide it with a loving nurturing childhood in order to prepare it for a wholesome Life. Life is more than just survival. Moreover, of extremely premature births (under 26 weeks of the normal 37 weeks pregnancy) less than four-percent survive to normalcy, according to one study.[4] Yet Christian parents and doctors go to extreme lengths and suffering, attempting to prolong a preemie's life 'until God decides to take it'.

Consequently it seems to me that those who believe the prime purpose of Life is life-after-death should recuse themselves from participating in issues concerning life-before-death. They have a conflict of interest, and thus should disqualify and remove themselves just as honorable judges recuse themselves from hearing cases where there may be the slightest appearance of a conflict of interest. Specifically afterlifers are conflicted between their natural human desire that each child have a happy healthy loving Life versus their belief that the child has a soul distinct from their body destined to continue on after their body dies. If Christians were scrupulously honest they'd see that their "right to life" slogan is really for a "right to life-after-death" else why would the Church oppose abortion[5] yet at the same time oppose contraception. The best way to stop the admittedly heinous practice of abortions is to stop unwanted pregnancies in the first place through responsible contraception. Yet unconscionably the Church's solution is abstinence for both married and unmarried couples.[6] Those celibate guys just don't get it—they have only their fantasies of sex. If Catholic priests, both men and women, were married[7] they'd understand that human love is much more than just sex. But until then the Church will persist in its view that sex is primarily to create souls to serve God.

The Popes painted themselves into a corner with their 1870 self-proclaimed infallibility (playing God) and, in spite of the changes in technology, now feel they'll lose-face if they reverse themselves on contraception. Yet the Pope embraces other modern technologies—for instance he doesn't walk or ride a donkey, he rides in his pope-mobile and jet-plane. The irony is the more the Church clings to absurd beliefs, the more they discredit themselves. If they faced up to the reality of change acknowledging that they aren't infallible, rather than dragging their feet and lagging behind, for instance over four-hundred years, they could truly become leaders. They might even go so far as to see God in Life's evolution (more on this toward the end of the chapter). It might allow them to pro-mote responsible human love and parenting yet decry abortion, and put an end to their ridiculous contradictions and calls to recuse themselves.

Death Control

At the other end of our lives—the terminal end—is death. Of course many believe it's not really the end but a new beginning, and instead they believe in life-after-death—"they passed, they've gone to Jesus/God"—that they just 'moved' spiritually to Heaven (or hell or purgatory). As I've said repeatedly I think they're kidding themselves, that they're heavily into denial. Nonetheless, incredibly their belief pervades our society and restricts persons' right to control their own death. They allegedly believe only God decides when you can go, when your 'audition' is over and you can leave the 'stage'.[8] Yet at the same time many of them used to believe in capital punishment,[9] that society can murder someone if there's 'just cause'. Admittedly executions are now as painless as possible, a vast im-provement from the days of the Inquisition when 'heretics' were tortured and burned-at-the-stake to persuade them to recant and be "saved from the eternal fires of hell." I don't mean to castigate today's Church for their predecessors' practices curtailed two centuries ago, but rather to expose the folly in respecting the authority of today's Church which still retains their antiquated mind-set. They're still reticent to allow terminal patients to relieve their tortured dying and die with dignity.[10]

I have another issue with the Church saying that only God decides who gets born and when they die—it's a cop-out, they're shirking their re-sponsibility for making hard decisions and blaming God for their indeci-siveness. If they truly believe God gave man intelligence, aren't they in-sulting and blaspheming Him by evading using that intelligence even though at times it may be excruciatingly difficult? "If you can't stand the heat, get out of the kitchen"[11]—if they can't or won't make hard decisions, they shouldn't pretend to be an authority.

Death is a part of life—if we can "Choose Life" why can't we also choose our own time and form of death?[12] Everybody's got to go sooner or later so rather than just accept death passively—even "rage, rage against the dying of the light"[13]—why not make death our last great adventure? In Chapter Ten I alluded to the reported 'near death' phenomenon wherein people who've come close to death but revived told of numinous experiences.[14] But there are other experiences too dangerous to try unless we're about to die anyway.[15] I'm not referring to extreme-sports risk-takers who are addicted to ever greater thrills—avoiding life with their death wish—but those who are truly at the end of their lives, have discharged all their responsibilities but still have just enough vitality left to 'enjoy' death. We should live 'til we die—what if when we come to die we find we've never really lived?

The operative word is 'choose'—only the subject person should get to decide when and how they die. There may be others who would coerce that person to end their life—their relatives and loved-ones who want to relieve their suffering and/or are weary of caring for the person, their heirs who want their property, their medical insurer who wants to cut-costs. Even those who favor assisted suicide are circumspect to distinguish between suicide and murder—the proverbial 'slippery slope'—but as said, adroit 'skiers' can face up to 'slippery slopes'. A person may long to die but be fearful because of their belief in an after-life.[16] Then why shouldn't a compassionate Church grant them a plenary indulgence remitting all presumed punishment for their sins? Before the Counter-Reformation the Church sold indulgences[17]—why not now give them away? If the person believes it, why not "Grant them eternal rest"? Or at least peace-of-mind so they can "Rest In Peace"? Alternatively the Church could re-baptize them with *extreme unction*—recall from Chapter Three's note 53 that Constantine delayed baptism until a few weeks before his death so that all his sins would be remitted.

And another thing, upon death why should their property pass to the deceased's heirs? The traditional answer is cited above—to retain land control. Today's answer is that when a person's alive it's their property to do with as they please—presumably their creativity, acumen and effort produced the value, so 'if not for them' that value wouldn't exist.[18] Upon their death, absent alternative provisions, the default is to pass it to their heirs (after taxes). But their heirs didn't choose to be born to that person and probably did nothing to earn or acquire the property, so why should they get it? The environment in which the deceased operated—their education, the free society that enabled them to operate, others' prior accomplishments that they built on, and so on—all contributed to their success without which (if they'd lived in another time or place) they might not have succeeded. In other words wittingly or unwittingly, they were 'a courier in evolution's trajectory', as explained in Chapter Ten's section on 'Prototheism and Life Urge'. But to collect their 'debt to the past owed to the future', rather than let society impose a 'death tax', better that that person themselves determine how best to carry forward their lifework, their legacy to the future. Maybe their heirs *are* the best couriers to pass their 'baton' on to or maybe some foundation can better pass on some enduring value or beauty—it should be the person's informed choice rather than society's. Of course there are risks—that the person didn't create the value but only purloined it as a 'hunter-gatherer'; or weren't truly 'a courier in evolution's trajectory', only an opportunist; or are leaving it to their heirs out of guilt from neglecting them in life—but the alternatives pose the even greater risk of repressing creativity and industriousness as the Soviets learned to their detriment. If what they create is not theirs to dispose of as they see fit, they might be discouraged from creating as in *Atlas Shrugged*.[19]

Between Birth & Death

'Between' is where most of us are, so let's focus on our Life's long phase. Advancing Life's trajectory should begin with ourselves by leading a healthy lifestyle—a challenge in today's industrialized world. For instance like most animals our early ancestors accumulated fat in goodtimes and burned it off in lean-times, but now we have mostly good-times so we're inclined to keep accumulating more and more fat. 'A waist is a terrible thing to mind'—pardon the pun.

Both my parents were raised on pre-industrial farms, meaning that all power came from animals—except for a deafening one-cylinder engine in a work shed—no tractor or electricity. The energy to do all the chores, farming and maintenance came from high-calorie meals—morning, noon and night. Even though my parents each moved to the city, after they married my mother still cooked like her mother did on the farm ("You can take the girl out of the farm but you can't take the farm out of the girl") so my die-maker father had his first heart-attack at age forty-eight and his last at fifty-eight. I of course developed a taste for high-calorie food but fortunately my wife, also of farm-raised parents, wisely changed our own family's menu to healthier lower-fat foods (and I took up running in earnest). My brother's wife didn't and he too died at fifty-eight (they both smoked). The point is, of today's population most were conditioned to like fat-rich high-calorie foods but lead sedentary lives, so obesity is epidemic.

Consequently fast-food places cater to fat-rich high-calorie tastes—and even when they add healthier items to their menu they don't sell. Thus many of the diseases of later years are 'self-inflicted' like heart-attacks, strokes, hypertension and congestive-heart-failure, and likely diabetes, putting a strain on medical costs. These will surely exacerbate as the baby-boomers age, but even teenagers are overweight. 'If you don't take care of your body, where are you going to live?' Something's needed to improve the average lifestyle.[20] Maybe medical insurance should be rated as is car insurance—high-risk drivers pay a premium, why not high-risk lifestyles?[21] If people had to pay to 'enjoy' their indulgence, maybe it'd induce them to change. Americans are free to live the way they choose but why should others of us pay for it? Or maybe there could be a tax on fat-food like the tax on cigarettes with the revenue going to pay medical expenses—the higher price of cigarettes discourages smoking, might it work for fat?[22]

A healthy lifestyle improves vitality so we have an active outgoing Life Urge to notice and revere the everyday beauty of Life. We're enabled to do more challenging physical and mental activities, and lose less sick-time. It likely extends vitality into old-age whether or not it extends age. (Some coach-potato quipped that practicing a healthy lifestyle you may not live longer but it'll sure seem longer!) With increased vitality and longevity we can be a more effective courier or executor of evolution's trajectory, of Life's advancement—moreover we'll enjoy it more.

Animal Rights

Until a century ago horses were the prime source of non-rail land traction. Even in the 1930s horses were used by street vendors and on my grandmothers' farms. A century before then black slaves were in use in the south, counted as three-fifths of a person with rights not much better than farm animals. It took a century of struggle to win Afro-Americans equal-rights to vote, and to education, housing and jobs as citizens in our free society. But a similar effort won't elevate horses or dogs or other animals to citizen status because they haven't evolved to the human level. Even in ancient Rome the Stoics and Christians won rights for slaves but never questioned the institution[23] just as today we generally support animal rights but don't question our right to own and enslave them, and—except for vegetarians—even consume them.

Where do I stand on animal rights? I'm an unabashed carnivore although for health reasons I moderate my intake (I'm better classified as an omnivore, and perhaps a semprevore). Well, we've all got to eat something—animal Life lives on Life! Even as vegetarians if we restrict our protein intake to grains and legumes—the wheat's, rice's, oat's, bean's or pea's 'babies'—we're still consuming Life. So it's not a question of whether we consume Life but what level of Life.[24] One of my daughters doesn't eat mammals but does eat poultry and fish—hardly anyone eats humans anymore. Our species evolved at the top of the food chain—eating flesh gave us the energy to evolve big brains as described in Chapter Eight. That's who I am—who we are. On the other hand I like the practice—attributed to some American Indians—of explaining, apologizing and thanking the animal before they killed it. But of course, butchers do my killing for me and I doubt that they apologize.

Moreover I don't keep pets although I realize a dog or cat would be better off with me than feral outdoors all the time—they evolved as symbionts of our species, so they need our protection and support.[25] I'm troubled by enslaving any animal, human or not, even though I realize they're dependent on us. I do feed the birds and squirrels outside my study window, and wouldn't hurt a mouse—unless it's crapping all over my kitchen counters. I also 'talk' to insects—bees, spiders, centipedes (no, they don't answer)—but I vacuum up flies and meal-moths, and swat mosquitoes. Thus I accept human's privileged position in evolution's trajectory—along with the heavy responsibility that goes with it, namely to not squander the involuntary sacrifice of those non-humans that give their lives that I might live, and not to usurp their freedom unnecessarily.

Our early ancestors' practice of eating other animals nourished the evolution of our big brains, with the resultant consciousness and perspicacity—by eating other animals they elevated us to 'higher' animals, albeit unwittingly. I've argued that our early ancestors 'blindly' advanced the evolution of Life's trajectory, so now that we're no longer 'blind' it seems to me we're obliged to justify our taking—directly or indirectly—other animals' lives. So consider again the food chain—virtually all the energy on Earth's surface comes or came from the Sun much of which is converted into hydrocarbons by plants, many of which are eaten by herbivores, and some of those animals are eaten by carnivores, like us—generally complex Life feeds on less complex Life.[26] This food chain is a rough analogue of the hierarchy of intelligence—eaters are often smarter than eatees as an alternative to being bigger, stronger or faster. The Sun's energy was converted by evolutionary progression over eons through the 'lower' levels of Life into the 'higher' levels. We now command those heights—at least for a little while—the beneficiaries of evolution's blind faltering struggle to inexorably advance Life. We've become evolution's executors. We have the privilege to speak for nature coupled with the awesome responsibility to fairly, unselfishly and insightfully represent Life's best interest. Evolution has conferred a 'nobility' on us, and thus *noblesse oblige!*

This is a 'slippery slope' indeed! If we justify killing other animals to serve our 'higher cause', we must be certain that ours is truly a higher cause and that we're truly serving it, not just rationalizing. And if we can justify using other animals for our 'higher cause', we might easily 'slip' down that 'slope' and justify using 'lesser' human animals to serve our 'higher cause'—the less intelligent/educated, the retarded or disabled, a 'lower' social-class or ethnic group, an embryo or fetus—eugenics and slavery are only two examples from just the past two centuries.[27] Yet like it or not, we're on that 'slippery slope'—to pretend we're not and close our eyes is sheer folly, inviting disaster. As described in the previous chapter under 'Innovations—Bodies & Brains', the day is fast approaching when 'designer children' could found an elite caste, a master race[28] served by a caste of inferior humans competing with intelligent robots untrammeled by human or animal rights. Rather than allow 'natural' humans to fall behind and become an inferior caste—three-fifths human and two-fifths animal or whatever—plan now to make medical advances available to all humans world-wide so that generations hence they're not faced with this dilemma and our human species can advance as one rather than split into two or more species.

But "power corrupts!" How often once leaders obtain power they exploit the offices' privileges—it's an almost irresistible temptation, easily rationalized—do you serve the office or serve yourself? As evolution's executors do we carry forward our legacy or squander our inheritance? Looking at today's world it seems we're more inclined to the latter than the former—rampant materialism, global environmental wastage, exploitation of resources, and so on—with little regard for how, or even if we're advancing Life. When it comes to other animals' lives we have schizoid behaviors—most love their pets (some inordinately) and/or wildlife, yet eat lots of meat that once was animal.

Education

In the feudal society of the Dark Ages the simile of the folk as 'sheep in a meadow' and the clergy as shepherds, was quite apt. The clergy were virtually the only educated people—even most nobles were illiterate—and the few books were meticulously copied out by hand on parchment mostly by monks. But with Gutenberg's movable type, cheaper paper and use of the vernacular rather than Latin, literacy began to spread infusing the talented populace with knowledge hitherto retained by the Church. The 'sheep' broke out of the 'meadow' and the 'shepherds' couldn't stop many of them. The Reformation and peasant revolts followed, and eventually the redistribution of the nobles' and the Church's lands, along with less patriarchal, more representative forms of government, the Enlightenment.[29]

Crucial to self-government are citizens who are enlightened and responsible which education presumably confers. Once literacy was spreading the Church led in propagating education, from universities down into parochial schools, but of course with a heavy dose of religious indoctrination[30]—'the best defense is a good offense'—and apparently it worked considering how ubiquitous theistic belief seems to be. Today education is compulsory through high school and most is secular. Periodically religious zealots attempt to insinuate prayer—directly or in the Pledge to the Flag's "under God"—The Ten Commandments and creationism into public education on the pretext of teaching 'values'. Maybe time *should* be allowed in schools to teach theism, atheism and prototheism if done equally and objectively by a competent teacher, or lacking such objectivity, by a team of teachers of various persuasions.

Ethics & Values

Ethics is usually seen as only applying to behavior between us humans but if you were the only person on Earth and there were no God, would there be any ethics? If an ant crossed your path would you step on it? Would you trash your environment? I see ethics in a broader context than just among humans. What sort of person do we strive to be, even if no one's watching?—that's our personal ethics. Would we want everyone else to behave as we do?—that's the ethics we wish for in our ideal society. Yet regardless of how everyone else behaves, it's our one Life to live in the here-and-now, regardless of any here-after. As I've said, evolution by virtue of our consciousness has granted us the privilege and responsibility of being its 'eyes'. What would we like our world to become and how might we affect that outcome?—that's our calling, our mission in Life—base our ethics on that, our polestar.

Churches endeavor to imbue their congregants with morals, ethical behaviors and social values which are based on revelation as interpreted by the Church and its clergy. But as technology and society change at an ever-accelerating rate the Church must constantly reinterpret revelation. It seems they're usually behind the times rather than in the lead, such as with Galileo. This is to be expected. Even if the 'revelation', the insights and judgments of a venerable elder were valid back then, they may now be obsolete necessitating reinterpretation thus making them vulnerable to the reinterpreter's biases and hidden agenda. Take for example the Ten Commandments, ostensibly rules prescribed over three-millennia ago to discipline a large throng of exuberant escaped slaves as they attempted to cross the Sinai desert with minimal wilderness survival skills.[31] To interpret wilderness survival rules into rules for today's world is like translating rules for riding a horse into rules for driving a car. Some may be applicable but which are and which aren't? To decide takes a broader understanding of horses and cars, or with revelation, of human nature based—not on a paradigm of a God 'out there' and life-after-death—but on the Life Urge 'in here' and Life's evolutionary trajectory.

Would a change from belief in God to belief in the Life Urge make people more ethical? Certainly belief in God is no guarantee considering the atrocities of war and terrorism perpetrated in the name of God, or rather one people's God versus another people's God each 'created in their own image and likeness' respectively. But than, as cited in the previous chapter's 'Bodies & Brains', the Nazis committed atrocities in the name of advancing evolution, back then called eugenics or Social Darwinism but now called the Holocaust.[32] The Nazis were trying to establish Aryans as the 'master race' in Hitler's totalitarian Third Reich. Evolution can be pretty nasty whether natural or planned. So belief in either God or the Life Urge can be used by demented people to rationalize their own unconscious drives.

What safeguards are there against misinterpreting either God's will or the Life Urge? Reputable theists will pray and consult confidants before taking action. But as I've argued, praying is attempting to search one's own unconscious and if the confidants one consults share the same warped ideas, they're just talking to themselves, their alter egos. I suspect this happened in the Crusades, and certainly in the Inquisition, and with the Nazis and Al Qaeda (aka al-Qaida). So what's the answer? As emphasized in Chapter Ten's 'Know Thyself', we must try to expunge our hangups and to seek counsel that's honest and objective, not just yea- or naysayers. But it seems to me the crucial difference between the God and Life Urge paradigms is whether the paradigm is based on revelation or on scientific thinking and verification. Revelation accepts some premises as absolutely true whereas science accepts nothing as absolutely true, and any 'truth' it does embrace is only tentative until displaced by a more comprehensive truth. Revelation is stagnant looking backward, science is dynamic looking forward. Both should eschew arrogance.

Is science adverse to religion? I think it's the other way around. Four centuries ago the Church labeled Copernicus, Bruno and Galileo as heretical because they opposed the Earth-centered-Universe concept. A century-and-half ago the Church of England's Wilberforce ridiculed Darwin because he opposed creationism (Creationists still are). A century ago the Catholic Church condemned industry/modernity. Now they're opposing birth control, abortion, cloning and so forth. Yet in order to survive, religions sooner or later quietly 'evolve' their beliefs in the face of widely accepted scientific realities.[33] Of course religion *should* feel threatened by science. One by one, science keeps pricking holes in religion's balloons so their creedal beliefs deflate or blow-up in their face. Discrediting religion may not be science's purpose, but that can be a result.[34] Now prototheism proposes a science *of* religion which assaults the very basis of belief—unless organized religions are willing and able to make the paradigm shift suggested in Chapter Ten and below.

Back to the Nazis—when orders come down from omnipotent authority, God or *der Führer*, to be unquestioningly obeyed, our only 'ethical' concern may be, not whether what we're told to do or not do is right or wrong, but whether we should obey or face the music.[35] Does ethics only apply when we have a free uncoerced choice? What about the alternative—are we more interested in the 'ethics' or the reward for doing good? If good behavior presumably gets us into Heaven, are we being ethical or just prudent?

Locating the source of ethics in the depths of one's purged and enlightened Self, 'in here', requires taking responsibility for expressing our own Life Urge, not shifting credit or blame to God 'out there' or to anyone else. Of course we humans are great rationalizers—some of us are very good at justifying whatever we want—so conservatives will make outcries similar to those made a couple centuries ago when democracy was first proposed: "People are too irresponsible, ignorant, lazy, self-centered, dishonest or whatever to be trusted to make good decisions—at least we have a well established and long tested code of ethics/morals, but venturing into untested ethics is a 'slippery slope', a Pandora's box." Those may all be true but they're not all that's true. I'm not proposing jettisoning all traditional ethics—some were actually based on the Life Urge misinterpreted as God's word—they were right even if for the wrong reasons.

Traditional ethics in general come from a paternalistic, authoritarian, hierarchical age-old culture, jealously guarding what they see as their prerogatives, and deeply suspicious and mistrustful of common folks (perhaps because they're projecting their own impulses and conduct onto others). Of course it's a self-fulfilling prophesy—if folks aren't given much freedom they don't learn how to use it prudently and may even go a little wild at the first chance—like Moses' Hebrew ex-slaves. Wise parents teach their children ethics and values by their own example, and by letting them learn in graduated, escalated steps where they can fail-safe and learn from small mistakes before being faced with bigger decisions and feeling they have to rebel.

Money

"You cannot serve God and mammon" the Scriptures teach, though many professed theists sure try to. Or maybe they intuitively realize something the Evangelist didn't. Under my notion—that, what we call 'God' is really the Urge to Life—can money be used to serve that Life Urge? We need to take a careful look at what money really is and at its influence in our society to see if and how money might serve the Urge to Life by motivating prototheistic values and ethics.

Intrinsically what we use for money of itself has very little utility. Take gold and silver, the Sun-god's blood and sweat,[36] the traditional forms of money. As King Midas found, you can't eat gold. To keep us warm we don't wear or burn gold or silver. We could build a house of them for shelter if we had enough. We can't ride them to travel about and they're probably too heavy to make a practical boat. Gold and silver do have practical uses but their value as money was greatly exaggerated. Money has value because enough people tacitly agree it has value—it's a little like a confidence game. If enough people think that paper has value, paper currency and private checks have value, and now plastic cards have value as well as electronic bits. Money's value is not in its form but in its fiction, in what we believe it represents.

Money's a medium of exchange but it's often treated as a fetish. The Zuñi Indians of the southwest US in the 1800s valued fetishes—small natural or carved objects which resembled prey animals and often had feathers, beads and arrow-heads tied to them. The Zuñi believed a fetish conferred on its possessor mystical powers over their prey enabling the hunter to track and kill the game animal depicted by the fetish.[37] Similarly many moderns imbue money with powers beyond its face value as a medium of exchange thus endowing the possessor with authority, prestige, legitimacy, and even respect. And it's not just those who have money but most everyone is complicit in this delusion.

We've come to desire money even if we don't know what we want it for. But since money's fungible we don't need to know what we want it for beforehand. And certainly it's good to have enough for your children's education, for your retirement, for a rainy day or what have you. Yet how much is enough? 'You can never have too much money' is the prevailing attitude. To some the acquisition of money is an end in itself. I believe people who measure their lives in money are indeed very poor in the things that really count. Rather than treat money as a fetish, why not view it simply as a medium of exchange. If a person's exchanging their time and energy—their one and only life—just to accumulate more money that they may never need and probably can't even spend, or to spend on more stuff that's not really satisfying, attempting to use money to buy things that money can't buy, maybe they should look at how they might better spend their precious limited time.[38] Certainly there are some folks whose favorite activity generates money just as a byproduct—that's great! But I've known people who cling to a well-paying job they hate rather than face the struggle and angst of looking for something more satisfying. 'Sometime you have to chew off your foot to get out of a trap.' Better to lose their 'foot' than waste their one and only life. Even if another job pays less, consider the 'lost' money as 'spent' on job satisfaction.

History

Long before money, among non-kin, goods were exchanged by barter. If I'd been around back then and had surplus grain I'd try to find a neighbor who wanted it and who had something I wanted, then try to strike a deal. If what I had wasn't easily divisible like grain but was whole like a pig, and my neighbor had a cow I wanted which we both agreed was worth more than my pig, I'd have to throw something extra into the deal like some grain, or among the Aztecs it was cacao beans, called commodity money.[39] Gold and silver were valued as commodity money because of their durability and luster (and because they came from the Sun-god?) but it was difficult to assay their purity and weight. About 640BC the kings of Lydia (now Turkey) began stamping standardized certified gold-silver coins whose value was accepted throughout the realm. In addition they established marketplaces. Back then I could take my grain or pig to town on market day and have a good chance of finding a buyer. But the buyer didn't need to have some goods I wanted, only coins which I could use with other sellers, then or later. Because of the prospect of an easy market for their surplus goods, folks produced surpluses of their specialty thus leading to increased wealth all 'round. Not surprisingly Lydian elite squandered their wealth on conspicuous consumption which lead to King Croesus' hubristic attack on the Persians and Lydia's downfall in 546BC.[40]

Next the Greeks adapted neighboring Lydia's inventions of coins and markets, particularly the Athenians with their nearby silver mine. In Athens' agora not only was there a free exchange of goods but of ideas.[41] The Greeks spread their money economy throughout the Mediterranean, then the conquering Romans unified and standardized it. But the city of Rome didn't produce anything, it only took in and consumed. So after they ran out of worthwhile conquests, they began debasing their coinage and went into slow decline, particularly in the west.[42] Medieval feudalism ensued for almost a thousand years with little use for money especially among the serfs.[43]

Gold and silver retained their mystique but their weight and vulnerability made them difficult to transport. Thus after the Crusades the virtuous Knights Templars' hundreds of widespread castles served as linked depositories for the wealthy providing banking services until the Templars were burnt-at-the-stake and plundered in the 1310s by France's Philip IV.[44] Next Italian families like the Medici devised ways around the Church's prohibition of usury and provided similar banking services enabling 'bills of exchange' to serve as paper-money until 1494 when the Medici were looted—again by the French.[45] With the flood of gold and silver from the Americas beginning in the 1500s, the proliferation of coins facilitated commerce down into the lower classes.[46] Then quasi-national banks like the Bank of England provided services backed by their alleged gold reserves but they too succumbed to politics justified by the First and Second World Wars, decoupling their paper-money from the gold standard.[47] Similarly until the Civil War the US government issued only coins leaving paper-money the prerogative of state chartered banks. Thereafter the newly issued US paper-money would be exchanged on demand for gold or silver up until the mid-1900s when ironically "Payable to the Bearer on Demand" was dropped and "In God We Trust" was added to our currency—a cynic might say the fiction of gold was supplanted by an even more ethereal fiction. The gold at Fort Knox and elsewhere is window dressing—it has nothing substantive to do with the worth of our money.[48]

Future

In reality the worth of our money is based on our confidence in that money and in the people we allow to govern us. Devaluation (inflation) results either from shortages of goods or an abundance of money from governments justifying over-issuing it in wartime or for other perceived public benefits, basically legal counterfeiting and hidden taxation. Some less astute governments and kleptocracies may flood their economies with money causing hyperinflation. Those hurt most by inflation are those who deal primarily in cash like the urban poor, are on fixed incomes or are owed fixed amounts (bonds, land contracts and the like). But people who have most of their wealth in investments which raise with inflation are buffered. Yet it seems strange that there should be any *in*flation. After all, as productivity improves, the price of those products decreases so there should be *de*flation as during the nineteenth and early twentieth centuries.[49] Are some politicians offsetting the price decreases with 'hidden taxes', spending the proceeds on pet programs?

With so many nations letting their currencies float free and with expanding global markets needing to exchange those currencies, a new species of currency trader has evolved. Speculating in electronic money in cyberspace it's said they lurk in bull pens at the monitors of their idiosyn-cratically programmed computers and on phones, day or night everyday, scanning and anticipating fluctuations in the world's currencies. Not even hunter-gatherers, they're more like some immobile reptile awaiting prey to come within reach of its rapacious grasp. They live off transitory trifling shifts in huge amounts of funds. National banks futilely attempt to counter these market-driven swings in their currencies at their taxpayers' expense but consistently to the traders' benefit.[50] There are earlier species of specu-lators in commodities and corporate stocks, most recently computer-armed day-traders. They're all basically gamblers but rather than just get their thrills by mindlessly risking their funds at a casino's slot machine or a state's lottery, they bet their funds and shrewdness against the markets. Some assert they inadvertently benefit society by generating financial and commodity markets without which, for example they argue, investors would be reluctant to put money into corporate stocks for fear of being un-able to get their money back out at will.

There are those who are apprehensive about the future of money, not only the proliferation of free-floating national currencies but the prolifera-tion of private forms of money—tokens, credit cards, debit cards, prepaid cards and smart cards as well as 'near money' like frequent-flyer-miles and who knows what's next.[51] It seems to me we need to keep in mind what money actually is—a medium of exchange—and not a fetish nor 'play-money' for speculators. I can see how each of us can demythologize money so it loses its appeal as a fetish without losing it function as a medium of exchange. But offhand I don't see how to take the greed out of speculation without hampering currency markets. In reality we don't take greed out of markets but out of speculators, but than they wouldn't be speculators, they'd be investors.

Even though money's importance may be exaggerated, it does play important rôles in our lives. As said, it facilitates exchanging our special-ized productive capabilities for discretionary purchases—we can sell our specialty, our work and time, for money, then use that money to buy oth-ers' specialties—imagine trying to do that without money, we'd be back to bartering. Thus money fosters and facilitates cooperation in society by providing a medium for exchanging *motivation*—a person is motivated to produce materials or services expecting they can exchange them, via money, for others' materials and services. It's also a 'democratic' system in that people 'vote' with their money by bidding on the value of others' ma-terials and services thus 'electing' what our affluent society values. More-over we can use some of our money, past and future earnings, to buy tools—capital goods that increase our productive capacity both in our work and private-life. Furthermore we can store some of our money for later use by loaning it to or investing it in others' enterprises so that hopefully our money's not only available in the future but increases. These rôles are so routine in this new millennium that we may not appreciate them until we look back only a few centuries or at today's third-world and post-communist countries.[52]

Still money's power to motivate people to go to work every day and do all sorts of other outlandish things—'to sell their souls for money'—would be unbelievable if it weren't so common. For a moment try to somehow detach yourself mentally from our money culture and look at it as would an extraterrestrial—the proverbial man-from-Mars—in disbelief that people would prostitute themselves for the stuff. There's no way it could work except people believe that it works, so it works. Yet in the past the Church convinced people to work to earn credit in Heaven[53]—some religious devoted their lives to it—so anything's possible. Maybe we could invent and promulgate some kind of currency for advancing Life's trajectory. Money is the medium for material values and sin/indulgence is the medium for afterlife/eternity values—what might be the medium for measuring Life's values? An entrepreneur is thought of as operating in a money milieu but, given a 'currency' that measures the advancement of evolution's trajectory, more entrepreneurs just might be motivated to operate where success is measured, not only by their business acumen, but by their contribution to Life's progress. Indeed some do now without such inducement.

Institutions

Recall in Chapter Nine's 'Symbols, Music & Language', whereas tools were characterized as extensions of our body, institutions were characterized as extensions of our group or society. In our journey through Life we travel a wide assortment of institutions—family, school, marriage, workplace—either partnerships or corporations. Let's examine some aspects of just a few of these institutions to speculate how they might be affected by a shift from an often implicit theistic or atheistic paradigm, to an explicit prototheistic paradigm.

In our passage through Life's institutions we encounter many other fellow passengers. We relate to some of them in diverse ways from the casual transitory situations—a smile or frown at a passer-by, chitchat at a grocery counter—to more formalized relationships such as marriage, school, church, work, or club. In these various situations we put on rôles, assume personas we've learned as described in Chapter Ten's 'Know Thyself'. We move from the casual unstructured situations—where we're somewhat free to more or less be ourselves or to put on whatever rôle suits us and the situation—to structured institutional relationships—where the rôles are prescribed, scripted more or less by that institution and by norms of society. During these involvements we form attachments, we may even be very close to some for a while, but those dissolve as we or they move on—graduation, job change, new neighborhood, divorce—even if you meet again it's not the same. One or maybe both of you, even soul mates, have diverged and changed or grown in different directions with new interests; the old times are nice to reminisce over but it's not the same. In these encounters throughout Life's passages we seek relationships that foster Life, that accentuate positives and minimize negatives.

In analyzing our institutions what at first may seem like a technicality is, When does an organization take on a life of its own and become an organism? Since the theme of this long essay is Life, this is not a trivial issue—Life is instantiated in organisms. Single-cell archaea, prokaryotes and eukaryotes are organisms described in Chapter Six. Chapter Seven went on to describe multicell organisms wherein individual eukaryote cells differentiate and specialize (except germ and stem cells), and physically join together to function as a single entity. (They may also harbor resident symbiotic prokaryote cells.) Individual cells die and new cells are cloned continuously but the multicell entity maintains its integrity until the whole organism itself dies. Broadening this definition, a beehive or ant colony is therefore an organism with individual bees or ants specialized even though they're not physically joined together, and individuals dying and being replace. But they can't survive for long without the others—except the queen, the germ 'cell'.

We humans similarly specialize, and join and leave schools, clubs, businesses—organizations which have lives of their own, continuing on after we leave. In most older cultures individuals were bound for life to a family, community or organization in specialized rôles. In today's culture, we're even more specialized but less bound to any one family, community or organization—we change towns and jobs freely. But the community and organization goes on with or without us—they have 'lives' of their own. Are they organisms like the beehive and we're kind of like worker bees? Unlike Orwell's novels *1984* and *Animal Farm*, in free societies we're free to migrate as nomads. But are we fungible—one specialist practically indistinguishable functionally from and interchangeable with another—while the corporate 'organism' continues on in perpetuity? We grant a corporation—which is a legal fiction—some characteristics and rights of a citizen, even more in some ways, of a supra-human organism—limited liability, freedom-of-speech, perpetuity, among others. And now with ubiquitous communications, corporations are going beyond the beehive metaphor—even going beyond multicell organisms where every cell is in contact primarily through intercellular chemical signal particles. Corporations' workers are now in constant instantaneous contact[54] via cell phones. But of course we're not just anonymous 'cells' in some multicell organism (despite our cell phones). We're each independently thinking sentient human beings—unless we choose not to be and essentially relinquish our autonomy to the authority of a fictitious supra-human organism.[55]

What are these fictitious supra-human organisms? I think that marriages don't qualify. But traditional extended families can come close—where marriages are arranged and the individual family members and their loyalties are subservient to the 'family'. The 'family' goes on for generations with its property and hereditary trade but without legal status separate from the family head, usually a patriarch. (The family was the model for dukedoms and kingdoms.) Nor are partnerships supra-human organisms although some also come close.

The supra-human organisms I'm thinking of are the corporate forms nominally overseen by an elected board and executives, and utilized in government, education, business, religion, clubs and such. In government there are villages, towns, cities, counties, states and nations with their elected boards being the town or city council, the county commission, and at the state or national level, house and senate; and the executive being the elected mayor, governor or president. There are also auxiliary quasi-governmental 'authorities' for housing, building, economic development and so on. In education there are school boards, and college and university trustees with school superintendents and college presidents. In business there's generally a board of directors, a CEO and maybe a CFO. Religious organizations run the gamut from hierarchical like the Catholic Church where the diocese owns and runs everything by fiat answerable only to the Vatican, to congregations where a board of congregants runs the operations and hires a minister. Social clubs, labor unions, social institutions all utilize corporate forms which constitute them as a fictional entity, legally a 'person' endowed with many of the rights of a citizen, except voting. In today's society these supra-human organisms are ubiquitous—we each are involved to varying degrees, one way or another in many of them at any one time. Let's examine a few of them to consider how prototheism might apply.

Marriage & Family

Society instituted marriage to propagate and perpetuate itself. Couples formed a unit which back then generally could be dissolved only if one member couldn't or wouldn't have children. What rights and privileges does society now grant marriages that aren't enjoyed by unwed couples? It used to be sex, but no longer. Modern contraception has separated having sex from making babies with profound affects on society. Non-childbearing couples—both hetero- and homo-sexual—can increasingly freely cohabit, can jointly own property (women couldn't a century or so ago), can have reciprocal powers-of-attorney and wills, and pretty much everything else. What than does marriage provide that can't be had by other means?

An unwed couple in their fifties who jointly owned their house, when I asked why they were getting married agreed with Pascal, "The heart has it's reasons that reason cannot know."[56] The instinct for couples to bond has roots that go far back and deep into our animal origins which evolution selected to perpetuate, not because those couples desired offspring, but because their offspring inherited their parents' trait to bond. Not all animal species evolved bonded couples but ours did because the prolonged rigors of successfully raising human offspring required such a commitment, as described in Chapter Eight. So the trait has survived into modern humans.

Even so, children aren't the only way of being productive and advancing Life's trajectory. Indeed it could be argued that bearing children beyond a couple's ability to provide for them and to provide them with a good start in Life is counterproductive. Alternatively the intimacy of a bonded couple may nurture other creative drives in one or both thus contributing more to Life's evolution than children might. Perhaps society should just trust that the intimacy and support of marriage, hetero- or homo-, just might foster benefits. So why not afford homosexual couples the status marriage confers? If that offends conservative sensibilities, call such marriages something else—like 'wedlock': they've 'wedded' their futures and are 'locked' together. But then what would we call childless heterosexual couples? We might avoid the controversy over 'gay marriage' by enacting laws that give gay couples the same legal rights as marriage, but called 'legal couples'.

But sometimes wedlock comes unlocked—marriage is by no means necessarily forever—some couples don't 'live happily ever after'. When love goes sour it can get rotten. Some divorced couples hate each other and haven't spoken in years in spite of shared interests in children and grandchildren. What a waste—poisoning the rest of ones Life. Other divorced couples get over it, understand that the love and interests they once shared diverged, that they had some good years together but things changed, and they're now friends. My ex-wife and I go out for a bite and a movie each year on what would have been our anniversary. Life's too short to harbor a grudge. We're still both good people, we're just no longer companions on Life's passages.

'Family' however implies children. Parenting has non-monetary rewards and so most couples have children even though parenting's grossly under-paid (as is teaching—surrogate-parenting). Then will the world's human population continue to increase? The answer you'll get depends on the assumptions about future human behaviors and policies.[57] China for example reined in its population growth by imposing a one-child-per-couple policy (although it's said it produced a self-centered generation). What kinds of behaviors would prototheism encourage and how might those affect population growth? A Life dedicated to knowledgeably responding to one's Life Urge would prescribe a circumspect, healthy lifestyle throughout Life. For example if couples delayed parenthood until their maturity, affluence and health reach an optimal balance, and then only reproduced themselves (two-children-per-couple) that would slow population growth. On the other hand if medical technology continues to improve vitality and extend longevity, that would delay population decline until a new equilibrium is reached. Such practices could lead to a society of vigorous sages devoted to advancing Life's trajectory (more on this below).

Education

It's been quipped "Children have to interrupt their education to go to school"[58]—a droll observation that children's natural zest for learning can be thwarted by mindless schooling. (On some school boards, those in charge of K-12 education are uneducated.) But it needn't be so. The challenge for parents, educators and society is to avoid stifling children's in-born Urge to Life while stuffing their heads with as much knowledge as possible during their early peak learning years. As described in Chapter Nine's 'Early Development', a child not only has an insatiable neocortex but needs enriching experiences and cultural exposures to 'feed' their neocortex, else its growth will be stunted. But there's so much to learn, what should we teach?[59] It seems to me, if as adults they're to be contributors to advancing Life's trajectory, they'll not only need skills (language,[60] math, computers) and an understanding of history and society, but creativity and a grasp of concepts.[61] Their precious time shouldn't be squandered on busy work and obsolete religion[62] (which has problematic benefit in teaching values and ethics—witness the wars being fought in the name of religion and the urban crime with store-front churches on every other block). Their teachers needn't be experts in all these subject but guides skilled in the use of resources, not only books but all the other technology that's becoming more and more available as aids to learning. But the most important lesson is to learn how to learn on one's own or with the help of others. Much of what they learn in school will be obsolete before they can use it so they need to become proficient at learning to learn (autodidacts).

Yet it can be overdone. Nowadays even play is structured by adults. When I was a kid we played baseball in the vacant lots next door, arguing about every pitch and play, not so much learning baseball as learning social skills. Now kids develop athletically while learning baseball (of minimal value in later Life) and only observe social skills between their coach, umpires and parents. And I'm not sure what to make of the structured computer games I'm told some kids spend hours at instead of outside in unstructured play. We evolved as unstructured hunter-gatherers in the wild—it seems to me it must still be essential to a child's growth. Computer games undoubtedly teach skills that will be useful in their future,[63] but the violence of some games (TV and movies) must be feeding their latent vicious appetite.[64] How do we persuade the game makers to develop and market more wholesome products? We restrict alcohol and tobacco, why allow feeding them violence?

Children are rightfully shielded from some adult practices until they're less susceptible to addiction and presumably can exercise prudence.[65] But prudence isn't infused overnight when they reach their majority, it's learned incrementally by repeated trial and fail-safe error. Alcohol for instance, in most states parents can be arrested for serving their minor children. But I believe kids should learn about alcohol at home under their parents' guidance (like Europeans?) long enough before their legal drinking age so booze doesn't take on the mystique of forbidden fruit leading to binging at their first opportunity.

Similarly sex education should be taught at home—who better than their parents in spite of some possible embarrassment ('Old people don't do *that* do they?'). Perhaps parents' best source of information for guidance is candidly reminiscing about their own adolescence, transposed into today's more permissive and explicit culture. Like everything else, kids learn about sex from a variety of sources—from what they're told by 'authorities' and companions, from what they read or see at movies, and from their own tentative experiences, fail-safe if they've been adequately and honestly informed. Lying to them about consequences is a cop-out (they won't 'go blind'). Contraception has made abstinence unnecessary and a waste of youthful passions—parents can be less concerned about their adolescent's unwanted pregnancy or fatherhood, and focus on helping them learn about love versus lust. Parents don't want to encourage promiscuity, rather they want to teach that sex is an expression of love and of the Life Urge. The dilemma is how to help an adolescent learn to make prudent judgments while their hormones are raging and the executive part of their brain, their prefrontal cortex, is undergoing a disorienting growth spurt.[66]

But children grow up and move on. When they become parents, heads-of-household and working full-time, they have little leisure for education even for keeping up with developments in ones own field. With multiple children, mothers are particularly susceptible to being subsumed by the family organism. Educational TV and historical movies might be the only recourse aside from magazines and an occasional book. Upon retirement suddenly we have the luxury of time to learn at our leisure if we've kept our mind active—and learning helps keep it active (like reading this book).

Somewhat related to continuing education are news media. Our Founding Fathers believed that a free democratic society must be made up of well informed citizens—they knew the importance of a free-press, and guaranteed it in our Constitution. But they didn't *fund* it! Back then publication of pamphlets and newspapers was funded mostly by sales to their readers. Today the price of most magazines and newspapers, especially subscriptions, barely covers the cost of distribution—the publishers get most of their revenue from advertisements crammed onto the pages up to the saturation limit of their readers' tolerance, and we've been conditioned to tolerate a lot. Newspapers are really *ads*papers with a little news sprinkled in. 'Free' information—on radio, TV, web-pages, signs, in junk-mail and wherever else it can be crammed—isn't really free. We pay for it with our time and attention/distraction, with the visual, noise and trash pollution of our environment, and with rude manners to fend-off aggressive sales people such as telemarketers.[67] And of course if we buy any of those goods and services, the cost of their advertising is included in the price.

The problem stems from the runaway materialistic society we've become. The cornucopia of goods and services has to keep flowing in order to sustain our economy. So suppliers cast their bait into the public waters in the hope of hooking customers. Apparently they must hook enough customers to make it worthwhile else a supplier would stop advertising. Maybe part of the problem comes from extending the right of free-speech to fictitious 'citizens' like corporate entities some of whom abuse it. I don't know the answer. I suppose if enough of us boycotted the offensive advertisers they might get the message and change their ways. Instead of the suppliers coming at us with their shotgun advertising, we could go to them when we're shopping, yet we'd still need to find them somehow— yellow page, Internet or whatever—so we need to strike a balance. But then why would they fund 'free' media, we'd have to pay for it directly, which is fine with me.

Community

Historically local churches and taverns were the community centers where services were held mornings and evenings respectively. There were also closed societies like Freemason lodges, as well as monasteries and convents offering succor and refuge. Today's churches, aside from their 'religious' function of Chapter Ten, also provide quasi-religious functions[68] notably officiating at weddings and funerals, teaching values/ethics, and socializing. Let's look at these ancillary functions to see how they might be provided in a prototheistic milieu, instead of traditional churches.

If you want 'pomp & circumstance' for your wedding, a church is hard to beat with its organ rolling, a white 'carpet' rolled down the center aisle leading up to the raised flower-bedecked sanctuary led by a procession of bridesmaids. But what come with it are all the religious trappings and maybe a sermon. Some non-traditional couples create their own ceremony—for example a couple I know had theirs in the evening on top of the mountain at the upper end of the ski-lift-gondola at Snowbird with the whole wedding party around them, a justice of the peace officiating over their reciting the vows they composed, and the alpenglow on the Wasatch Mountains for backdrop. Quite a 'cathedral'!

When I attend a funeral service,[69] if there's a priest or minister presiding, I'll try to sit so I can quietly step out during the 'commercial' (similar to using the mute button on my TV remote). But I've also attended services with extemporaneous remembrances by friends and relatives without any religious 'commercial' about afterlife. I believe a funeral service should help grieve the loss and let go, not pretend that the dead are still around in spirit form. Scattering their ashes back to nature can help— better than putting them in the ground under a tombstone where allegedly they'll be resurrected for the Last Judgment (although the old Catholic cemetery across from my house makes a peaceful park).

The issue of values/ethics was discussed earlier in this chapter. Preaching theistic values and ethics based on revelation required either a good knowledge of the Bible or of the prescribed theology supposedly derived therefrom—probably some of both depending on a church's sect— along with an understanding of human nature. In a prototheistic milieu teaching values/ethics requires an appreciation and grasp of science and of historical trends along with an intuition of the numinous. Science and

humanities are usually regarded as antagonistic yet needn't be, as I'm trying to show throughout this work.

But it's in social functions where churches excel—Protestant more
than Catholic until recently. Folks and their children dress up in their
Sunday-go-to-meeting clothes and practice 'proper' social behavior.
They'll likely get acquainted with others who share their values and may
participate in rummage sales, bridge clubs, dances and ice cream socials,
and may even find a mate and marry. Running volunteer activities enables
learning leadership skills. The minister usually functions as a counselor in
troubled times and manages an informal network of volunteers to aid the
needy. But none of these functions are unique to churches—other organizations can provide them too—yet theistic worship provides the *raison
d'être*, the magnet or justification for the congregation's socialization.[70]
Could a prototheistic Life Urge provide such a magnet?

Why not? As described in the previous chapter both Unitarian and
Quaker churches with their emphasis on individuals' consciousness of
'life' or the 'inner light' are just one step away from recognizing it as their
Life Urge, although I acknowledge for some that would be a very big step.
Then too there are undoubtedly clergy whose faith may have been waning
for years but who saw no alternative until now; who feel trapped by the
decision made in their youth to follow a vocation which has lost its vitality and meaning, but who have seen no way out, indeed see no other way
of even earning a living. They might find the courage to lead their congregation to a new understanding of 'spirituality' and 'faith'.[71] But what
about mass and the Eucharist—if Jesus wasn't divine isn't a Catholic
priest's daily ritual since ordination pointless? The mass ritually reenacts
Jesus' Last Supper or Passover meal, which early Christians informally
reenacted in their homes; only later the orthodox leaders formalized it into
the Eucharistic mass. An intrepid priest might forget about the divinity
and concentrate on the humanity[72] by returning the practice to a communal service wherein Jesus used the sharing of bread and wine as a metaphor for the oneness of his group. An alternative to reforming established
churches is to form new ones. Either way there probably should be a body
to certify a prototheistic leader's authenticity and to discredit incompe-
tents—a credentialing organization as have most professions.

Still what many want their church to offer as the core of its religious
practice—aside from the above ancillary functions—is 'magic and mystery', the mystique they identify with religion. The need perhaps goes far
back into our species' past when our early ancestors danced around a blazing fire to the rhythm of crude drums, or crawled deep into a cave to encounter torch-lit beasts drawn on the walls and ceiling. Or filed into a cathe-

dral to the toll of the steeple's bells and the roll of the organ, into the dim haze of the morning light through the stained-glass to gaze high up the columns to the scenes of heaven painted on the arched ceilings. That was mystery and magic. Their descendants now don't want reason to dispel the mystique. They want something to engage their unconscious, to stir their liminal imagination. Is it the same sensations one gets from a 'spiritual' movie but sanctified as a religious experience? Some folks I know shop for just such a church. Should prototheist 'churches' consider incorporating into their service practices described in Chapter Ten on 'Religion'?

Work

Most men and now many women have/had to work to earn a living for themselves and their dependents. Rather than just put in our time to get paid, why not accomplish something more with work? If you can find a worthy occupation you might make it one of your missions in Life, a *raison d'être* and your quest. Some years ago the musical "The Man from La Mancha" about Cervantes' fictional Don Quixote had great appeal, especially the song "To Dream the Impossible Dream," suggesting that the desire for an all-consuming quest—regardless how farfetched—burns in many hearts. But one needn't go off the deep end as did Quixote, jousting with 'malevolent' windmills. True, it may be necessary at times to attack evil and greed, but I prefer a positive approach of building rather than tearing down, in the hope of outpacing or converting the negative influences into something more positive and productive.

There are many reasons for working than just to earn a living or some extra cash for whatever use. It's something to do, to keep busy, to get out of the house and for companionship. It's a way to gain some identity without which some feel empty, as well as prestige and career advancement. Some take pride in their work of serving society—police or fire protection, the military, medical or teaching. Others take pride in accomplishing something—building cars, houses or highways. Both hopefully advancing Life's trajectory in some way. But buried deep in a large organization it may be difficult to see how what we do relates to the whole, we're just cogs in the wheel, ciphers, 'worker bees'. So we find other more satisfying things to do—gossip, run the football pool or homework—or play office politics to advance our career. Participative management ostensibly overcomes alienation and builds team spirit by collectively drafting mission statements that relate each team's work to the whole organization. But some managers exploit it in an attempt to get more work out of the workers which backfires if the workers see through it. Moreover some workers don't care to see the big picture, they're more interested in their family or hobbies and only work to support them. In private firms profit sharing attempts to motivate workers—providing there's a profit.

But even in large hierarchical organizations it may be possible to use one's position to carry out one's own mission regardless whether management understands or even cares about it—a closet entrepreneur. Yet projects that several of us toiled at for years I've had scuttled, just as they were reaching fruition, by a new administration which didn't even bother to understand the project. Again, "A greedy man never knows What he's done." There's a danger in large organizations that people get promoted more for their longevity (the 'Peter Principle')[73] and/or career maneuverings[74] than for their competence in their position's mission. And the bosses who promote them got there the same way so they're unable to judge any other way—it's self perpetuating. Whereas in professional sports-teams and other performance based operations, managers are paid less than the players/performers; in most business firms just the opposite prevails—pay and prestige enforce the hierarchy. If the overall operation is successful or at least solvent, such employees can carry on for years until the moribund organization faces a challenge it's unable to respond to—then the whole structure can come down taking competent and incompetent people alike (often the competent go first). If one finds oneself in such an organization better early-on to search for a healthier situation elsewhere. As I observed earlier, 'Sometimes you have to chew-off your foot to get out of a trap'.

In organizations that truly practice participative management—regardless whether they call it that—employees are valued for their grasp of and contribution to the entity's mission, even for their ability to modify the mission when warranted. Such an organization is a supra-human organism attempting to bring out the best that's in every human in its ranks by allowing each as much personal initiative as practicable. Whether they collectively advance Life's evolution, though depends on their organization's mission, and that mission can be influenced by all enterprising employees, but most typically by top management and in planning/development units. Belief in the ultimate worth of the mission can infuse a religious zeal, an added dimension and energy to the firm's operations. The previous chapter gave a hint of how an organization might function as one of evolution's executors, though I barely scraped the surface on innovation and advancing Life's trajectory.

Work can be in the public or private sector, or something in between like a privately-owned public utility.[75] Until a couple centuries ago it was believed that the public interest could best be served by the public sector until Adam Smith published his *Wealth of Nations* in 1776 in a time of many small craftsmen and merchants, and before the industrial revolution.

He advocated that free enterprise and the profit motive fostered competition among entrepreneurs which—as through an 'invisible hand'—raised the general standard of living. But abuses of the industrial revolution prompted a reversal to public control in socialist and communist countries that ended in failure only in the last decade or so. What seems to work is a 'light rein'—regulations to prevent exploitive monopolies and collusion, but otherwise free enterprise to encourage entrepreneurs to do their best, in some ways akin to participative management. Free trade is spreading worldwide.

In our society free enterprise is an extension of the individual freedoms we cherish. But why is it extended to a fictitious corporate entity not a real person much less a natural citizen in itself, even though that corporation is owned by and composed of citizens, whether US or foreign? It's not simply to shelter its owners by limiting their liability to their investments. True, it encourages investment in anticipation of substantial returns—by accomplishing some dream, by appreciation and/or by profits—those are the investors' motivations. However society's motivation in allowing such fictitious entities is to benefit society by encouraging innovative risk-taking, rallying suppliers to optimize the value to consumers of their materials and services. Profit is society's reward to suppliers for supplying value (profit being the difference between the price consumers are willing to pay and the suppliers' costs).

Value ' ... is in the eyes of the beholder', the consumer, who not only must distinguish true-value from pseudo-value—*caveat emptor*—but must decide whether what they're exchanging their hard work for is worthwhile, as described above in the section on 'Money'. Also recall from earlier chapters how evolution works in economics—just as mutations present alternatives to their environment from which their environment selects which will survive, suppliers present alternatives to the consumers who by their combined purchases decide which products or services survive. So it's up to us collectively to influence what suppliers supply—thus we get the products and service we deserve. If we buy frivolous products, we encourage suppliers to produce frivolous products. Whereas if we buy products that support or advance Life's evolution, we encourage suppliers to invent and produce such products. I could go on about this, but that's enough for now.

Play

Recreation is intended to 're-create' strength and spirit. My own preferences in the last couple decades have been running, cross-country skiing and canoeing. (I'm not much of a sports-fan, except of the ones I practice—

sitting in the stands or in front of television watching others' performance doesn't re-create me. Although I appreciate their athletic abilities I just don't care who wins.) Before that it was mostly knocking about in nature with my young kids, recapturing my own childhood ways: "follow the children." (Early-on I tried golf but gave it up when I realized I had only a few years to enjoy my kids before they went off on their own, and also I developed an incorrigible slice.[76]) Physical activity with others builds rapport, whether it's athletics or a canoeing 'expedition'. A couple guys I ran with most mornings for years just weren't my type (a fundamentalist and an ultra-conservative) nor I theirs, yet we cut through that, came to esteem one another and value our companionship.

The compulsive feeling that we have to 'win' or improve our performance turns play into work.[77] Within limits it has health benefits but if overdone can nullify the benefit through constant injury or worse. Better to find a playful activity we enjoy that's convenient so we're motivated to do it regularly. Pleasant surroundings and/or companionship are also good inducements. I like running because it requires little equipment and it's right out my door either into the cemetery across the street or to the nearby park—just a couple miles seems to clean the 'sludge' out of my system. Weekday mornings before work I used to meet up with those two guys but even if they didn't show, it still got me out. Sunday mornings for years I'd drive to a parking lot where our running group gathered to start out promptly at 8am, then naturally separated into smaller groups for long runs in Bloomfield Hills and Cranbrook—a local treasure. The talk and frolic enhanced our activity, and afterward we'd meet for breakfast.

While we may not think of athletic games as 'institutions', competitive sports are a less violent outlet for a human trait than the alternative, the 'institution' of war which runs deep in our nature.[78] The sports-fans that get all pumped-up and go nuts when their team wins as if they themselves actually played in the game, must be responding to such primordial instincts. I suppose competition is sometimes necessary but it's overrated—cooperation always has been far more important. Yet offhand I can't think of any sports event that features cooperation between teams rather than competition.[79] Maybe we should find some and promote them, though it might be tough finding sponsors.

Retirement

Until early in the past century retirement was a luxury few could afford even if they were lucky enough to have lived to retirement age. Now with Social Security and pensions, along with longevity, it's the norm. Yet after all those years of working some folks have trouble making the transition, but I didn't. I bought a new Saturn 'wagon and traveled to visit my out-state kids, and to go canoeing and XCskiing. As I explained at the beginning of this book, I also wanted to study some topics yet didn't want to turn it into 'work'. Before long however I found that the casual approach wasn't getting the results I sought so I capitulated, outfitted a study in my home—my *sanctum sanctorum*—and 'went back to work'. In effect I launched into another career, but I still make some time for play.

Retirement can be a time of leisure and reminiscing. With reasonably good health we can be active but not like we were in our youth—gradually we'll slow down and/or contract some debilitating ailment. Yet that doesn't mean we can't still make some invaluable contribution to society.[80] True, our kids or grandkids may have to help us use new technology like computers, DVDs, cell-phones, and palm-pilots, but we have something they won't have for years—we have judgment and wisdom; in short each of us could be a sage.[81] [Obviously I'm addressing older readers.]

As mentioned earlier, preliterate societies valued their elderly as sages, as repositories of information and knowledge—memory banks. Today we store far more information in libraries and computers than hundreds of sages could keep in their heads—we're in the information age. But who has time to read and assimilate very much of it? Certainly busy working parents don't, but we retirees do. Moreover information isn't knowledge or understanding—it takes judgment and wisdom to sort out what's valid and applicable to our kith, kin and community. We retirees have the leisure to study broad subjects, have years of experience to put that information in perspective and the judgment to make the connections. Thus as an 'old geezer' we can once again be an asset to society if we've cultivated an open and active mind. Obviously you have since you're reading this—so you're a sage. Now if only other folks knew and appreciated it ...

Being a sage doesn't automatically confer recognition as one—there's no certificate we can hang on our wall nor can we hang out our shingle with office hours when we're available to dispense our wisdom. Moreover there are professional sages—pundits we're competing with—expounding on TV and in newspapers, magazines and newsletters, and now on the Internet. What chance does an amateur sage stand? Not much with a national audience, so start small, like with oneself. We've all said "If I knew then what I know now ..." Well, we can't change the past but maybe we can change the future a little by being a little wiser at least a little more of the time. And even if no one else knows it, at least we can feel a little wiser in our own private observations, in our understanding of what's really going on, seeing through the 'good reasons' into the 'real reasons'. And maybe some of it will show and maybe some of our friends or relatives will ask and even listen. Than again maybe not. Yet every once in a while opportunities will arise extemporaneously. (In offering advice I find it's best not to say what they should do, but tentatively what I *think* I'd do.) Don't preach or lose our sense of humor—"Many a truth is spoken in jest."

Than again, maybe we *should* be a little crotchety—in old age we can get away with being somewhat outspoken, if we don't overdo it. I find I can strike up casual conversations with strangers, and at my age they're usually not threatened and will respond. We each need to find our own style—try different approaches and see what works—we probably need a variety of approaches for different situations. The important thing is to speak up—there're things that need to be said that too often we don't because they're impolite or 'politically incorrect'. And we may not have to say much—a few choice words, or sometimes just a glance, can create cognitive dissonance in our audience that might germinate over time. But if nobody ever says anything, not much will change. Younger society may think we're irrelevant and marginalize us anyway, so what've we got to lose? Look at it this way, we owe it to younger society to raise their awareness—somebody's got to do it! "If not us, who? If not now, when?" Make it our mission in old age. Like modern-day alchemists, we can turn our leaden years to gold.

Still there may be niches aging specialists might carve out. Throughout this long tome I've harped on advancing Life's trajectory, being evolution's 'eyes'. Maybe each of us should mount a mental retrospective of our specialty and consider what might have been done differently that would have better advanced Life's trajectory. Then armed with that insight consider how that vision might be applied in the future. What you do with that vision depends on your talents and contacts. If you still have contacts with you old place of employment, maybe you could meet with younger colleagues and gently introduce your ideas—say over lunch as a start—to see if your ideas find fertile ground. Or if you're still active in your profession, you might draft a paper to present at a meeting and/or to publish in their journal. The Internet may provide an avenue so pilgrims and neophytes come to your website instead of to your sage's cave or tepee. You get the idea. From being a specialist you become a generalist in your field, a sage in the niche you carve out, 'eyes' for evolution in your specialty.

Government

Belief in God seems to pervade our nation's culture and society. Nonetheless in the late 1700s our Founding Fathers,[82] having recently experienced the tyranny of imposed beliefs and the sordid history of state religions, made separation of church and state a cornerstone of our system of government. Even so, today some of the righteous faithful regularly need to be reminded that 'freedom of religion' applies not just to them but to all of us including the non-religious.[83] (Recall how in recent memory we discovered that the vociferous 'moral majority' was neither?) Many of the non-religious and semi-religious, it seems, have been intimidated into acquiescence or silence by the theistic hegemony. For example over a century and half after the 'separation of church and state,' with little dissent Congress in 1954 inserted "... under God ..." into our Pledge to the Flag and in 1955 ordered inscribing "In God We Trust"[84] (replacing *e pluribus unum*) on our currency.[85] Was this the righteous faithful managing to insinuate their beliefs into our nation's fabric— just good old American aggressive 'marketing' by those in the religion 'business'? This was a time when any who might have been opposed risked condemnation and even reprisal, the very thing our Founding Fathers sought to avoid. The McCarthy era had just ended and we were pitted in the Cold War with the atheistic Soviet block in a struggle to preserve freedom; we needed all the help we could invoke. That was then, but what about now?

Our system of government is based on the democratic ideals encapsulated in our Declaration of Independence's second paragraph's first two sentences—"... that all men are created equal ... endowed ... with certain unalienable rights ... [including] life, liberty and the pursuit of happiness. That to secure these rights, governments are instituted among men, deriving their just powers from the consent of the governed ..."[86] (The issue of "... endowed by their Creator ..." is discussed in the note 82 to 'Founding Fathers' above.) Democracy (*demos* = 'common people' and —*cracy* ≈ 'power' in Greek) it seems to me, implicitly affirms that the Life Urge emerges and begets consciousness in each human being. Further it implies that each person has the right to be free to express their Life Urge as they choose.

This is consistent with what we know of our early ancestors' temperament. They evolved in the wild as nomadic hunter-gatherers, prized their individual freedom and lived in small troops which were egalitarian (at least among adult males) as mentioned early in this chapter. Not until the agrarian revolution did they adapt the family model—with its dominant head—to their society, only ten-millennia ago. For the first three-thousand-millennia of our evolution we were free and egalitarian, and for the past quarter-millennium we've been trying to recapture that form, adapted to a greatly expanded and interlinked society. We easily forget how innovative, how experimental and how rare such democracy was and still is—we take it for granted.

The catch is that in a democracy most citizens must be responsible and in order to be responsible one must be knowledgeable, presumably through education. Hence compulsory education is imposed in the hope that by the time a young person's old enough to vote, they'll be knowledgeable enough. Until 1965 literacy tests were common.

Our system of government is called a democracy but it's not a 'pure democracy', it's really a republic in that we don't vote on every single issue but rather we elect representatives at the various levels of government to identify issues, investigate and debate them, and arrive at solutions. Do we want representatives who simply do our bidding, who vote on issues the way we would if we sat on that legislative body? Or do we want representatives who can do better than we could, who have the time, sagacity and statesmanship to govern, who are not just followers but leaders? Some special interest groups prefer the former. Corporations, unions, associations and such can't vote at the polls but rather 'vote' with their membership bloc and with their dollars. And because of the high cost of campaigning, their dollars can influence citizens' votes through TV commercials, ads and campaign literature, and if successful put that politician virtually in their pocket. The wise citizen shouldn't be duped by TV sound bites and politicians' pandering, but rather identify and support candidates who come closest to the latter type of representative—a daunting task with all the hype that's thrown at us, like trying to drink from a firehose. Hopefully the Internet[87] is beginning to play a greater rôle in choosing candidates and thus diminishing TV's influence and the attendant inordinate campaign expenses.[88] It's been said 'We get the politicians we deserve' meaning if we vote for facile candidates or don't vote, we elect shallow, hypocritical politicians; whereas if enough of us choose wisely, we elect statesmen.

An issue I've alluded to several times already is the rights we grant fictitious supra-human organisms such as business corporations. The US Declaration of Independence posited "... that all men ... are endowed ... with certain unalienable rights [including] life, liberty, and the pursuit of happiness." How is it that we've come to accept that these corporate fictitious entities 'are endowed with the unalienable rights of virtual life, extensive liberty, and the pursuit of profits'? Because a corporation's human members individually have these rights, does it follow that they jointly have these rights if they're subsumed for a time into a supra-human organism? I certainly agree there are benefits but in exchange some of these corporations trample our rights—what are we giving up for what we get? A supra-human organism is not truly alive, rather the humans who constitute it are and they determine whether their corporation contributes to Life's evolution—whether it's an agent of synergy or entropy, evolution or devolution. Humans *are* responsible, and must be *held* responsible for their corporate actions, and not just to the limit of their investment. If I knowingly loan a malicious person a lethal weapon and they use it, I'm culpable and not just subject to the loss of my weapon but as an accomplice. Similarly if I knowingly put my money into a malicious corporation, shouldn't I also be culpable, and not just subject only to the loss of my investment?

Back to the of separation of church and state. Philanthropic, educational and religious organizations are indirectly subsidized by taxes in at least four ways. In Michigan and I assume most states, churches and other religious properties are exempt from paying city property tax most of which goes for police and fire protection extended indiscriminately to all properties in the city. If a church has a break-in or needs police to direct funeral traffic or has a fire, they get the protection but don't pay for it. Because they're not bearing their share of the costs of these services, the other non-exempt properties must pay a disproportionate higher share, in effect paying the religious share—subsidizing religion. Secondly religious organizations as non-profits don't pay federal or state income taxes yet receive the same benefits as the rest of us without paying for them, so effectively we're paying their share—subsidizing religion. Thirdly clergy can deduct from their taxable income the portion of their salary that covers housing cost—the 'parsonage exemption'.[89] Fourthly contributions to religious entities are tax exempt so some of what that taxpayer would otherwise pay to the government instead goes to subsidize religion. Even though separation of church and state is a cornerstone of our government, these indirect subsidies may persist on the notion that religion benefits all society by promoting ethical behavior and social values—Constantine's and the Medieval church's conviction enduring even today. As discussed above under 'Ethics & Values' that's a dubious premise, but it may be the 'good reason' used to condone these subsidies, though the 'real reason' may be the theistic hegemony's unconstitutional promotion of religion.

Global Perspectives

Ideally prototheism would encourage people worldwide to venerate the Life Urge in all living things. In people of different beliefs, traditions and ethnicity, not just tolerate the differences (or worse, hate them) but delight in their varied cultures and ways of expressing their idiosyncratic

Life Urge. In other animals and plants, respect their right to Life even though sometimes taking it for a higher calling. Thus prototheism should promote peace, and environmental awareness and responsibility, lessen the drive to exploit peoples and resources, and instead seek viable ways of facilitating and nurturing their Life Urge.

While North America and Europe may be ripe for a paradigm shift toward prototheism, there are convincing arguments that much of the southern hemisphere—Latin America, Africa and even Asia—is retro-gressing toward a Christianity more akin to the early church: pentecostal, evangelical and conservative, dubbed 'jungle religion'.[90] It seems to me this may be a 'good-news/bad-news' predicament. The good news is they're more in touch with the numinous aspects of religion. The bad news is they're being led to believe it emanates from outside themselves—God, Jesus, Mary and saints—not from the depths of their being. How to head-off such a calamity? Well, I also understand that these emerging economies will bypass some phases of our technology—for example rather than wire-up the entire countryside for telephones, they'll leapfrog directly to wire-less communication between low-cost devices and antennas or satellites.[91] So perhaps we could reach the more progressive younger-generation via the Internet—the 'global village'. But to be creditable we need to 'practice what we preach'—the shallowness and consumerism we currently export via American movies and franchises contradict the prototheistic mes-sage—conspicuous consumption needs to be turned from a trendy ideal to a stigma.

The global economy is led by multinational corporations whose pri-mary allegiance is to their stockholders, but those too may be faceless fi-nancial entities—pension-funds, mutual-funds, trust-funds, insurance companies and the like. If they're speculators trying to 'beat the market' there's little hope of recruiting them. However most are longer-term in-vestors desiring appreciation of their funds of course, but more concerned that the money is there when they need it. Certainly advancing Life's tra-jectory will advance the free-market global economy in the long-run but that may be longer than those entities' 'long-term'. Another avenue is cor-porate image—most of these entities need to be perceived as beneficent by their constituents and by the nations they operate in. Protesters at World Trade Organization meetings have raised heretofore disregarded broader concerns than just profitability yet some of the WTO pronouncements may only pay lip service. So prototheism needs to get Life's progress on the WTO's and others' agendas.[92]

Giant multinational corporations traditionally aren't innovators pre-ferring to let others do the spadework, then move in to take over through acquisition, overwhelming capital infusions or dumping in emerging markets. Therefore the giants can be led by gutsy innovative entrepreneurs. If prototheistic entrepreneurs are not just motivated by profit but also by Life's progress and are willing to risk pioneering ('pioneers get all the arrows') they can induce the giant multinationals to follow suit. Such entrepreneurs need the daring-do of explorers and the zeal of missionaries, but they also need the support of investors who share their vision—armchair entrepreneurs.

Democratizing

Human institutions are like interlinked nested organisms. In our passages through Life we join, then leave these institutions. We start out naturally in a family, then gradually broaden our involvements with other kids in our neighborhood and schools, then into educational and work institutions, into marriage with our own family, and with communities and governments. We're continuously negotiating the tension between our primordial instinct to be independent and our need to participate in ever expanded groups. We evolved as free egalitarian hunter-gatherers, then surrendered much of that when the agrarian revolution adapted the family model of ever enlarging hierarchical organizations subjugating most humans as slaves or at best in hereditary trades, 'worker bees' in their respective organisms. Now we're trying to recover that free egalitarian model—somehow evolved into democratic institutions—in our workplaces and governments.

What comes to mind is an analogy of living cells' evolution. Single cells were first free, then were joined with others in multicell organisms where stem-cells differentiated irreversibly into dedicated somatic-cells, as part of some organ in the body of a larger organism. Humans have been somewhat like stem-cells giving up their freedom to join ever larger groups, becoming part of some unit in an organization that functions as a supra-human organism. Now we're trying to revert to be like those stem-cells, or rather more like reversible stem-cells that can dedicate ourselves to one function for a while, then to another or several others as and when we choose in our passages through Life.

The hierarchical family model was reinforced by the Church with God the Father in Heaven, the Pope (= *papa* in Latin) as absolute spiritual authority on Earth, a pastor as 'father' in each parish and finally paterfamilias as head of each family. The Protestant Reformation challenged that model and the Enlightenment's Deism challenged the omnipresents of God, relegating Him to an absentee 'first cause' or designer. Pre-agrarian hunter-gathers and aboriginal farmers (= pagans from Latin *paganus* ≈ peasant) believed their gods were all around them everywhere and that gods were mostly anarchists. Greco-Roman polytheism was traded for Judeo-Christian monotheism by Constantine the Great—largely for political reasons—which prevailed ever since.

But it's time to move on and fully democratize our institutions in order to empower them with the best each member has to offer by enabling each member to realize their Life Urge's full potential. Just as in Constantine's day anarchical polytheism was inconsistent with the Empire's hierarchical government, today hierarchical monotheism is inconsistent with democratic governments and organizations. As I've argued throughout this tome, in order to change mind-sets from 'top-down' to 'bottom-up' thinking, we need to forsake monotheism and convert to prototheism emphasizing both individual freedom and responsibility. Our supra-human organisms can then become fully and truly democratic.

Yet there are those who contend that democracy too will be replaced—as the majority become instantaneously interconnected via the internet—with what they call 'plurarchy' which "... in its purest form is a system in which every individual player decides over him or herself, but lacks the ability and opportunity to decide over any of the other players. The fundamental notion of democracy, whereby the majority decides over the minority when differences of opinion occur, is therefore impossible to maintain."[93] Alternatively democracy's 'oppression by the majority' could be minimalized if we respect and guard individual rights as much as possible and not just tolerate but exalt in our differences.

Propagating ProtoTheism

I don't know if you're convinced yet of the logic and value of prototheism, but I can only assume you're still with me and wrap it up. But first in case there's any lingering confusion about the distinction between prototheism and the Life Urge, I'll repeat what was said at the outset. Prototheism itself is not a religion but is a science—a science of religion that asks, Where does religion come from? If not from 'out there' than what is it 'in here' that's misconstrued as gods/God? My hunch is that it's our own Life Urge which is the *sine qua non* of all Life and which emerges spontaneously in all Life. That thesis is developed extensively throughout the book. Then if what's worshiped as 'God' is in fact our own Life Urge, could our 'Life Urge' be the basis of a new or revised religion? If so that religion might be called 'Life Urge' (or some such name) and the science called prototheism. But I suppose it's unavoidable that the science and the religion overlap and be conflated, particularly when individual scientists, professional and amateur, explore and analyze their own 'religious' experiences.

Still sciences have well established methods of propagation—presentations and peer-reviewed publications, collaboration among scientists with similar interests including seminars, research grants to explore and test ideas, professorships and college courses, textbooks and popular books like this one, and so forth. Whereas formal religions establish inflexible doctrines, science is a work in progress inviting challenges and change (not without contention).[94] Hopefully prototheism will grow from an idea into a mature and reputable science.

Therefore as a science prototheism should also ask, Besides the Life Urge, what alternative prototheistic basis might there be for belief in gods/God? An answer from a century ago would be Bergson's *élan vital* infused by God. Some don't see that it makes much difference which one is the prototheistic basis. But as I see it there's a crucial difference whether it's "our Father Who art in Heaven" working *through* us or it's our individual Life Urge working *in* us as evolution's 'eyes'. Who's in charge, who's responsible? If it's God with us as His sometimes agents, maybe we can sometimes duck responsibility. But if it's we, than we're now responsible for evolution's trajectory with our runaway material 'progress', for better or for worse.

Yet either way it's not my intent to make up a new religion. It's not a task I'd want to take on, nor should I. But somebody's got to do it. Who? Theism may have been the only recourse until the last few centuries, but now it's not only obsolescent but irresponsible, I think. Still I don't believe it's my prerogative, much less responsibility to make up a new religion. Rather I want to provide a prototheistic framework and to prompt others to think about revising their religions or making up new ones. If I truly believe that 'religion' flowers in each person, then each person is responsible for their own religion, and not I nor some dead prophet's revelation—not a hierarchical religion but a democratic (small 'd') religion—consistent with today's democratizing society worldwide. How might we get from here to there?

As explained in Chapter Ten, I believe 'religion' is each person getting more connected with their own Life Urge in whatever ways work best for them, and then expressing their Life Urge in whatever ways they're inspired to and capable of, both individually and in concert with others, as explained in Chapters Eleven and this. Still while each of us is responsible *for* ourselves, rarely can we achieve such objectives *by* ourselves alone. We not only need companions—fellow travelers—but probably teachers, guides, tutors, coaches or whatever.

So let's consider a fanciful scenario. Recall from Chapter Three how Christianity was just another upstart religion until Constantine adopted and adapted it, and converted the whole Roman Empire from paganism to Christianity. Might a modern-day Constantine II[95] somehow lead the conversion of Christianity to a prototheistic religion? Where might such a leader come from? Well, most of us never heard of Angelo Giuseppe Roncalli, a seventy-seven year-old minor cardinal of peasant stock, until he was elected as interim Pope, took the name John XXIII and launched his *aggiornamento*—which later was scuttled by the Curia and Pope JohnPaul II.[96] Might such a dark-horse be elected Pope by an insurgent majority of Cardinals or would he have to stage a brilliant political coup not unlike Constantine's shrewd military coup? Such a Pope Constantine II would then reinterpret Jesus and might proclaim that God works through the Life Urge propelling evolution (which I don't quite buy, but it's a good start—the 'camel's nose').[97] To emphasize the paradigm shift he might canonize Copernicus, Bruno and Galileo as pioneers in man's search to understand nature. And the sycophants would climb aboard just as they did with Constantine I. You get the drift. It'll never happen but it'd make a good novel.[98]

An alternative scenario might be patterned on the Reformation when leaders such as Luther—who *protest*ed against the Roman Church's practices—started their own religions collectively called *Protest*ants. Then the Roman Church launched its own reforms called the Counter-Reformation. A vigorous prototheist movement might induce Rome to resurrect changes John XXIII began, *Aggiornamento II*, perhaps even going as far as suggested in the previous paragraph. Sometimes it takes a crisis, an 'enemy at the gates' to induce change.[99] If you're apprehensive about revolutionizing the Church, take heart—that's what Buddha, Jesus and Luther did with their respective 'churches'.

Now that I've gotten that off my chest, let's get real. Rather than look for the coming of one or even several charismatic figures to lead us—a messiah, Christ-figure or *führer*—why not all be leaders, change agents in our own small or big ways?—ordinary folks who've internalized an understanding of Life's trajectory and not only apply it in their own lives, but can step forward to intervene when needed to overcome 'entropy'—ordinary folks who've become extraordinary. This is more consistent with the democratic ideals espoused above—bottom-up rather than top-down. In earlier times with limited literacy, charismatic leaders could rouse the masses. Just in the past century Hitler's Nazis burned books and controlled the media with their propaganda[100]—more recently Chinese[101] and Islamic[102] leaders have done much the same. The best protection against such totalitarian leaders is the free exchange of information and knowledge. We grumble about the theistic hegemony but as long as we safeguard our nation's democratic ideals, they can't succeed in curtailing religious freedom. We're now in the information age—we must learn to better use it, and speak-up and stand-up for what we believe.

But are there models for change we might emulate? Atheism has been around for millennia and atheists have made many important contributions perhaps because they see the world differently with open minds. But it hasn't caught on possibly because *a*theism's message is negative ('a-'=not/without)—they're against religion without providing a replacement—so organized atheism has relatively few acknowledged followers (although I suspect there are many 'closet' atheists[103]). Another persuasion that's likely existed since before humans and whose adherents also have made important contributions because they too see the world differently, but that's lately coming out into the open, is homosexuality.[104] (Interestingly until just a few centuries ago atheists were burned-at-the-stake as heretics, with homosexuals purportedly thrown onto the fire as fagots.[105]) Perhaps there are lessons to be learned from the Gay Rights Movement.[106] Like atheists, gays asserted their right to not be harassed but gays also assert a positive right to practice their belief. By definition atheists don't have a positive belief to practice, they're basically just against religion, though many embrace Humanism mentioned in a previous chapter. While my idea of a prototheistic religion also doesn't believe in a God 'out there', it does have a positive belief in a Life Urge 'in here'. Since there are similarities should prototheism employ some of the gays' tactics?

I'm not comfortable with, much less in favor of some of the gays' 'in-your-face' confrontations, marches, demonstrations and what have you. (That's how some early Christians got themselves killed!) Some gays seem insensitive to, even provoke, the strong homophobic feelings that can erupt into blind rage which have resulted in assaults, even assassinations. Prototheism also risks evoking strong feelings of fear which are expressed as anger and rage. It's akin to the Copernican revolution when people were told that the Earth wasn't solid ground beneath their feet but was a huge ball somehow floating in space, as described near the ends of Chapters Two and Four. We're telling them there's no "Father in Heaven"—think of the reaction of a small kid when their mother leaves them in childcare, except these are adults. So rather than 'in-your-face' confrontations, why not show compassion for their distress—leave them their beliefs if that's what they truly want. We're not imposing our beliefs (well, maybe tweaking with a little cognitive dissonance), though certainly not accepting theirs. Agree to disagree—tolerance—that's what freedom of religion's all about. Instead, address those folks who already question theism.

There's another prospect besides converting dubious theists and agnostics to prototheism—from acquiescing to or skepticism of a God 'out there' to embracing their own Life Urge 'in here'. There's also the prospect of conversions in the opposite direction, namely of converting atheists to prototheists—from a denial of a God 'out there' to the recognition that what's called 'God' might be the Life Urge 'in here'. As I've commented already, some atheists understandably seem prickly, guarding their seemingly lonely independence. Perhaps such atheists might 'come in from the cold'—not as gushy theists would have it to the 'loving arms' of Jesus or 'the Father'—but to the warmth of their own Life Urge glowing deep inside themselves and in kindred humans. I'm sure some atheists implicitly know all this—why not make it explicit?

Probably because of my long involvement with corporate development, an important way I see of propagating prototheism is to help entrepreneurs and executives understand how they're affecting the trajectory of Life's evolution. Does their business promote or demote Life?[107] Prototheism could be taught in business schools producing graduates who'd seek out progressive employers searching for Life-promoting ventures. Some of those graduates might some day launch their own ventures. Financial advisors, mutual funds and venture capitalists might specialize in such evolutionary endeavors. Consulting firms could become competent in, and advise their clients on ways of promoting Life's evolutionary trajectory.[108] A prototheist perspective might even prompt them to identify growth opportunities which otherwise might not occur to them. They needn't necessarily sacrifice profit—the fast-growth phase of a product's life-cycle often allows a high margin to at least partially recover development and start-up costs. So in addition to the intangible benefits as executors of Life's evolution, they may reap the more socially acceptable monetary rewards. Still the sad truth is that many new ventures fail which is socially unacceptable. Yet a failure may provide a stepping stone for a subsequent success.[109] Sage entrepreneurs know and appreciate this, even though not the naïve with their 'sports-fan' mentality. Perhaps a professional society could be formed, a network of men and women, both working and retired, who embrace the ideals of advancing the trajectory of Life's evolution and can constrain their competitive juices enough to support one another, especially their novice members.

But in order for business-types, politicians and others to begin considering becoming deliberate executors of Life's evolution, first we need to heighten awareness of the Life Urge and evolution's trajectory. I say 'heighten awareness' because I believe we're fundamentally aware of our Life Urge but have been misreading it, as explained *ad nauseam*. This book of course is a start targeted at science-minded skeptics. Hopefully short articles will be published addressing various other audiences, and maybe collaborations both on more technical and on popular versions of this book, and on a novel as mentioned above and on children's books as mentioned in Chapter Ten. I envision a few demographics that find time to read: Some college faculty might see this book as below their academic standards but nonetheless their students might take a course in prototheism if it's offered by venturesome faculty. Progressive clergy might not only read some of my stuff but introduce it to their congregations (hopefully in a positive manner) which might intrigue some to pursue it further. And some autodidactic retirees might not only study prototheism but lead discussion groups and forums, and even join groups of retirees to press onward. Then there's television and radio hopefully for interviews and maybe an edutainment documentary. And just as two millennia ago the system of Roman roads provided a medium for the spread of Christianity, today the Internet provides a medium for the spread of prototheism. We'll see. "We are the stuff As dreams are made on."[110]

Finally, the end. Or hopefully the beginning. Leading this faltering 'expedition' up the 'mountain' of knowledge we humans are amassing, I've learned a great deal and immensely enjoyed it as I hope you have. Through this long essay I've tried to give you my insights gleaned from digging into how our world came to be and thoughts about where it might be going. Now you can use my spadework to research and arrive at your own conclusions. Of course I believe these concepts are preferable to the explanations upheld by Christianity. Yet I acknowledge that my ideas may be off in some ways and flaws may be exposed as knowledge advances. Nonetheless it's the best I can offer at this time; it's my take on it, my perspective from the heights we've climbed. In order to earn the right to criticize, I feel I'm obliged to suggest alternatives that remedy what I'm criticizing (though not always, as you've seen). So these are my suggestions. If you don't buy mine, than what do you suggest? In either case, we all need to work both individually and jointly to find better ways, then each do what we can to improve our own corner of the world. In these last chapters I've suggested a few ways I see of advancing Life's trajectory as examples intended to stimulate your thinking about ways of your own. Naturally we must each find our own way, what we each can do best.

So shall we proceed? "Far better to light one candle than forever curse the darkness."[111] (See blank pages at end of book.)

Appendix A

Protestant &
Eastern Christians

Are there issues that warrant a separate appendix for Protestant and Eastern Christian? Obviously you're reading such an appendix, but mostly because the question needs to be addressed. The main body of the text speaks directly to readers with a Catholic heritage (because I'm who's speaking and that's my heritage) but the sub-subtitle addresses "... other Christians ..." As cited in Chapter Three, from the start of Christianity there were differing interpretations and sects which under Constantine were amalgamated into an orthodox doctrine. Even so, there continued to be different interpretations which the orthodox deemed to be heresies and attempted to suppress, often violently.

Constantine had moved the Roman Empire's capital from Rome to Byzantium in 330 which he renamed Constantinople (now Istanbul). Still, even after the fall of Rome in 476 the consecutive bishops of Rome claimed primacy based on their tenuous direct succession from Peter "the rock, upon which Christ founded His church." The final schism didn't come until 1054. Meanwhile the Roman-Byzantine Empire endured cycles of expansion/contraction and prosperity/decline for over a millennium. Even after the Turks finally conquered Constantinople in 1453, its patriarch was recognized as the religious and political spokesman for Christians throughout the Ottoman Empire. But as the Turks lost control, the local patriarchs reasserted primacy over their locales with Constantinople's patriarch first among equals, unlike Rome's pope.

Today Eastern Christians include Eastern Rite Churches affiliated with Rome (Armenian, Ukrainian, Chaldean ...) and Orthodox (Greek, Russian ...). In both, priest may be married (not patriarchs) and rites are generally in the local language, but Orthodox Christians deny the Pope's primacy and infallibility. Still in all, the faithful are theists believing in God 'out there' along with Mother Mary, the saints, angels and devils.[1] But there certainly are skeptics, notably the late Nikos Kazantzakis and his fictional Zorba the Greek.

The rise of Protestantism is also blamed on the Roman Church's corruption, arrogance and intransigence. Luther didn't set out in 1517 to break with the Church and start a new religion but only to reform his beloved Catholic Church.[2] However his success had as much to do with literacy, the printing press and paper as it did with him, just as today's protesters benefit from TV coverage. Moreover the German barons welcomed a rationalization to curtail the flow of funds to Rome so here too political expediency was a contributing factor. After Luther came Calvin, the Anabaptists and Anglicans, and many others fomenting bloody conflicts and wars until the Peace of Westphalia in 1648.[3] Most all Protestants were theists then, even the Deists and many Unitarians, as are today's Protestants—although I suspect there are more skeptics among them than recognized.

Even though I've already written a page-and-half of this appendix, it seems to me very little adjustment is required to transpose the text's Catholic perspective to a Protestant or Eastern Christian perspective.

Appendix B

Prototheism for Skeptical Jews

As emphasized at the outset, this book is not addressed to fundamentalists, neither Christian nor Jewish.[1] This second Appendix is addressed to disenchanted, estranged or disaffiliated Jews who no longer can, or never could accept the Jewish religious beliefs but still are more or less connected with Jewish society and culture while immersed in the secular world. Most of what was said in the book's main body applies to any religious background except for instance where the Catholic Church's practices are discussed. This Appendix attempts to initiate a transposition of the Catholic/ Christian experience to the Jewish experience. I won't pretend to have a visceral understanding of the Jewish experience—that's not my heritage— but I'll do my best to relate what I've learned of Judaism to the ideas put forth in this book.

Judaism has a long history of dissidence—indeed the earliest Christians were Jewish—but to my knowledge all were theists. Not until Spinoza in the 1600s and the beginning of the Enlightenment did an earnest skeptical tradition emerge.[2] Today that skepticism is intensified by our ever-increasing knowledge thus casting doubt, even ridicule on biblical explanations. And at the same time, unlike the climate in Spinoza's day, today skepticism is permitted, indeed in places encouraged in our free society. This is not to say that it's easy—"We live with the power of entrenched religious establishments that confer respectability upon those who join churches and synagogues and say they believe in God."[3] Nonbelievers are put on the defensive about what they *don't* believe, but needn't be if they're clear about what they *do* believe.[4] Yet is there a germ of truth in Jewish tradition? Just as the founding Christians, I suspect, misinterpreted the revelations (read intuitions) that emerged into their consciousness, did Jewish prophets also misinterpret their intuitions? Worse still, were those intuitions intentionally misconstrued and embellished to support political ends?

Chapter Three describes the Jewish situation at the time of Jesus when Christianity germinated. But of course Jewish history began long before, as recounted in what Christians broadly call the Old Testament and Jews call the Books of the Hebrew Bible.[5] However, just as the Christians' New Testament in recent years has been subjected to much scrutiny, as described in Chapter Three, so has the Hebrew Bible. Political expediency played a hand in both. The following sketch is based primarily on Finkelstein & Silberman cited in the Bibliography.

There's now compelling evidence that "... much of the biblical narrative is a product of the hopes, fears, and ambitions of the kingdom of Judah, culminating in the reign of King Josiah at the end of the seventh century BCE. ... the historical core of the Bible arose from clear political, social, and spiritual conditions and was shaped by the creativity and vision of extraordinary women and men. Much of what is commonly taken for granted as accurate history—the stories of the patriarchs, the Exodus, the conquest of Canaan, and even the saga of the glorious united monarchy of David and Solomon—are, rather, the creative expressions of a powerful religious reform movement that flourished in the kingdom of Judah in the Late Iron Age. Although these stories may have been based on certain historical kernels, they primarily reflect the ideology and the worldview of the writers. ... the narrative of the Bible was uniquely suited to further the religious reform and territorial ambitions of Judah during the momentous concluding decades of the seventh century BCE."[6]

For example "... in the story of Joseph's sale by his brothers into slavery (Genesis 37:25), camels are ... described as beasts of burden used in caravan trade. We now know ... that camels ... were not widely use in that capacity ... until well after 1000 BCE."[7] While the Bible identifies locations in northeastern Egypt where the Israelites allegedly worked in captivity, the detailed and comprehensive Egyptian records have no mention of Israelites much less of their mass escape.[8] "Sites mentioned in the Exodus narrative ... were unoccupied precisely at the time they reportedly played a role in the events of the wandering of the children of Israel in the wilderness."[9] The story that "... the Israelites followed the command of God as conveyed to them by Joshua, marching solemnly around the high walls of the city, and on the seventh day, with a deafening blast of the Israelites' war trumpets, the walls of Jericho came tumbling down ... there were no walls that could have come tumbling down" then.[10] As for "... the grandeur of David's city and of Solomon's Temple" in spite of intensive and extensive excavations and searching, archaeologist can't find them, and instead believe that the Bible describes cities such as Samaria to the north in prosperous Israel, the envy of Judah.[11] And so on. Great literature, poor history.

What's amazing is that these stories have sustained the Jewish people for nearly three millennia, if not more. In addition they provided a foundation for both Christianity and Islam.[12] Some say it speaks for the power of God but I think it speaks for *The Power of Myth*[13] if well-crafted, as those creative writers produced in late seventh century BC Judah. Moreover it seems to me, it attests to the power of the Life Urge, albeit misinterpreted and projected out onto 'the one God in Heaven' (Judaism, Christianity and Islam are all nominally monotheistic). Certainly there were other factors[14] such as the need for a parent-figure—even though imaginary—who would look after them (if they kept the Covenant) and to whom they felt they could turn when all else failed. Still I would attribute their 'faith' in God 'out there' to their disowned Urge to Life from deep in their own human nature which was exploited by the kings of Judah, as it has been many times since by their Jewish, Christian and Muslim successors.

Let's put this in synergistic complexity terms. The Life Urge may be acting as what might be called a 'pre-gestalt' in search of a percept or concept on which to form. The only percept/concept it's offered is of 'God' and so the Life Urge unbeknownst precipitates onto 'God', it emerges into consciousness as 'God' and is experienced as faith in God. To once again use the example of 'sunrise', if the only known concept of the Sun is as a flaming sphere coursing across the heavens, the concept of the Earth as rotating might never occur to us. What I'm advocating is that, just as we had to shift our paradigm or concept from a moving Sun to a moving Earth, we have to shift our concept from God 'out there' to our Life Urge 'in here'. The Life Urge should be felt and prompted to coalesce as a gestalt on one's Self, as described in Chapter Ten's 'Prototheism and Life Urge'. (Perhaps that's what the Kabbalah originally was about.[15])

With the Romans' destruction of the Second Temple in 70AD and devastating suppression of the Jewish revolt in 132–5, the priests were discredited and the rabbis emerged emphasizing communal and spiritual life. The rabbis taught that individual Jews could achieve salvation while awaiting God to bring about the messianic redemption of all Israel. Synagogues replaced the Temple. The diasporas, the rise of Islam, Maimonides, the expulsion from Spain, the Enlightenment, the Holocaust and Zionism all shaped modern Jews into Orthodox, Conservative, Reform and Reconstructionist denominations of Judaism—all monotheistic.[16] However

"The meaning of Jewish history, as it was conceived by the rabbis, presents many problems ... Supernatural guidance of natural events is not a credible idea ... there is no evidence that the experts of the present are inferior to the experts of the past ... to maintain that priest, prophets, and rabbis were the chief actors in the Jewish drama is to ignore the secular dimensions of the Jewish experience ... Traditional scholars ... simply assume that what the Bible and the Talmud claim to have happened did happen ... In light of these objections to the rabbinic approach to Jewish history, Humanistic Jews provide different answers ..."[17]

Consequently in the last thirty some years a new persuasion, Humanistic Judaism, has been instituted which de-emphasizes God's three-millennia divine Covenant with Jews and instead emphasizes human dignity within Jewish traditions.[18] This has been a major accomplishment at much social cost to the leaders and those Jews who dared follow them. But does it go far enough? In Chapter Ten's section on 'Non-Theistic Religions' I surmised that Unitarian Universalism and Humanism seem to lack an overarching doctrine. Similarly without a focus on the divine or Jewish survival or Zionism, it seems Humanistic Judaism suffers from lack of a compelling ideology.[19] Can prototheism provide that ideology?

Prototheism asks, What is the origin of theism, of belief in God? And my answer, as developed throughout this book, is the Life Urge. Jews long have celebrated Life with their wine toast "L'chaim," To Life! And at least since World War II (the Holocaust?) some have worn the Hebrew symbol חי for L'chaim, as described in this book's first note. Yet for millennia the Jewish people have lived Life with their dogged determination to survive and prosper even though misconstrued as belief in God's 'promise' rather than their own Life Urge.[20] So I submit that Humanistic Judaism already has the ideology they seek if only they disconnect L'chaim from any misplaced illusory dependence on God and look to their own Self. Of course Humanistic Jews already disconnect—they just haven't connected their Life Urge as a conceptual ideology as I'm suggesting.

Some Humanistic Jews may take offense at my adopting and adapting their secular חי symbol of Life to a prototheistic symbol of the Life Urge on the dedication page of this book—I apologize, no offense is intended, only esteem. Rather I'll put a different spin on it. Consider that Jews were likely the first to adopt a monotheistic belief. Yet I maintain that it was their own Life Urge misattributed to one God, YHWH or Yahweh, as explained in Chapter Ten's 'Poly- to Mono-Theism'. In other words, they intuited their Self but, given their then 'bicameral mind',[21] they misconstrued it as God. If so, then Jews have a long tradition of identifying their Life Urge, albeit misinterpreted. Thus Humanistic Jews could proudly claim Judaism's primacy and play a leading rôle in promoting prototheism as an ideology to replace theism.[22] So it looks like Jews were right all along!

Judaism is much more than a religion—it is foremost a people. "Membership in the Jewish people is determined by birth, not by any creedal test or ceremony of initiation ... Today the Jewish nation has become a world people ... the overwhelming majority still live in the Diaspora, primarily by choice ... While the majority of Jews still give nominal assent to the rabbinic tradition, a large minority have rejected the premises and practices of this tradition. Many of these dissidents remain fervently Jewish in a secular way."[23] Then could it be that secular Jews are uniquely positioned worldwide to assert their renowned *chutzpah* and lead a paradigm shift to prototheism, just as millennia ago they led the shift from polytheism to monotheism?[24]

It's not mine to say, but isn't it an audacious conjecture? Jews once again taking the lead—as did the legendary Abraham with monotheism,[25] Spinoza with the Enlightenment, now secular Jews with prototheism. I'd go along with that.[26] (Also see my suggestion for Holocaust museums on page 361 note 32.)

Appendix C

Prototheism for Skeptical Muslims

Except where the Catholic Church's practices are discussed, most of what was said in this book's main body applies to any religious background. This Appendix attempts to initiate a transposition of the Catholic/Christian experience to the Muslim experience, but I leave it to those with an Islamic heritage to complete that transition. As stated at the outset of this book, because of my marginal exposure to Judaism and my extremely limited exposure to Islam, I've relied on sources who're conversant with those religions and who're deeply skeptical or apostate (again, this book's not addressed to fundamentalists[1]). In the case of Islam I've relied primarily on two very recent sources. In Ibn Warraq's three books he has examined, translated and published the works of scholars of Islam and other skeptical Muslims, as well as his own assessment. The other source is Nevo and Koren discussed below.

In his latest book Warraq[2] compiled testimonies of forty-five Muslim apostates from throughout Islam and the West who were all "... comparatively well educated, computer literate ... and rational, with the ability to think for themselves. However, what is most striking is their fearlessness, their moral courage, and their moral commitment to telling the truth. They all face social ostracism, the loss of friends and family, a deep inner spiritual anguish and loneliness—and occasionally the death penalty if discovered. Their decisions are not frivolously taken, but the ineluctable result of rational thinking."[3] Islam has a low tolerance for the slightest expression of dissatisfaction which is seen as apostasy.[4] Indeed the mullahs come down hard on any questioning of their religion, a tacit admission, it seems to me, that it can't bear much scrutiny (reminiscent of the Roman Catholic Church's Inquisition from the 1400s to 1600s). Yet, just as with the Bible, as Muslims' critical thinking and knowledge increases, the credibility of the Koran, Syrah and Hadith decreases. In his two earlier books Warraq questions Islam's teachings by citing some scholars referenced below.

An even more recent book by the late Yehuda Nevo and Judith Koren has a comprehensive, exhaustive and revealing analysis of Islam's beginnings based on contemporaneous inscriptions, coinage, and non-Muslim chronicles, letters and texts. Nevo and Koren, like other recent scholars, assert that explanations based on Islamic scripture cannot be correlated with explanations based on objective sources. Indeed they agree that the Koran, Syrah and Hadith are not history but literature, legends composed to rationalize the Islamic state just as the Jewish Bible was composed to rationalize Judaism (see Appendix B). For example Islamic literature tells of the 'conquest' with many great battles and warriors. But they're not recorded in any non-Islamic writings, or commemorated in monuments or on coins—did no one else at the time notice such epic events?[5] Islamic literature tells of the many pagan tribes in the *Hijaz* (central and western Arabia). But extensive archaeology has yet to find any such evidence in the *Hijaz*—rather they find it in the Negev (southeast Palestine).[6]

According to Nevo and Koren, the nomadic Arab tribes had no common origin-legend until Jews told them of Abraham's 'illegitimate' son Ishmael.[7] Traditionally Jews descended from Abraham's second son Isaac by his wife Sarah (and later sons by Keturah). Arabs descended from Abraham's (aka Ibrahim) first son Ishmael by his (Egyptian?) concubine Hagar whom Sarah drove off into the desert.[8] Whence Arabs, though 'cousins' to Jews lost their birthright and were nomadic herders (Bedouins) given to warfare.

Nevo and Koren begin their explication in the fourth century AD in the far reaches of the Byzantine, the eastern Roman Empire. Rome was overextended so wanted to pull back its military and reduce administrative expenses without jeopardizing the security of their southeastern fringe areas.[9] The Romans gradually replaced Byzantine soldiers with tribal 'allies' (*foederati*).[10] The civilian population was largely Christian of various sects whereas the tribal Arabs were mostly pagan. To avoid losing Christians to paganism, the Byzantines required that the tribal Arab ruling elite convert to some form of monotheism.[11] Since their founding-father Abraham was the first monotheist, this was acceptable and they initially adopted a simple Judeo-Christianity, regarding Jesus only as a prophet and not divine.[12]

As the Byzantines pulled back, the local Arab tribes took-over, not only militarily but administratively by continuing the Byzantine system with the local Byzantine acculturated population.[13] Moreover in the 620s Rome destroyed the aggrandizing Sassanian Persian army and departed, having killed their king and appointed a new friendlier king while leaving their civil administration intact but undefended against the Arabs.[14] By the mid-600s an Arab strongman from Damascus, Muawiyah, had consolidated Arab tribes under his monotheism and became the first caliph[15] in 661.[16] When he died in 680, civil war again broke out until Abd al-Malik in 685 prevailed as the second caliph.[17] In order to provide a focus for Arab unity Abd al-Malik had a shrine built over the rock upon which Abraham was believed to have nearly sacrificed his first son, whether Ishmael or Isaac. The Dome of the Rock was built over the Jewish Temple Mount.[18] Around the Dome's inside Abd al-Malik had inscribed Judeo-Christian text but around its outside put Arab verse including *Muhammad rasul Allah*. Nevo and Koren argue that at that time '*muhammad*' was not a name but an epithet or rôle: 'the chosen one', the one desired to speak for God (more shortly).

When Abd al-Malik died in 705 the next caliph, Walid, not only was anti-Christian but was also anti-Byzantine.[19] Then in 724 Hisam became caliph and scholars like Ibn Ishaq began gathering material for an Arab history.[20] But Hisam and the Abbasids (after annihilating the Marwanid royal family, Abd al-Malik's dynasty) shifted the emphasis from an ethnic Arab history to a history of the Islamic 'empire'.[21] If Islam was to become a multinational religion it needed a mythology.

As mentioned, when Abd al-Malik inscribed *muhammad* on the Dome of the Rock in the 690s, it was not meant as a person's name but as a rôle.[22] Indeed even in the Koran 'Muhammad' is only mentioned four times whereas Allah "... no less than 300 times ... Ibrahim 79 times ..."[23] But the Arabs needed a 'prophet appointed by God' to rally around. So the Abbasids had their scholars invent one.[24] They chose as their model a man who had fought with al-Muxtar against Abd al-Malik in the early 660s but who was not political. He had an exemplary reputation and his name just happened to be Muhammad, Muhammad bn al Hanafiyyah.[25] Moreover he was from an area, the *Hijra*, that was sparsely populated so there were few who could contradict their story, per Nevo and Koren.

Other recent authors propose that the Muslims patterned their legend on the Jewish Pentateuch[26] (with some Christian elements) but changed the venue to western Arabia (the *Hijaz*).[27] The Biblical version of God's test of Abraham to sacrifice Isaac in Jerusalem (or Syria?) in one version became Ishmael and the Kaaba at Mecca.[28] Moses became Muhammad, Mt. Sinai became Mt.Hira, the Ten Commandants became the Koran (aka Qur'an), and Egypt and the exodus to Judea became Mecca and the *Hijra* to

Medina.[29] Still even though the 'conquest' began in the early 600s, the Arabs' political/religious system wasn't codified until the 800s in what became known as Islam,[30] two to three centuries after the Arab take-over began.

A footnote to Chapter Three's section on Constantine asserts that political expediency was the principal reason not only for Christianity's proliferation, but also for Judaism's before and for Islam's after, as described in these Appendixes. The traditional Islamic stories are vehemently upheld by conservative Muslims. Here's what some of those recent researchers suggest as the scenario: Muhammad, known later as 'the Prophet', was born around 570 purportedly in Mecca. But some scholars believe he was from northwestern Arabia perhaps near ancient Petra in what's now Jordan.[31] He became a warlord who united Arab tribes and Jews in the recapture of Jerusalem from the Byzantine Empire but he split with the Jews over reuse of the Temple site[32] (some things never change). His united Arab tribes went on a 'conquest' into Mesopotamia (now in Iraq), though it was more of a migration since the Byzantines and Sasanian Persians had largely abandoned its defense.[33] Arabs became a dominant though small minority in their 'conquered' lands (intermarriage was common?) and so over a couple centuries evolved a political/religious system amenable to the inhabitants who were disposed to change the Byzantine system.[34]

Thus beginning in the 620s the Arabs took-over the southern Byzantine territories and evolved a religion that began as simple monotheism and by around 800 had been forged and codified as the state religion known as Islam. (Perhaps because we Americans enjoy the principle of separation of church and state, we've trouble appreciating how prevalent the state-church tie was until the First Amendment of our Constitution, a little over two centuries ago—and still is in a few countries.) Islam became a world power expanding westward across Africa and into Spain, northward across the Bosporus almost to Vienna, and eastward into India and beyond. While at the time Christendom was stuck in the Dark Ages, Islam blossomed (preserving the Greeks) with philosophy, poetry, architecture, mathematics, astronomy ... But now it seems the situation has reversed—the West has pretty much thrown-off the clergy's other-worldly stranglehold while Muslim clergy still control some governments and courts.

Militant Muslim's contempt for, even hatred of the West in recent years has exhibited itself in terrorists' activities including suicidal fanatics willing to blow themselves up (and go to paradise) at bus stops, in restaurants and markets, at embassies and on airplanes, and even to use airplanes as missiles that destroyed New York's Twin Towers financial 'hothouse' September 11, 2001. Certainly the West deserves some of militant

Islam's contempt, with our "infectious greed" as elucidated in Chapters Eleven and Twelve, and our self-righteous attacks on Afghanistan and Iraq. But Islam's mindset is where Christianity's was over half-a-millennium ago when Christianity used the Inquisitions and earlier Crusades to enforce its belief in its version of God and an other-world. Efforts to modernize Islamic society are resisted by its theocrats[35] just as the Catholic Church's clergy tried to hold onto its medieval power, and still tries. Today's technology with satellite television and the Web[36] are making their hold ever more tenuous. However of course I believe the answer lies not just in modernizing Islam but in translating theistic beliefs into prototheistic concepts, as expounded throughout this book.

Thus what was said at the end of Appendix B applies here too. Muslims' 'faith' in God 'out there' could be equated with their disowned Urge to Life from deep in their own human nature which was exploited by the Arab rulers, as it has been many times before and since by their Jewish, Christian and Muslim counterparts. Again let me put this in synergistic complexity terms: The Life Urge may be acting as a kind of 'pre-gestalt' in search of a percept or concept on which to form. The only percept/concept it's offered is of 'God' and so the Life Urge unwittingly precipitates onto 'God', it emerges into consciousness as 'God' and is experienced as faith in God. What I'm advocating is that, just a we had to shift our paradigm or concept from a moving Sun to a moving Earth, we have to shift our concept from God 'out there' to our Life Urge 'in here'. The Life Urge should be prompted to coalesce as a gestalt on ones Self, as described in Chapter Ten's 'Prototheism and Life Urge'.

Notes and References

References to books listed in the Bibliography are shown as the author's surname(s) and page number(s) thus: Aczel: 987 or Adams & Laughlin: 987. If an author has more than one book listed in the Bibliography the referenced book's year of publication is shown after their name thus: Armstrong'01: 987. Journal and Internet* references are self-explanatory.

1. חי at the head of the dedication page is the Hebrew symbol 'chai' as in 'L'Chaim!'='To Life!' popularized by the song in the musical "Fiddler on the Roof." As you read the book you'll begin to see why I'm adopting it. I'm also adapting it by incorporating a swoop under it—an upraised gesture under חי flinging Life upward, connoting Life evolving onward and upward. Perhaps it'll be registered as a composite icon or logo. The only reference I found on חי's origins was from the toast "L'chaim!" to a condemned man reassuring him that the drink he was being offered wasn't the executioner's potion (see Blech: 342). Several erudite Jews said חי has no religious connotation and has only become popular since WWII. חי appeals to me because it's a symbol of Life, whereas the cross and crucifix are symbols of death with a hope for life-after-death.

2. This is the last line of the inscription over the gates of Hell in Dante's *Inferno III 9* (c1315). I've also hung it over the archway to my study (my *sanctum sanctorum*). Both Merriam-Webster's and Oxford's translation is "Abandon all hope, ye who enter!" and Hollanders' is modernized "ABANDON ALL HOPE, YOU WHO

---

*I am sorry to advise you that the AT&T Worldnet references are a problem. I assumed, apparently erroneously, that AT&T Worldnet maintains an archive that could be accessed using the date cited in the endnote. However it's been called to my attention after I'd mostly completed the endnotes that this isn't so. AT&T Worldnet daily carries ABC News and Reuters articles, but none of the threes' web pages shows a link to their archives so I'm at a loss as to how to access those articles directly. What I suggest is that their date of publication be used to research contemporaneous publications.

ENTER HERE" (their capitalization). But to my non-Italian ear *speranza* seems closer to 'aspirations' though I prefer 'illusions'. And so I'm asking you to abandon—or at least set aside—any lingering illusions in entering into the reading of this book, with an open mind and suspended judgment. Dare to be disillusioned (altho' since you're reading this book, you may already be way beyond that stage). However I'll not ask, as five lines later Virgil said to Dante "Here you must banish all distrust, here must all cowardice be slain." Instead, remain skeptical and apprehensive.

Chapter One—Some Preliminaries

    1. Concepts are alternately defined as "... mental representations that tie together specific instances ..." into categories like 'tomato' and 'apple' according to Paul Bloom's review of Gregory L. Murphy's *The Big Book of Concepts* in *Nature* 16Jan'03. Rather than just simple recognition of something, my use of 'concept' goes beyond to an explanation of what it is (even if wrong). Where Murphy uses '*con*cept' I use '*per*cept', what we *per*ceive. As used in this book 'concept' is how we explain what we perceive—see Ch. 9's 'Emerging Consciousness'.

    2. Why me?—If you're wondering, here's a brief sketch of how I came to be who I am. Both my parents were raised on farms in Québec and Michigan where French and German were spoken respectively. They wound up in auto factories in 1920s Detroit where they perfected their English and where they met. My father was Catholic. My mother was baptized Lutheran but joined the Methodists and although married in the Catholic Church she never converted. My sister, I and my brother soon ensued so I grew up during the Great Depression and World War II (but was too young for military service). We lived in Gesu parish run by Jesuits from the adjacent university; thus my education was under IHM nuns in grade school and Jesuits in high school and college. I received my bachelor's in mechanical engineering followed by an MBA after which I joined Ford Motor helping plan and launch the Edsel. I also patented a few inventions. Of course I married a Catholic girl so we had six children by the time we were married $8\frac{1}{2}$ years and thus started questioning the Church's teachings. We built our dream home in St.Hugo's parish where we were both very active including my co-leading the parish Synod (Pope John XXIII's program for updating the Church, his *aggiornamento*) along with serving as a commentator at mass (now called a lay reader). Two incidents stand out as opening my eyes, my epiphany. I had been reading some of Teilhard de Chardin's works when I came across a passage (which now I can't find) that seemed to say man had not yet evolved to attain life after death. It happened that a visiting priest at St.Hugo's was reputed to be an authority on Teilhard de Chardin. So after mass in the sacristy I showed him the passage and was astonished when he said my reading was correct! The other incident occurred as I was strolling with my children in a pastoral setting near our home one beautiful Sunday morning in summer. It hit me that if there is a God, He's to be found there and not in a stuffy church. No longer could I lead the *Credo* and so stepped down. Still

I went through years of antagonism and angst in letting go of the Church's teachings even though they were patently obsolescent. After Edsel I went into corporate development at Stanford Research and then to the gas company where trying to change the organization cost me my job and our dream home. We moved to a racially mixed neighborhood in Pontiac where I worked in community and economic development helping turn the city around. And of course I took up jogging, still do. After some thirty years of marriage Mariette and I divorced amicably. Retirement has given me leisure to study the issues covered in this long essay—I've always been a science buff. Thus I'm audacious enough to believe my real world experience along with a searching mind as a science/religion buff may enable finding a fresh perspective more relevant to our world and times.

3. Names of the scientists whose works I'm building on are generally not included in the text (unless it's a household name like Einstein) based on my own experience that citing many 'strange' names distracts from the explanations of the concepts (less is more). Hopefully I give due credit to those 'strangers' in these notes.

Chapter Two—Gods

1. The likely origins of humans' belief in a fire god &al will be explored in detail in later chapters on human evolution.

2. The translation of Virgil's *Aeneid* that I found illuminating was Robert Fitzgerald's read by Christopher Ravenscroft on audio-cassette from HighBridge 1995 (from a local public library).

3. Abstracting from the Sun-god to a dematerialized, ethereal entity may have been a logical progression from the belief that the Sun passed overhead just above the clouds to the realization that it was very much farther away, 'infinitely' far away in the heavens. For that matter, the transition from a fire-god to the Sun-god was quite natural considering that only less than a century ago was it realized that the Sun isn't a fire but is nuclear fusion—Zirker: 16–20.

4. Many gods vs one God—monotheism still has many lesser 'gods' such as angels, devils and saints, but they're not in charge of natural phenomena as were the polytheistic gods; rather the one God is.

5. The denial of the reality of death in our culture is much more pervasive than just human death. Even though we consume a large proportion of meat in our diets, most of us have trouble facing up to the necessity of killing an animal to get that meat. We don't do it ourselves but instead employ butchers to kill and dress it out for us. If we can't face the reality of an animal's death to get the food we need to live, we're even less able to face the reality of our own death or of a loved one's ("They've passed" "They've gone to God").

6. Live life for afterlife—Rather than live a good life based on love of God or morality, it'd be based on reward vs punishment like a business transaction, 'If I do this, God will do that', *quid pro quo*.

7. Regarding accepting responsibility for this world, "The Evangelical Environmental Network ... is also at work nationwide changing stereotypes while sharing the Christian gospel." reported 8/18/99 by EnviroLink. Even so their concern derives from a new interpretation of the gospel; are they just adding another requirement for the 'afterlife' rewards, the stewardship of Earth? For other such groups see ENN's website's features 7/13/00. The Kellert & Farnham collected essays assert man's stewardship of Earth, as does Kellert: 137.

8. "All the gods are within us." Joseph Campbell to Bill Moyers/PBS.

9. Angry faces—"Abused Kids See Angry Faces Everywhere"—AT&T Worldnet News Jun17'02 citing a report the same week in the *Proceedings of the National Academy of Sciences*.

10. A mostly secular, current example of teaching children to believe in a 'god' is Santa Claus. They're told stories of how Santa will bring them presents at Christmas if they're good, they're taken to sit on Santa's knee &c. They want to believe so they'll get presents (if they don't, they won't?). And of course it all happens just as the adults said. Eventually they figure out that it's all a hoax but should they risk letting on that they know and losing out on the presents? Perhaps what we think we're teaching them is not what they're learning: We're teaching them about rewards for good behavior but what they're learning is about false gods and skepticism toward authorities. So maybe it's a good lesson after all. (If this custom is presented as a make-believe game children and parents can pretend and play together, it's a fun way to show love, albeit vulnerable to commercial exploitation. How'd I get off on this?)

11. A revelation can be a sudden insight, an intuition, so obvious—"Why didn't I think of this before?"—that it feels like it didn't come from one's own mind but was 'revealed' from elsewhere, from the beyond. I heard the fiddler Jay Ungar tell how his haunting "Ashokan Farewell" (featured on the soundtrack of Ken Burn's PBS series "The Civil War") didn't feel like his, that he couldn't take credit for it. It just came through him and for several months after whenever he tried to play it he'd break down in deep sorrow. (Told at his and Molly Mason's 1997? show in Waterford, Michigan.)

12. Revelation—Maslow'64: 19–25 attributes revelations to peak-experiences and the ensuing organized religions to non-peakers.

13. On the gods speaking to men, see Jaynes: 72–5, 85ff & thru-out; some of his ideas are now superseded. See Schlagel: 297–9 for a synopsis of Jaynes' ideas.

14. On the mythic stage of man's evolution, see Donald'01: 295–8.

15. Theist is the term for one who holds a gods- or God-mentality. Thus one who doesn't hold such a mentality is a 'non-theist'. I prefer non-theist to the more common term 'a-theist' which seems to carry too heavy a burden of negative connotations. So often atheists come off as contentious no doubt because they're often attacking, or under attack by, zealous theists. The term 'a-gnostic' ('don't know', coined by T.H.Huxley in 1869—Browne: 309–10) seems to me too indeterminate, as if trying to dodge an attack by theists. But I believe we can't just shrug off belief in gods/God; at minimum we need to set such beliefs aside so we have an open mind

in our search for truth. The term for a person of this last disposition is 'free thinker'. However my endeavor is neither to oppose nor ignore religion but rather to uncover the roots of religious belief—the antecedent of the gods/God mentality—in our human nature by tracing that vein back through evolution to its source. Hence rather than use a negative term such as 'non-theist', instead I'm coining the positive term 'proto-theist' to more aptly depict my disposition to find what's called 'God' deep in our human nature, 'in here' not 'out there'. (Prototheist sounds a little like 'protagonist' which may turn out to be not just a coincidence.)

16. Science *and* religion implies that they're separate realms, a Platonist or Cartesian view, or a scientist's ploy to dodge the wrath of the religious. Science *of* religion regards religion and gods just like any other phenomenon which can be scientifically explored. Yet as will be argued, in using the discipline of science, I'd like to retain the numen, the marvel that religion can engender.

17. Unless one truly has the courage of their convictions as I'm suggesting here, they'll probably play it safe and implicitly adopt Pascal's wager. Blaise Pascal's wager in his *Pensees* is translated as follows: "If you bet that there is a God, and you are right, you gain everything; If you bet that there is a God, and you are wrong, you lose nothing; If you bet that there is no God, and you are right, you gain nothing; If you bet that there is no God, and you are wrong, you lose everything. Thus, given the consequences of possible infinite gain against possible infinite loss, preoccupation with thoughts of God is prudent." (Avise: 204–5; Kors'97: p.9,II.C.3) But according to Kors, Pascal was an unhappy, miserable man torn between hate of all his fellowmen and self-hate. If you're not wallowing in hate, you might have a more positive, optimistic outlook rather than be preoccupied with thoughts of a God 'out there', angry, vengeful, and needful of obsequious propitiation. That's a rather pitiful concept of God. For a more optimistic wager see Avise: 209, "If mortal life is all that exists for individuals, we lose nothing by seeking to make that life as meaningful and rewarding as possible. But if eternal life exists, we have lost nothing by seeking a fulfilling existence here on earth. Thus, one might wager on the richness of life here and now."

18. The image of Christ as the "Good Shepherd" and of us as "Sheep in a meadow" has been perpetuated by churchmen desirous to have their 'flock' docile and subservient, a rather derogatory conception of humans. More's the pity, most of those churchmen truly believe it; that's why a bishop carries a shepherd's crook, a crosier, and the head of a parish is called 'pastor' from the same Latin root as 'pasture'—one who's in charge of the flock in the pasture.

Chapter Three—Christianity's Beginnings

1. There is an overwhelming amount of material covering the subjects of this chapter. I poured over about a dozen recent books which appeared to be most relevant and objective (listed in the Bibliography). I found Fox's *Pagans and Christians* (1986) and Shorto's *Gospel Truth* (1997) resonated best with my disposition (Shorto's is a good, readable synopsis of current opinions). Frend's *The Rise of*

Christianity (1984) provides exhaustive detail but his description of Jesus' life appears to rely uncritically on the *New Testament* so I'm suspect of the reliability of other parts of his work. Moreover throughout Frend's book unlike other authors he seems to put undue emphasis on the 'inevitable' progress of the orthodox Christian Church. The Jesus Seminar is attempting a laundering of the *New Testament* to wash out the half- and un-truths but since their results are based on votes of 'believers' who have a vested interest in Jesus, they too are suspect (see *free inquiry* winter 1998/99 p.9). Even so they find that "... only 18% of the words ascribed to Jesus in the Gospels may have actually been spoken by him." as reported by TIME in their article on the Jesus Seminar April 8, 1996: 52–60. Schonfield's *The Passover Plot* (1965) gives an interesting Jewish perspective but without the benefit of more recent findings. Others not referenced below were Barnes, Brown, Hoeller, Hornblower, Mack and Pagels. And since drafting this chapter new books have been published deconstructing Jesus hagiography but I've moved on and have only read MacDonald's and Crossan & Reed's (referenced below). Intriguing though, are Earl Doherty's *The Jesus Puzzle:* ... ; Alvar Ellegard's *Jesus: One Hundred Years Before Christ* and Acharya S.'s *The Christ Conspiracy*. Accessing any of these on Amazon.com will lead you to others and their reviews. They appear to go beyond earlier investigations. After completing a working draft of this book, I bought and perused Schlagel'01—he does a thorough scientific up-to-date analysis of both Jewish and Christian Scripture, pages 79–215. Also see Eisenman's *James the Brother of Jesus*,Watkins, 2002, and Ehrman's *Lost Christianities,* Oxford, 2003.

2. Flat world—While the general population at that time saw the Earth as flat, those few who had a Greek education would know about Aristotle's concentric spheres concept as refined by Claudius Ptolemy in his c130AD *Almagest* (later title); see Kuhn'57: 72–3 and Sellers: 32.

3. On the invisible gods see Brown: 9, 16 & 18; on dealing with gods see MacMullen: 13 and on 'give to the giver' see Fox: 38.

4. The Oracle at Delphi apparently got high on natural gas for her prophecies and divinations—*NewScientist* 1Sept'01: 40–2 and *Scientific American* Aug'03: 66–73.

5. For a more vivid account of the ancient world see Cahill'98 also available on audio cassette. Or listen to a reading by Christopher Ravenscroft of Robert Fitzgerald's translation (1983) of Virgil's *The Aeneid* (abridged) on audio cassette (HighBridge Classics 1995).

6. Jewish history and legends are also being reassessed and demythologized. For example see Finkelstein & Silberman: 23 for their thesis, elaborated thru-out, namely that the Hebrew Bible was written "... to further the religious reform and territorial ambitions of Judah during the momentous concluding decades of the seventh century BCE." so that earlier "... stories of the patriarchs, the Exodus ... of David and Solomon—are ... creative expressions ..." But than Dever: 40–4 refutes Finkelstein without benefit of their recent book. (Dever: 293 sees himself as a positive secular humanist.) Also see Appendix B herein for an elaboration of Jewish history.

7. Israelite 'monotheism'—Finkelstein & Silberman: 2–footnote.

8. Messiah prophecy—Schonfield'65: 22.

9. Herod the Great's nasty personality is now believed to have been exacerbated by chronic kidney disease per Jan Hirschmann of the U.of Washington at a U.of Maryland conference as reported by AT&T Worldnet Jan25'02. Both Herod's parents were Arab but he converted to Judaism for political reasons—MS Encarta.

10. The Septuagint (LXX) translation was commissioned for the Alexandrian Library by Ptolemy II Philadelphus (285/3–247BC). Like earlier Hebrew texts it incorporated the interpretations and modifications of its seventy-two translators—see Basbanes: 17, Mitchell: xxviii and Staikos: 64 & 73.

11. BC—I've not felt compelled to substitute BCE (Before the Common Era) for BC (Before Christ) nor CE (Common Era) for AD (*Anno Domini* = 'year of our Lord' in Latin). Which 'common era'? Roman, Chinese, Aztec, Inca ... or Christian? So why not say which? All calendar numbering systems are arbitrary. Ours was based on beliefs held at the time it replaced the previous numbering system of AUC (*Ab Urbe Condita* = 'from the founding of the city' of Rome = 753BC). (Jews and Muslims use lunar calendars.) I appreciate that those who use BCE and CE are trying to secularize our calendar but I'm not bothered by it. See Gould'97: 106 and Steel: 114–5.

12. The prophecy of a virgin birth was based on a mistranslation of the Hebrew into the Greek of the Septuagint. The Hebrew referred to a women who had not yet given birth, a primipara, not to a virgin—Shorto: 30–2. For Jesus' siblings see Shorto: 100

13. Some argue that Jesus' birth occurred in the spring, perhaps mid-April (see Steel: 329–34 and Dec21'02 PBS show "Mystery of the Three Kings" citing evidence for April 17, 6BC). But a few centuries later as the Church gained dominance (under Constantine; Steel: 109) they decided to proclaim it as December 25. This was primarily to supersede the celebration of the birthday of *Sol Deus Invictus* (the unconquered sun-god; Steel: 85) or Mithras (the Persian Sun-god who had become popular especially with the army—Kriwaczek: 119–28 & 130–41 and Shorto: 28), which of course was the winter solstice (roughly). (It's also near Hanukkah, the Jewish Feast of Lights.) Perhaps though, the Church believed that these feasts foreshadowed Christ and that He was the culmination of man's longing. In any event Jesus' birthday came to represent the rebirth of hope. Hence in the winter darkness this is the time to light candles and the Yule log, and celebrate the return of the Sun, the restoration of the light and 'evergreen' hope. It is truly a marvelous celebration even though it's been usurped and misconstrued by the Christian hegemony, not to mention overly commercialized. For past Christmases I've given certain of my Christian coworkers pairs of handmade beeswax candles (a son was a beekeeper) with a note like "In this season of dwindling light and impending chill, may these candles warm your heart with love and enkindle hope for the New Year" (recalling the adage: "Better to light one candle than forever curse the darkness."). See *NewScientist* 25Dec99: 82 for a review of two books both titled *The Star of Bethlehem* and ~ 22/29Dec'01: 6 on the cover-up of the 'Christmas star' which appeared Mar20 and again Apr17, 6BC.

14. Shorto: 45 refers to the *Via Maris*, the Way of the Sea, as the principal trade route through lower Galilee to Sepphoris. However Foltz' map of—what only a century ago Ferdinand von Richthofen dubbed—the 'Silk Road' shows the western end of the main route going from Baghdad up the Euphrates and over to Aleppo (Halab) which is some 260 miles NNE of Nazareth. But the Silk Road was actually a network of roads which came out of China across India and Persia to the Mediterranean beginning centuries before Jesus' time. To cut over to Nazareth from the Euphrates the route would have had to someway cross the Syrian Desert. The Silk Road caravans transported not only long-distance trade-goods and travelers, but also their diseases and cultures including their religions. For a history of Buddhism and the Silk Road before and during Jesus' time see Foltz: 36ff.

15. Young Jesus as rebel—Shorto: 100.

16. Jesus' baptism—Shorto: 105–6 & 132. He was 'born again'.

17. In grade school I recall a nun railing against the use of Xmas believing it demeaned Christ as an unknown: X. Years later I realized it was the first Greek letter 'chi' in the Greek word 'Christ'. This is the same as in the Catholic symbol ☧, 'chi-rho', the Greek abbreviation for Christ King, called a Christogram.

18. Jesus' miracles—Shorto: 134–8.

19. The story of the loaves and fishes is heralded by some as one of Jesus' greatest miracles. Allegedly with five loaves and two fishes offered by a small boy he fed a multitude of five thousand and then collected scraps that filled twelve baskets. Shorto: 140–2 sees this as hyperbole. But years ago I read a more plausible explanation in an historical novel by Douglas: 280–3. Each family or group that made up the multitude prudently tucked some food in their clothing before they ventured out into the countryside to hear this Jesus. Not realizing that most everyone else had stashed food too, they kept theirs out of sight until offered some of the little boy's. Then, declining the boy's, they took out theirs and shared with those who had been less prudent. Douglas portrays this as "… a miracle! Jesus had inspired those stingy, selfish people to be decent to one another! It takes a truly great man to make one harmonious family out of a crowd like that!"

20. Jesus staging a confrontation—Shorto: 271.

21. Crucifixions—Shorto: 197–201.

22. Our reaction to the crucifix is interesting: If we see a photo of an 'uncivilized' New Guinea warrior with a shrunken head hanging from his neck, we think it's ghoulish. Whereas if we see a most gruesome crucifix hanging from a 'civilized' Christian's neck, we think it's devout. But a fetish is a fetish. Or what about a severed head stuck up on a pole versus a grisly crucifix over an altar?

23. Jesus' Messiah calling—Schonfield'65: 41–6 and Shorto: 266. Stevens & Price: 42–6 ask "Was Jesus mad?" and conclude he wasn't schizophrenic but wasn't entirely normal either.

24. Jesus' daring scheme—Schonfield in his *The Passover Plot* 165–172, describes how Jesus' highly placed accomplice, a Joseph of Arimathea, owned a new tomb next to a vegetable garden nearby Golgotha, the hill of crucifixion. Joseph

arranged to have Jesus drugged on the cross from a sponge to induce the appearance of death, then got permission from Pilate to take the alleged corpse down from the cross. He promptly had it taken to the tomb where he arrived with linen and spices for a kind of 'first aid'. Later that night as planned the gardener moved Jesus' body from the tomb to a safer location for revival. Jesus had expected to recover but the centurion's precautionary lance into his side while still on the cross proved to be his undoing. Rather than risk returning Jesus' corpse to the tomb, they interred it somewhere else leaving the mystery of the empty tomb. It's a compelling theory which Schonfield seems to have thoroughly researched for his 1965 historical novel based on what was known then.

25. Jesus' corpse—Shorto: 205–9.

26. See TIME, April 8, 1996: 55 citing Crossan's *The Historical Jesus*.

27. "Seeing the Gods" is the title of one of Fox's chapters wherein he describes this then common occurrence as an 'epiphany'.

28. The stories that grew and were circulated about Jesus conform to the classic hero myths as outlined by Nugent in Lecture Six: The Heroic Ideal. She describes these characteristics from Lord Raglan's 1934 *The Hero* (reprinted in 1975). These include a virgin birth, fathered by a god, attempts to kill the child, exile to a far country, victorious return, cruel death (on a hill) and entombment in a sepulchre (with the potential to rise again). Susan Wood of Oakland U. (Mi) in a lecture November 20, 1997 "Mortals, Empresses & Earth Goddesses" cited specific gods associated with these myths. More recently a compelling argument has been put forth by MacDonald: 190 that Mark, the author of the earliest gospel sometime after 70AD (which was used by the other three orthodox gospels' authors), modeled his stories of Jesus directly on Homer's epic tales, the *Iliad* and *Odyssey*. "Mark crafted a myth to make the memory of Jesus relevant to the catastrophes of his day." False memory problems are still prevalent, see Schacter thru-out.

29. 'Kingdom of Rome'—Crossan & Reed: 273–6. The Jewish concept was that God owned the land and allowed his people to use it (but not to buy or lease it) for the benefit of all. The Romans took the land from the Jews and applied their own laws for the benefit of the few.

30. The devastation of Jerusalem, the destruction of the Temple, and the slaughter of much of the population forever changed Judaism from the sacrificial 'temple' religion of Jesus' time to a legalistic 'rabbinical' religion evermore dispersed—Shorto: 54 & 193. In wiping out Jewish nationalism (in 70AD followed by the Second Jewish War in 135AD), it took with it the messianic interpretation of Jesus, lead by his brother Jacob/James—Schonfield'74 thru-out. This left the field open for the re-emergence of Paul's Christianity which had been losing ground—Schonfield'65: 239 and Frend: 162.

31. Paul's epiphany, it seems to me, occurred when he projected an unconscious, suppressed part of his own personality out into the sky, and then reingested it in a traumatic episode that changed his life. Epiphanies were common then—Fox: 380, 398 & 678.

32. Paul prevailed—Frend: 110.

33. Gehenna or Sheol for Hebrews but with the advent of the Pharisees came the belief in resurrection of the dead—Wine'95: 22. Also see Kriwaczek: 198.

34. On the 'underworld', see Hornblower: 209–11 & 667–8, MacMullen: 18–9 & 70, Shorto: 75 and Stevens: 167. Elysium, see MS Encarta.

35. Original sin is an idea coined by Tertullian in the 2nd century and elaborated by Augustine early in the 5th, namely that Adam's and Eve's defiance of God by tasting the forbidden apple not only got them expelled from paradise but the taint of that sin is transmitted down the generations by the act of procreation—MS Encarta. Jesus' mother Mary supposedly was exempt from original sin because of her Immaculate Conception so she couldn't transmit it to Jesus in his conception by the Holy Spirit ("What a tangled web we weave ...")

36. Early Christians seen as atheists—MacMullen: 15, Fox: 425 and Frend: 148 & 178.

37. Interestingly monotheistic Jews were exempt from the pagans' requirement because theirs was an ancient religion—Fox: 428.

38. Confessors—Fox: 458. I recall from religion classes that the sacrament of confession came about by using the words attributed to Jesus, "Your sins are forgiven" as giving priests the power to forgive sins, but it may be a misinterpretation. Jesus may have meant not that He was forgiving their sins but simply that if the person forgave themselves and stopped feeling guilty then their sins were lifted from them. "Whose sins you shall forgive, they are forgiven and whose sins you shall retain, they are retained" may also have been a simple statement of fact— if you hold a grudge and don't forgive, then the person may still feel guilty.

39. Christians' percent of population—Fox: 335, 586–7, 590 & 592.

40. For the various 'heresies' see MacMullen: 93; Fox: 332, 407, 602 & 638 and Frend: 212–8, 314–8, 492–8 & 653–9. Ehrman's *Lost Christianities* unread as yet.

41. Orthodox Christians—MacMullen: 93.

42. 'Dramatic narratives' is a term used by Brown and by Shorto: 174 for 'creative stories' about Jesus. See also Schonfield'65: 244. But even though ours is not an oral culture, we shouldn't be too smug considering for example stories about George Washington and the cherry tree. Today's advertising and public relation types regularly interpret and present (spin) the 'facts' to fit their objectives. (At Edsel back in the mid1950s the market research guys would sarcastically put on their assignment reports, "These are the conclusions on which I base my facts.") For that matter according to Merriam-Webster the term 'propaganda' comes from *Congregatio de propaganda fide*, Congregation for propagating the faith, established by Pope Gregory XV who died in 1623. D.S. Wilson: 215 quips "When it comes to altering a sacred story, it seems that nothing is sacred—at least during the early stages of religious evolution."

43. Ghostwriting was an accepted practice then. "Writings ... were placed under the names of apostles ... as demonstrating that these represented the true workings of the Spirit and therefore guaranteed orthodoxy." Frend: 243. (But again we shouldn't be too condescending: Chief Seattle's oft quoted 1854 'speech' about the Earth was written by a screenwriter, Ted Perry, in 1971, according to Ridley'97:

214.) If the gospel writers (redactors) in their time freely attributed what they wrote to apostles or Jesus, then it seems that their predecessors in earlier times were even more likely to attribute their pronouncements to God as revelations (see Appendix B). That was the accepted practice and they believed it. It was their way of seeking endorsement back then, just as today I seek out recognized authorities to endorse my point of view.

44. Christian mobs allegedly pillaged and burned the Great Library at Alexandria. It is believed to have contained a vast collection of papyrus scrolls, the works of most of the great thinkers of antiquity, which are irrevocably lost to civilization—see Basbanes: 17–8, Sagan'80: 20–1 & 333–7 and Staikos: 57–89. (Hypatia is thought to have been its last librarian though she's not so titled in Dzielska or Staikos. She was brutally murdered in 415AD by the patriarch Cyril's (or Theophilus'?) thugs perhaps somehow blamed for Alexandria's series of earthquakes that began in 320AD.) Fortunately we know that a few works were hidden from the purge such as those found at Nag Hammadi in 1945—Crossan & Reed: 7 & 123, Hoeller: 16–23 and Pagels: xiii–xxxv & 150–1.

45. The phenomenon that Constantine and his entourage saw was probably a combination sun pillar and parhelion (sun dog), visual phenomena caused by sunlight scattered by ice crystals in the air, described by Steel: 86 and in his letter to *Sky & Telescope*, Oct'99: v98 i4 p12. Or maybe it was a meteorite—*NewScientist* 21Jun'03: 13.

46. Constantine's campaigns—Barnes: 42–3, Fox: 611–27 and Frend: 482–8

47. Constantine's leadership of Christianity—Fox: 624–5 & 664–9 and Frend: 488.

48. Constantine's "overweening ambition"—Frend: 475.

49. Government inconsistent with polytheism—How can you have an orderly government if the gods pit leaders against one another?

50. Religious 'overachievers'—Fox: 449 & 558–9.

51. Constantine and orthodox Christians' organization—Frend: 231, 282, 249 & 479.

52. Spoke with the authority of God—Frend: 499.

53. Constantine delayed his baptism until a few weeks before he died in 337. But this doesn't necessarily betray insincerity. It was believed that baptism remitted all past sins and, as Emperor in a brutal domain, Constantine undoubtedly had plenty—Fox: 658.

54. For example Canon Theologian N.T.Wright of Westminster Abbey reportedly asked (on Peter Jennings' 'Search for Jesus' on ABCTV Jun26'00 9–11pmET) "If Jesus didn't rise from the dead, how do we explain the explosive growth of early Christianity?" For an answer look to Constantine's politics. D.S.Wilson: 147–57 looks at the early Christian Church's growth as functionally adaptive.

55. Hamilton: 213–6 argues that had Christianity continued to follow the early Greek Christians rather than the Roman, the Church would be altogether different today. "The Greeks wanted independent citizens who thought for themselves; the Romans ... wanted citizens who were not given to thinking, but to doing what they are told." D.S.Wilson: 214–5 claims that the Christians who called

themselves 'orthodox' ignored Gospels such as Thomas' "… which encouraged the believers to embark upon a journey of self-discovery rather than conforming to a close-knit group." Thus Constantine adopted Roman orthodox Christianity, adapted it and helped it flourish because its religious hierarchy complemented the empire's political hierarchy. Without him whether Christianity, Greek or Roman, would have flourished seems unlikely.

56. At expense of pagan temples—Constantine may have had an additional ulterior motive. According to Weatherford: 60–1, unable to finance his administration from taxation and looting new lands, he looted the temples of their gold and silver to mint gold coins.

57. Christian vs pagan—A curious aside is the choice of the Sabbath day. Jews of course observe Saturday (from sundown Friday to sundown Saturday). I don't know why Christianity—which grew out of Judaism—moved it to Sunday unless it was Constantine's influence. Initially he had regarded Christ and the Sun-god as the same, so did he choose Sun-day?

58. Christianity's perks—Fox: 623 & 667 and Frend: 487.

59. Jesus made into the ultimate broker—Shorto: 241–4.

60. Even though called 'monotheism', if we use the Greek, Roman, Egyptian or most other definitions of 'gods', we have to conclude that the Christians ended up with perhaps far more 'gods' than the polytheistic pagans. Specifically we have God the Father, God the Son, God the Holy Ghost, the Virgin Mary, Joseph, Mary Magdalene, all the Apostles, the many martyrs and saints, and a multitude of angels and devils. (By this definition were the Jews monotheistic in view of their legions of angels and devils?) This allowed the emerging Romanized Christian church to provide external targets on which to project archetypes of choice just as the pagans did, yet with a strict hierarchical 'polytheism' compatible with the Roman government's hierarchy.

61. For an elaboration on early Christians' behavior in time of pestilence and epidemics—McNeill'76: 121ff and D.S.Wilson: 153–5.

62. To condense the progression from Judaism to Christianity into today's idiom: What started as the Jewish left, left Judaism and became the Christian left who were opposed by both the Pagan and Jewish right, but ultimately ossified into the Christian right.

63. Christians' other-worldliness—Frend: 701 & 710.

64. Keys: 249ff argues that the Dark Ages and other world-wide upheavals were precipitated by a super volcanic eruption about 535AD, a 'proto-Krakatoa'. A round-up of other likely suspects is being lead by Mike Baillie of Queen's U. in Belfast, N. Ireland.

65. To vicariously experience what the Church's 'Dark Ages' mentality was like, watch a video of Kenneth Branagh's 1996 *Hamlet*. Early on, the scenes with the ghost and in the woods near the castle vividly depict how people of that day really believed in an afterlife and how their lives were controlled by that belief.

66. Indulgence—a plenary indulgence was promised to those who went on the Crusades (from *crux*=cross). The sale of indulgences to finance Church opulence precipitated the Protestant Reformation.

67. Deductive versus inductive reasoning: The method, attributed to Aristotle, of deductive reasoning begins with an assumption, hypothesis, axiom or 'revealed truth' and argues to logical conclusions; called *a priori* or top-down thinking. Francis Bacon's inductive reasoning proceeds from observations to generalizations or theories; called *a posteriori* or bottom-up thinking. (I found The Teaching Company's SuperStar Teachers® lectures on audio tapes useful listening while driving; particularly Daniel Robinson's and the 'Great Minds' series.)

68. McNeill'76: 257ff suggests "... that decreasing significance of epidemic disease, partly due to medical advances but mostly due to ecological adjustments ... , constituted an essential background for the popularization of 'enlightened' philosophical and social views ... A world in which lethal infectious disease seldom seized a person suddenly in the prime of life no longer stood so much in need of belief in Divine Providence to explain such deaths."

69. For the ensuing history I bought a few recommended books tho' I haven't read much of them: Where my analysis leaves off Fletcher picks up in the fourth century on the Christianizing of Europe. Roberts concisely covers the entire history of Europe and Bokenkotter covers the history of the Catholic Church somewhat from an apologist's perspective whereas Küng is more critical. Dolan and Morris cover American Catholicism.

70. The French of course have a phrase for the consequences of denial: *Chasser le naturel, il revient au galop*: Chase out the natural, it returns at a gallop.

Chapter Four—Some Fundamentals

1. Fundamentalists—Armstrong'00: ix–xvi provides an insightful analysis of Christian, Jewish and Muslim fundamentalists' concerns.

2. For the Copernican 'heresy' of advocating that the earth revolved around the Sun (among other things), Giordano Bruno was burned at the stake (to induce him to recant rather than burn in hell) in Rome in 1600. Also in Rome in 1633 Galileo Galilei, contemplating a similar fate, was coerced, bullied to abjure the same 'heresy' (although reportedly he muttered *"eppur si muove"*: "and yet it does move") and was put under house arrest for the rest of his life (Schlagel: 47 says during that time "... he managed to write and furtively publish his second book ..." that "... earned him the title of 'the father of modern science.'" In Kurtz'03 Moy: 139–43 and Rowland thru-out are less critical of the Church). (Copernicus had waited 'til on his death bed in 1543 before he published his theory, and/or maybe he was just a perfectionist who had trouble letting go of it—I can relate.) Copernicus' concept of the Earth as a 'floating' planet in a heliocentric solar system flew in the face of the Church's long-held belief in a static world beneath the dynamic heavens just above the clouds. The Church held onto that belief for a long time, in fact Galileo's views were not officially acknowledged until 1992—Reston: 60, 261ff & 283ff and Stock: 174. (Schlagel: 46 states "... a Polish Pope, John Paul II, in tribute probably to his countryman Nicholas Copernicus, finally exonerated Galileo from the false condemnation.") Two other historic novels

that describe the lives and times of Copernicus and Bruno are Banville's and Yanow's. For a technical elucidation see Kuhn's *The Copernican Revolution*. For less technical descriptions of Copernicus, Galileo &al see Sellers: 35–43 & 61–70. (Mar12'00 Pope JohnPaul II in a public ceremony "... asked forgiveness for the many past sins of his Church including its treatment of ... heretics ..." without being more specific—*Reuters*.)

3. In 1836? Tennyson penned the lines: "Move eastward, happy earth, and leave / Yon orange sunset waning slow; / From fringes of the faded eve, / O happy planet, eastward go, / ... / Ah, bear me with thee, smoothly borne, / Dip forward under starry light, / And move me to my marriage-morn, / And round again to happy night."

4. My son Michael and I tried contriving a more accurate term than 'sunrise'. The best we could do was 'anti-meridianal solar tangent'. Sunset would be 'post-meridianal solar tangent'. Admittedly, in the song from *Fiddler on the Roof*, there's more of a poignant lilt to the lines ♪"Sunrise, sunset ..." Well, we tried. It seems we persist in using misleading terms because we haven't found better ones. 'Day-break' isn't bad, more definite than 'dawn'.

5. Actually we're acutely aware of rapid fluctuations in the air pressure which we sense with our ears as sound, namely vibrations of the air pressure. Also we feel the change in air pressure when our airplane changes altitude.

6. It's symptomatic that the term 'suction' persists even though Torricelli, a protégé of Galileo's, demonstrated these properties of air in the 1640s. See Genz: 102ff

7. Even so there is a difference between the rocket's force and 'gravity' too subtle to feel. On Earth your feet are being squeezed together slightly more than your head because 'gravity' is focused approximately at the center of the Earth.

8. I first started thinking about this way of conceptualizing 'gravity' on reading Shlain'91: 329–30 and gestated it with Sartori: 261–80 and other sources. While I find it very useful in conceptualizing space-time, I'm not competent to vouch for its veracity so perhaps it's only a useful analogy and an exercise to stretch your imagination.

9. In grappling over the years with relativity and quantum physics, I read (or tried to read and oft times reread with only modest understanding) quite a few authors as referenced in the bibliography: Coleman, Davies, Einstein, Gardner, Gell-Mann, Gribbin, Hawking, Hoffmann, Infeld, Lindley, Narlikar, Pais, Prigogine, Rucker, Sartori, Shlain, Weinberg and Wheeler. However like Omar Khayyám I "... evermore / Came out by the same door where in I went." (q.27) Rather than take to drink as he did (also see *free inquiry* winter'02/3: 59–60), I 'drank' at Omnés' 'spring', his recent *Quantum Philosophy* (not without some difficulty). With a clearer head I was able to return to some of those earlier authors. Admittedly it was partly a matter of my readiness: "When the pupil is ready the teacher will come."

10. On the reciprocal nature of space and time: "... the intimate relation between time dilation and length contraction: neither effect could logically exist without the other, and either can be used to derive the other." Sartori: 88.

11. The corollary to "Mass warps space-time" is that "Space-time tells mass where to go" which will be used in the next chapter on Earth's formation. (Attributed to John Wheeler by Greene: 72)

12. Altho' some mornings getting out of bed, it seems that the force of 'gravity' 'pulling' me back down is unusually strong.

13. Earth's 'gravity' is the aggregate effect of all the masses of all the objects in and on the Earth. On Earth's surface or above it we experience this aggregate effect pushing away from the Earth's center. If somehow we were at Earth's center the pushing would be in all directions around us netting zero 'gravity' (but oy! the compression)—*Scientific American* Aug'03: 95.

14. Particle's mass curving space—*NewScientist* 17May'03: 30–1. Gravity's effect on neutrons was recently detected and, surprise! they fall in quantum steps— *Nature* Science Update 17Jan'02.

15. Newton's 'gravity' is a mathematical relation that operates *as if* it were a force acting at a distance. He couldn't explain a mechanism that could cause the action at a distance, but only the relationship so that the action could be predicted. Descartes posited a mechanism, that is, fluid forces in a whirlpool (like Einstein's warped space-time?) but didn't describe the relationship; from Kors' audiotape. Kuhn'57: 257–60, Omnès'99a: 34–5 and Weinberg: 169.

16. As I write new findings on the speed of gravity are being debated—*New-Scientist* 11Jan'03: 32–5 and *Nature* Science Update 16Jan'03. On gravity waves see *Scientific American* Aug'03: 25–6.

17. On young Einstein's thought experiment, *gedankenexperiment*, see Gribbin: 75–80, Pais: 131 or Sartori: 53.

18. Timeless light beam—Lindley: 148.

19. Supposedly in the 1920s when a reporter prefaced his question to Arthur Eddington (who in 1919 first substantiated a key prediction of Einstein's general theory of relativity) with "Sir Eddington, it is said that you are one of only three men in the world who understand Einstein's theories of relativity ..." Eddington wryly interrupted the reporter: "I'm trying to think: Who is the third?" Hawking'96: 108a, Kirshner'03: 54–6 & 269n3 or Rees'97: 69.

20. A refined test of general relativity is the Gravity Probe B project planned for launch in 2002—*Nature* Science Update 3Mar'01. For updates go to http:// einstein.stanford.edu/

21. Between microwave and infrared frequencies is 'terahertz' radiation until recently a neglected band with properties similar to X-rays without the hazards—*NewScientist* 14Sept'02: 34–7.

22. Quip attributed to Richard Gregory cited by Velmans: 141.

23. Photon's frequency/energy—Lindley: 37 & 42. But then you might ask: Frequency of what? What's vibrating? Regarded as a light wave, we're accustomed to waves having motion at various frequencies. But regarded as a particle or packet, is it pulsating like an ultra-tiny heart? Or third, should it be regarded as an ultramicroscopic vibrating string, per Greene? On shifting the frequency of light beams, see *NewScientist* 24May'03: 14–5.

24. Light's own perspective, see Gribbin: 79 and Lindley: 148.

25. There are recent proposals that in the early Universe the speed of light was greater than it is now and that particles can travel 'faster-than-light' using quantum tunnelling. See *NewScientist* 24Jul'99: 28–32, *NewScientist* Inside Science #147 19Jan'02 and *Scientific American* Apr'03: 28. Another proposal is that the speed of light varies with the photon's energy level—*NewScientist* 8Feb'03: 28–32 & 46–9.

26. Squeezed space and stretched time explanations can give an intellectual acceptance of 'gravity' but not necessarily an intuitive grasp; for 'intellectual' read mathematics. In physics the language of the intellect more and more is becoming mathematics.

27. Wave-particle duality—Lindley: 54 and Stenger: 49.

28. Entanglement—"... it is not correct to think of entangled particles as separate entities. In some respects, entangled particles do not have their own individual properties but behave as a single entity." "What does entanglement mean? What does it tell us about the world and about the nature of space and time?" "Entangled particles transcend space. The two or three entangled entities are really parts of one system, and that system is unaffected by physical distance between its components. The system acts as a single entity." Aczel'01: 198, 249 & 252.

29. Nonlocality and the uncertainty principle—Aczel'01: 76ff, Lindley: 152 & 21 and McFadden: 148–50 &c.

30. Einstein thought it was ignorance and spent nearly the last forty years of his life unsuccessfully searching for an explanation in the belief that "God does not play dice." Could it be that his belief in an omniscient, omnipotent God somehow got in his way or is it truly beyond our grasp? (But "Late in life, however, he concluded, 'In their struggle for the ethical good, teachers of religion must have the stature to give up the doctrine of a personal God.'" Larson: 89) However Loewenstein: 41–4 argues that *"... the randomness in deterministic chaos is fundamental; gathering more information won't help."* [his italics]

31. Good mechanic—The head of the mechanical engineering department where I was a student back in the early '50s decried what he called 'cookbook' engineering. He wanted us to understand why, not just how, something works. "... but quantum physics is taught as engineering ... don't try to think what's really happening ... Don't think. Calculate." Schwartz & Begley: 280. My professor would be appalled. But than he wasn't teaching quantum mechanics.

32. Over a dozen interpretations—McFadden: 211.

33. Quantum experiments—Aczel'01 thru-out.

34. With apologies to Robert Browning: "Man's grasp exceeds his reach or what's a metaphor?" At least so far no one's come up with a metaphor to 'reach' across this chasm so we can intuitively 'grasp' a concept of the microscopic realm.

35. Adapting to the microscopic—Omnès'99a: 164.

36. Help may arrive in 'string theory' as explored in Greene's fairly readable *The Elegant Universe*. (Interestingly I find no mention of 'string theory' in either of Omnès' books.) While string theory and its progeny provide comprehensive theoretical explanations for both relativity and quantum mechanics phenomena, so far they have not proved susceptible to experimental verification. And while it is interesting to pursue this vein of thinking, for our purposes we need go no further at

this point. Moreover Greene: 385 at the end of his excellent book speculated "... maybe there is a limit to comprehensibility." Omnès99a: 253 asserts that our mind is limited in its ability to invent concepts or paradigms and must resort to formalism, namely mathematics, in dealing with relativity and quantum physics. Also Lindley: 222–6, *Scientific American* Feb'01: 68–75 & ~Dec'02: 40–1, and *NewScientist* 29Jun'02: 30–4. An alternative to string theory called 'loop quantum gravity' is described in *Science* 8Nov'02: 1166–7 and *Scientific American* Jan'04: 66–75.

37. Light impervious to decoherence—Omnès'99a: 202 & ~'99b: 196.

38. Recently scientists are discovering that there are a great many life forms underground and at the bottom of the ocean that don't depend on the Sun for energy but thrive on other sources. In fact these life forms may predate Sun dependent life forms which will be explored in Chapter Six.

39. Reductionism—Stewart & Cohen: 33–46 and Weinberg: 51ff. Morowitz: 14 "The reductionist approach leads us continually to seek solutions at lower and lower hierarchical levels. To move conceptually in the other direction, we must apply pruning algorithms and seek for emergent properties or entities that become the agents for advancing another hierarchical level."

40. Synergy has gotten a bad name lately because corporations, such as Time-Warner and AOL, used the concept as a rationale for mergers predicting that it not only will produce economies of scale such as saving the cost of duplicate facilities, but more importantly will generate synergy such as increasing sales by linking markets. Even if the potential exists, the merged parts have to fit together, not easy when cultural differences and inflated egos are involved. As I write the 'synergy' of the AOL Time-Warner merger isn't the touted 1+1=3 but =0.7 (per Jan30'03 Newshour with Jim Lehrer).

41. See Holland'95 and ~'98 thru-out for a mathematical approach to emergence. Also see R.Coren: 80–5, Crick: 11, Donald'01: 32, Goodwin: 176 & 181–7, Johnson: thru-out, Lewin 12–3, Mayr'97: 19–20, Stewart & Cohen: 64 & 205 and Mark Taylor: 13–4. The term 'synergy' is used in a narrow sense in business (where I first encountered it), education and medicine to describe the effect of combining diverse inputs, "more bang for the buck" (see MW dictionary). Here I'm using the term to signify a unique quality that can emerge beyond any properties observed in the constituents. However Corning'83: 81–2 footnote & 397, argues that synergism is broader than emergence, in that a unique property or thing can emerge without benefit of synergy, but he doesn't cite any examples. In Corning'03: 5 & 103–52 he defines it in great detail and more broadly than I would. Morowitz thruout his book on *Emergence* does a commendable job of tracing 28 examples of emergence from the Big Bang onward, but with a teleological perspective saying that Teilhard de Chardin is his role model (p.15)—it's worth perusing but with the *caveat* that he's seeking God. Solé & Goodwin offer a lot more science with no religion as does Chaisson.

42. On the limits of reductionism, Horgan: 259 cites Philip Anderson's "More Is Different" in *Science* in 1972: "Particle physics cannot predict the behavior of water, let alone the behavior of humans. Reality is a hierarchical structure ... 'At each stage, entirely new laws, concepts, and generalizations are necessary, requir-

ing inspiration and creativity ... Psychology is not applied biology, nor is biology applied chemistry.'"

43. Plato in his *Republic* advocated that philosophers (read scientists?) should be the rulers, or alternatively that rulers should be philosophers. But in a democratic society all citizens participate in ruling, thus all citizens should be philosophers/scientists.

44. It's recently been argued that back then "... the center of the universe was not a position of importance. To the contrary, it was the lowest point—in Galileo's words, 'the sump where the universe's filth and ephemera collect.'"— *Scientific American* Mar'01: 24A. This seems more consistent with their hierarchical world-view back then: God was up above high in Heaven, the angels and saints (lesser gods) were in the clouds, man and beasts were on Earth, and the devil and damned were down below under the Earth. So depending on how one lived their life, after death they'd either be raised up or be dragged down (as shown in paintings of that day).

45. Ascribing these alternative worldviews to Aristotle/Ptolemy and Copernicus is an oversimplification for brevity's sake. For a more accurate elucidation see Kuhn'57 who traces the Copernican Revolution up to Newton. Also see *Science* 7Sept'01: 1769–70 on the affect of the Ptolemaic cosmology's loss on society then and now.

Chapter Five—Earth's Beginnings

1. The belief that galaxies are moving away is based on the red-shift in the light from distant galaxies which was first noted by Slipher, Hubble and Humason in the 1920s. Hubble concluded that the red-shift was due to the Doppler effect similar to what we experience standing at the side of a road as a car passes by. The pitch of its sound appears to drop because the sound waves that were being bunched together as the car approached are now being stretched as the car moves away. The faster the car moves away the more its sound waves are stretched out and so the lower their apparent pitch. The same thing happens with light waves: the faster their source is moving away the more the light waves are stretched toward the red end of the light spectrum—termed 'redshift' or 'z'. A balloon analogy is often used to envision the Universe's expansion: Take a partially inflated balloon and with a felt-tipped marker put dots on it. Then as you blow the balloon bigger the dots move away from each other. The farther two dots were separated on the partially inflated balloon, the faster they move apart as you continue to inflate the balloon. For example, mark any dot as your 'home' dot and note that another dot that was an inch away might now be two inches away but some other dot that was three inches away would now be six inches away. While the first dot moved one inch, the second moved three inches. So just as the whole balloon is expanding at the same rate, our Universe is all expanding at the same rate even though the parts farther away look like they're going faster. And just as the balloon started small,

our Universe must have started much smaller. Hence not only are distant galaxies moving away but the space between is being stretched out as their light travels through it to reach us. See Hogan: 50–1, Kirshner'02: 68–74 and Lunine: 15–6. Also the Universe's expansion rate appears to be accelerating—Kirshner'02: 234ff, *Science News* Mar31'01: 196 & Aug31'02: 139. For alternative proposals see *Nature* Science Update 2Feb'01.

2. The theory that came to be known as the Big Bang was first proposed by George Gamow in 1947. The man who dubbed the term 'Big Bang', Fred Hoyle, later proposed *nucleosynthesis*, the process by which the elements of matter were created in the Big Bang and subsequently in stars as described below. See Hawkins: 20 & 102, Maddox: 28–32 and Rees'00: 67–8. However Hoyle is among the dwindling number of cosmologists who don't believe the Big Bang theory; instead he and his colleagues propose a "quasi-steady state" model as described in *A Different Approach to Cosmology: ...* Cambridge U.Press, 2000 reviewed in *Science* 15Dec'00: 2079–80. For more on Hoyle see Rees'97: thru-out.

3. Cosmic background radiation—Adams & Laughlin: 17–20, Chown: 155ff, Hogan: 77, Kirshner'02: 114–7, and Rees'97: 49–54, and *Science News* Oct27'01: 261, *Science* 22Mar'02: 2223–5 and *NewScientist* 26Apr'03: 50–1. AT&TWorldnet Feb11'03 reported that a robotic NASA probe, called WMAP—the Wilkinson Microwave Anisotropy Probe, about a million miles from Earth was able to look back in time to just 380,000 years after the Big Bang determining the age of the Universe as 13.7 billion years and that stars started shining 200 million years after the Big Bang (or only 75my, *Science* 20Jun'03: 1906c); also see *Nature* Science Update 13Feb'03; *Science* 14Feb'03: 991, ~28Feb'03: 1333–4, ~7Mar'03: 1532–3 and ~2May'03: 730–1; *Science News* Feb15'03: 99–100 and *NewScientist* 15Feb'03: 12–3 (for a good explanation) and ~5Apr'03.

4. Even though we can't know what came before the Big Bang, some cosmologists still speculate. One idea is that the Big Bang was really a Big Bounce after an earlier Big Crunch so that our Universe goes through cycles of contraction and expansion—*Nature* Science Update 26Apr'02 and AT&T Worldnet Apr25'02. Another idea is that our Universe is just one of many *multiverses* and that ours just happens to be 'tuned' just right for life's emergence—Rees'00: 3–4. Still another regards space as pre-existing and the gravitational field as negative energy with all other energy as positive (which was then channeled into matter) so that at the beginning the net total energy of the Universe was zero—Davies'99: 61–2. And yet another employs string theory—*NewScientist* 3Jun'00, 24–7 and *Scientific American* Mar'02: 25–6. Still another employs 'braneworlds'—*NewScientist* 29Sept'01: 24–29 and *Science* 26Apr'02: 639. Also see Kaku: 350–3.

5. I'm puzzled by the use of 'seconds' in the literature describing the Big Bang. It seems to me that if space was enormously compacted, then time was enormously dilated and so 'seconds' has a different meaning than we commonly use. See Hogan'98: 55.

6. Early stages of the Big Bang—Adams & Laughlin: 3–13, Davies'99: 61–2, Delsemme: 19–21 & 289–4, Hawking'96: 148–9, Rees'97: 151ff and ~'00: 117ff. Also

see *Science News* Apr28'01: 261, *Science* 20Jun'03: 1910 and Kirshner'02: 254 (earlier estimate). On acoustic oscillations see *Science* 22Jun'01: 2302–3. On quark-gluon plasma re-creation see *Science News* Jun21'03: 387.

7. The status of proton, neutron, quark &c investigations is reported in *Science* 15Dec'00: 2083–4 & 2117–9.

8. Big Bang photons—Chown: 197–9, Delsemme: 289; *Science* 4May'01: 823 and ~22Jun'01: 2234–8.

9. Dark Ages—*Science News* Aug11'01: 84, *Science* 22Mar'02: 2194–5 and *Nature* Science Update 13Feb'03 saying 380,000 yrs is based on WMAP data (notes above & below). Also see *Science* 2May'03: 730–1.

10. The CMB temperature varies ±0.0002K which is interpreted as ripples or polarization of the CMB—*Science* 27Sept'02: 2184 and ~15Nov'02: 1349–50; *Science News* Sept28'02: 195, ~Dec21&28'02: 390 and ~Feb15'03: 99–100; and *NewScientist* 28Sept'02: 14, ~11Jan'03: 24–7 & 28–31 and ~15Feb'03: 12–3.

11. Most of the 4% baryonic matter consists of non-luminous components such as intergalactic gas, brown dwarfs and smaller free planets and asteroids, neutrinos and primordial black holes—see Hawkings: 138–9, Rees'00: 76–81 and ~'97: 104ff, and *Science News* Oct13'01: 234–6, ~Jan5'02: 5 and *Science* 20Jun'03: 1909–13. Also suspect are white dwarfs—AT&TWorldnet Mar22'01 citing a *Science* report of that date. The leading candidate for the other 23% dark matter is 'Cold Collisionless Dark Matter' (CCDM) of which a subclass is WIMPs (weakly interacting massive particles)—Kirshner'02: 130 & 138, *Science* 20Jun'03: 1909–13 and *Nature* Science Update 8Jul'03. And then there's 'dark energy'—*Nature* Science Update 2Feb'01 & 23Jul'03 and *Scientific American* Aug'02: 42–52, ~Mar'03: 50–9 & ~Jul'03: 20–1, *Science* 20Jun'03: 1914–8 & ~25Jul'03: 449, *Science News* Aug2'03: 67 and Kirshner'02: 254–9. WMAP (cited in notes above) "... shows that over 73% of the Universe is made of 'dark energy' — a mysterious force that appears to be pushing the cosmos apart. Another 23% is made of 'dark matter', a whole family of particles that has so far eluded detection by astronomers and high-energy physicists. ¶That leaves just 4% for the rest — galaxies, stars, planets and people, everything made up of atoms." *Nature* Science Update 13Feb'03. Also see *NewScientist* 5Apr'03: 30–3 & ~7Jun'03: 25 and *Nature* Science Update 26May'03.

12. Dark matter detected by warped space making our Milky Way galaxy spin faster than it should due to its visible matter alone. Thus it's theorized there must be invisible 'dark' matter surrounding our galaxy that warps our 'gravity whirlpool' deeper than would the visible matter by itself. (Explained below.)

13. Dark energy accelerating expansion—Kirshner'02: 255. An alternative explanation 'tweaks' Einstein's gravity which not only explains the acceleration currently but immediately after the Big Bang—*Nature* Science Update 3Jul'03.

14. This rubber sheet and BBs analogy is helpful in visualizing space-time warpage, but like most analogies it 'limps' and can be misleading. The weight of the BBs warps the sheet because of 'gravity' 'pulling' them down, but we're trying to get away from this concept of 'gravity.' Instead try thinking of matter as contracting the space all around it: "Mass warps space-time and space-time tells mass where to go."

However in the literature Newton's 'gravity' is frequently used as a shorthand description of the process and admittedly can be helpful in visualizing the process. Moreover Einstein's calculations are said to be much more difficult than Newton's inverse-square calculations. Recently it's proposed that magnetism 'stiffened' the 'rubber sheet'—*Nature* Science Update 12Jun'01 and *Science* 22Jun'01: 2230.

15. My description of galaxy and star formation is based mostly on Rees'00: 109–13 with some imaginative license. I also relied on recent evidence of acceleration in the expansion of space; see *Science* 26Nov'99: 1689–90. For recent alternative explanations and a taste of the complexity of galaxy formation see *Science* 7Jan'00: 61–91; ~1Jun'01: 1629–3; ~19Oct'01: 537–8; ~4Jan'02: 51–3, 63–91 & 93–98 and ~20Jun'03: 1893–1909. Also *Scientific American* Mar'02: 64–71 and ~Jun'02: 46–52, and *Science News* Jun8'02: 362–4.

16. Nuclear fusion is the merging or fusing of lighter elements into heavier elements. The most basic example is four hydrogen atoms, each with one proton and one electron, fusing (in two steps) into one helium atom with two protons, two neutrons and two electrons. The resulting helium atom has 7‰ less mass (roughly the two lost electrons) than did the four hydrogen atoms. This lost mass m is converted to energy E per Einstein's formula $E=mc^2$, so that a very large amount of energy is produced from a small amount of mass due to the extremely large value of the speed of light c squared. See Rees'97: 9.

17. Brown dwarfs—*Science* 26Oct'01: 801 and ~21Jun'02: 2154.

18. Neutrinos are also produced in stars &al but they have proved elusive to study—*Science* 12Jul'02: 184–7; *Scientific American* Jul'02: 70–7 and *NewScientist* 7Dec'02: 32–7, 38–9 & 40–3.

19. On red giants and the various dwarf stars see Adams & Laughlin: 42–50 & 58–6; Delsemme: 53–6; *Scientific American* Apr'00: 76–83 and *Science* 23Mar'01: 2293–4. Even smaller dwarfs of failed stars have recently been identified—*Nature* Science Update 3Apr'01. On simulations of white dwarfs see *Science* 3Jan'03: 53–4 & 77–81.

20. In fusing elements, starting with helium on up through iron each successive heavier element yields less and less energy from its production. Elements heavier than iron must consume energy for their production. Harwit: 13–9 and Rees'00: 44 & 47.

21. Supernova—in addition to type II, there's type Ia which is a white dwarf that's somehow increased its mass (by accreting a companion?) so it can become a star-size thermonuclear explosion. Kirshner'02: 28–31 & 140. On their lopsided egg-shaped explosion see *Nature* Science Update 13Aug'03.

22. Clouds between stars—*Scientific American* Jan'02: 34–43. Each successive generation of stars was 'polluted' by heavier elements from earlier generations so first- and second-generation stars were relatively 'clean'—*Science* 1Nov'02: 939–41. Also see *Science News* May24'03: 328–9, and Letters to *Nature* 17Jul'03 and AT&T Worldnet Jul16'03 on dust. 'Star stuff' was Carl Sagan's term.

23. On supernovae see Adams & Laughlin: 53–8, Delsemme: 48–54, Harwit: 19–20 and Rees'00: 44–5. On neutron stars and pulsars see Blair & McNamara: 79ff

and ENN News 7/4/00. Neutron stars can produce extreme magnetism—*Scientific American* Feb'03: 34–41.

24. Our galaxy, the Milky Way, is believed to have a massive black hole lurking at its center obscured by surrounding clouds penetrated only by radio- and X-rays. Improved imaging recently revealed not just one but many sources, perhaps a concentration of cannibalizing, exploding and collapsing massive stars per *Nature* Science Update 10Jan'02. More recently the decade-long tracking of stars orbiting the center of our Galaxy confirms the presence of a black hole several million times the mass of our Sun—*Nature* Science Update 17Oct'02 & ~17Feb'03, *Science* 30May'03: 1356–8, *Science News* Jun21'03: 394–6, *NewScientist* 21Jun'03: 24 and *Scientific American* Jul'03: 20–1 & 34–41. There appear to be other black holes in our Galaxy—*NewScientist* 5Apr'03: 20. On some other galaxies' black holes see *Science* 21Dec'01: 2516–8, ~1Mar'02: 1653–4 & 1688–91 and ~8Mar'02: 1874–7. Also see *NewScientist* 19Oct'02 Inside Science 154. On black holes at the cosmic dawn, see *Science* 2May'03: 752–3.

25. A quasar shines a beam of red-shifted light brighter than the rest of its galaxy—Rees'00: 112. On black holes at galaxies' centers see *Science* 1Sept'00: 1484–5. On high energy astrophysics see *Science* 5Jan'01: 65–92. On black holes in the early Universe, see AT&T WorldNet Mar13'01 and *Nature* Science Update 10Jan'03. For a counter opinion see *NewScientist* 19Jan'02: 26–30.

26. Gamma-rays, black holes—*Scientific American* Dec'02: 84–91. Also see *Science News* Sept28'02: 205.

27. Stars encircling Milky Way—AT&T Worldnet Jan6'03, *Nature* Science Update 7Jan'03, *Science* 10Jan'03: 183 and *Scientific American* Mar'03: 38.

28. Colliding stars and galaxies—*Scientific American* Nov'02: 44–51, *Science News* Dec14'02: 376–7 and *Science* 28Jun'02: 2350–4.

29. Other stars' planets—over seventy huge planets (≥Jupiter) have been spotted in our Galaxy outside our Solar System. Two spacecraft missions—NASA's Kepler and ESA's Eddington—are planned to search for smaller habitable planets. See *Nature* Science Update 15Jan'02 & 14Jun'02. It's looking as if Giordano Bruno was correct even before 1600—we may not be alone in the Universe.

30. For the abundances of the various elements see Harwit: 24–5. Notice that from carbon on, the even-number elements are more abundant because they are multiples of helium. There seems to be disagreement in *Nature* 21Feb'02 whether our Solar System disk was formed from debris of at least two supernovae (Yin, Jacobsen & Yamashita) or from ejecta of the inner solar nebula (Clayton).

31. "... the Sun accounts for about 99.9 percent of the mass of our Solar System, ..." per Hawkins: 118.

32. This explanation was liberally adapted primarily from Harwit: 21–35 & 413–434 as well as Delsemme: 69ff.

33. Gravitational waves are predicted by Einstein's general relativity but so far have not been detected; still the search continues—*ScienceNews* Jan8'00: 26–8, AT&T Worldnet Jan23'02 and *Scientific American* Apr'02: 62–71 & Aug'03: 25–6. Also see Blair & McNamara, and Thorne. But imagine in the rubber sheet analogy above what would happen to the BBs if you gave the sheet a good whack. That's

what a massive gravitational wave could do to the space of the protosolar cloud with its dust grains, and gas atoms and molecules. Magnetic fields and shock compression are also implicated; see Harwit: 413ff. Recent evidence points to a supernova explosion—*Science* 11Apr'03: 265–7.

34. Recently an alternative to heating and re-cooling has been proposed for the melting of dust grains and refreezing into chondrules, namely, that a nearby gamma-ray burst seared the dust into droplets that cooled into chondrules—*NewScientist* 11Sept'99: 17. Still another alternative is the cycling of dust grains into and out of dense gas clouds where their materials are processed by radiation—*Scientific American* Dec'00: 70–5. Also see *Science* 2Mar'01: 1776–9. Then again maybe meteoriticists are at a dead end—*Science* 31Aug'01: 1581–4.

35. Carbonaceous chondrites are named for their carbon-rich compounds which provided the base materials for life and perhaps 'fossil fuels' through fractionation—Gold: 38ff and Harwit: 428.

36. About a tenth of the cloud probably was ejected in clumps axially along magnetic field-lines that formed perpendicular to the disk—*Scientific American* Aug'00: 42–7 and *NewScientist* 17May'03: 26–9. Water may also have been involved to cool the forming star—*Science* 24Nov'00: 1513–4. From observations of stars forming in the Orion nebula it appears that our young Sun was a hundred times more active than today—*NewScientist* 15Sept'01: 10 and *Science* 21Sept'01: 2188–9. On the formation of Jupiter-like planets see *Nature* and ~ Science Update 4Jul'02, *Science* 29Nov'02: 1698–9 and *Science News* Jan25'03: 56–8.

37. ProtoSun blasts—"Based on data from NASA's orbiting Chandra X-ray Observatory, [of young stars in the Orion Nebula] it appears that the sun threw more tantrums than expected, in the form of powerful x-ray flares that zapped the surrounding disk of gas and dust." *Science* 8Mar'02: 1813 and *NewScientist* 19Oct'02: 23. For what appears to be an excellent book on today's Sun see Zirker thru-out, which I acquired long after completing this chapter.

38. Most meteorites are believed to have formed 4.567 billion years ago during the condensation of the protoSun's cloud and therefore provide samples for analysis of that time. Thus they yield information about our solar system's age, chemical composition, cooling rates &c—Delsemme: 76–82, Harwit: 31–5 & 427–32 and Lunine: 107b–110b; and *Science* 6Sept'02: 1658–9, 11Oct'02: 350–1 & 6Jun'03: 1513–4. This last citation asserts that 64% of Earth had formed within 10 million years after formation of the solar system 4.567 billion years ago and that by 30 million years Earth was fully grown when the Moon formed. But Earth's mantle has materials ratios not represented in meteorite collections implying that Earth must instead be composed of unsampled 'Earth chondrite' or 'Earth achondrite'—*Nature* 7Mar'02. Recently it's been argued that Earth's age is 20my older than believed—*Nature* Science Update 29Aug'02.

39. On the formation of Earth—Delsemme: 101–4, *Nature* Science Update 4Jan'01 and *Science* 6Jun'03: 1513–4.

40. The Moon is currently spiraling away from Earth at some four centimeters per year. Earth's rotation was probably speeded up by the protoMoon's impact but has since slowed considerably—shortly after the Moon formed a 'day' was

probably less that twelve hours; Delsemme: 104–5, Drury: 181, Lunine: 127b-130a & 209b-210a, Spudis: 164–9 and Ward: 221–34. Some even argue that initially Earth's 'day' was only three hours and the Moon's 'month' was only nine hours. Others contend that the debris that fell back to Earth tilted the Moon's orbit five degrees from Earth's orbital plane, per *NewScientist* supplements 7Aug'99 and 19Feb'00: 10. A more recent model gives an initial 'day' of five hours, per *Nature* 16Aug'01 as reported in *Nature* Science Update 16Aug'01 and AT&T WorldNet Aug17'01; also see *Scientific American* Nov'01: 18 and *Science* 4Jul'03: 84–7. (Actually there's also a smaller tide on the opposite side of Earth.)

41. The Earth would look pockmarked like the Moon does now if Earth hadn't 'healed' its wounds. Both bodies were pummeled by planetesimals but the Moon—being only one-hundredth Earth's mass—cooled faster and didn't retain an atmosphere, so its craters remain pretty much unchanged—Spudis: 16–21ff. It's recently been concluded that a flurry of impacts 3.9 billion years ago inundated the Moon and presumably Earth; see *Science* 1Dec'00: 1677&1754–6 and *NewScientist* 9Mar'02: 7. Given Earth's greater mass it seems we should have swept up a greater percentage of passing planetesimals than the Moon which might be explained if the asteroid punched thru erupting lava to cover the hole—*NewScientist* 14Dec'02: 16–7. There is recent evidence of a huge impact 3.5 billion years ago in what is now South Africa and Western Australia (back then Gondwana?)—*Science* 23Aug'02: 1325–7, *Science News* Aug24'02 and AT&T Worldnet Aug22'02.

42. On the comets and early atmosphere see Delsemme: 113–24 and Lunine: 130a–132a. On the Oort cloud of comets, see *Nature* 1Feb'01, 589–91. On the comets' organic compounds see *Science News* May19'01: 317–9 and *Scientific American* Aug'01: 44–51.

43. On the Earth's core see *NewScientist* 14Oct'00 Inside Science #134 insert and *Science News* Sept22'01: 191 citing *Nature* 6Sept'01. *Discover* Aug'02: 35–42 discusses a largely ignored theory that Earth's inner core is a nuclear reactor. Also see *Science* 14Mar'03: 1675–7 & ~2May'03: 789–91, *Nature* Science Update 8May'03 & 15May'03 and *Scientific American* Aug'03: 24–5.

44. Tides—*Science* 19Jul'02: 348–9.

45. Water sources—*Science News* Mar23'02: 184–6. It's believed that "Earth's lower mantle may store about five times more H_2O than the oceans."—*Science* 8Mar'02: 1885–7 and *Nature* Science Update 8Mar'02. Also see *Nature* Science Update 27Sept'99 and *Science News* Mar9'02: 147c-148b.

46. Currently the wobble amounts to twenty feet at the North Pole with a 433 day cycle per a report in the Aug1'00 issue of *Geophysical Research Letters* according to ENN News Jul18'00 and *Science* 4Aug'00: 710. Another recent study suggests that in addition to wobbling, the Earth's shell may slip around on the mantle while the core maintains its rotational axis thus making it look as though the pole wanders over the Earth. It is thought to be caused by "a mantle overturn event" which also affects the Earth's magnetism and triggers plate changes—*Science* 21Jan'00: 406–7 & 455–9 and ~27Jun'03: 2044–5 & 2084-6.

47. Earth's heat escapes to space as infrared radiation. The greenhouse gases act like the glass in your car on a sunny day: the glass lets in the visible radiation

which warms the seats &c causing them to radiate infrared which the glass blocks thus holding the heat in the car.

48. There is not just one form of crust as I've implied, but at least three: The type I've been describing is called primary crust none of which has survived. Secondary crusts form when heating by the core's crystallization and radioactive decay melts the interior into *basaltic lavas* which ooze from underwater vents to cover the ocean floors. Tertiary crusts form when surface layers are plowed back into the mantle by the moving plates (*plate tectonics*), are melted and resurface as low density, granite-like rock forming the continents. In addition a thick layer of very dense rock underlies the crusts of both the oceans and the continents—*Scientific American*, Jan'96: 76–81. How mantle slabs drive plate tectonics—*Science* 4Oct'02: 207–9.

49. See "Snowball Earth," *NewScientist*, 6Nov'99: 28–33 and *Scientific American*, Jan'00: 68–75 including the hyperlink to "The First Ice Age." However a Discovery News Brief 11/1/99 indicts increasing oxygen as the culprit for the snowball Earth 2.3 billion years ago and *Scientific American* Sept'01: 20–2 indicts 'methane addiction' as the trigger between 750- and 580-mya (million years ago). See also *Science* 10Mar'00: 1734–6 & ~31Mar'00: 2421. Doubts persist—*NewScientist* 9Jun'01: 12 & ~15Dec'01: 15, and *Science News* Oct19'02: 246.

50. For a compatible alternative speculation on what happened to reduce carbon dioxide see Schopf: 255ff or Ward: 113–24.

51. Rodinia and Pangaea—*Science* 30May'03: 1379–81.

52. Earth's interior energy is produced by cooling, by the latent heat of crystallization of the largely iron core and by radioactive decay—*Science* 14Mar'03: 1675–7 & *Nature* Science Update 8May'03.

53. On the chain of volcanoes formed by subducting ocean plates see *Nature* Science Update 16Sept'99.

54. Yellowstone has been hyped as "Created by the largest volcanic explosions in the planet's history—the Earth's greatest thermal spectacle ..." (PBS promo for Jan31'01 "The Living Edens" show: "Yellowstone: America's Sacred Wilderness"). Keys: 273 believes that Yellowstone will someday erupt again cataclysmically. But there are recent reports that it has no deep plume—*Science* 3Jan'03: 35–6; also see ~9May'03: 920–1 & 921–2. On Africa's Afar volcanoes see *Science* 12Oct'01: 287.

55. For this section I primarily used Lunine: 77–98, 165–176, 196–210 & 240–252. For a less technical but graphically descriptive overview see Dixon &al *Cassell's Atlas of Evolution*.

56. On supercontinent cycles and how the mantle shapes the Earth's surface, see *Scientific American* Jan'96: 81 and Mar'01: 40–7.

57. Himalayas' formation—*Nature* Science Update 26Aug'99.

58. Reflected Sun light and infrared light, 'Earthshine', is being studied as it reflects off the shaded part of the Moon; see *Nature* Science Update 29Jan'02.

59. The Sahara and Arabian deserts were caused by a slight change in Earth's orbit and the tilt of its axis thousands of years ago according to research reported by ENN 7/12/99.

60. There's convincing evidence that Earth's magnetic field reversed, flipped, many times in the past (paleomagnetism); see Denton: 198, Klein & Edgar: 68 and Lunine: 26 & 89b–91a. Then are we to infer that the VanAllen radiation belts collapsed with each flip exposing Earth to the solar winds and cosmic rays? Moreover the Earth's magnetic poles are not aligned with the Earth's axis—geomagnetic north is around 79°N, 71°W (it wanders around). Is this because the Earth's iron core somehow rotates on its own offset axis as it generates Earth's magnetic flux? Did the core itself flip periodically causing the magnetic flips but without the VanAllens' collapse? (The Sun's magnetic field is wild!) And is the Earth's core somewhat displaced by the Moon's 'gravity' like ocean tides as Earth rotates? Rather it's now believed that Earth's magnetic field is generated by dynamo action in a rotating electrically conducting field flowing in the molten iron inside Earth's mantle and core—*Science* 8Mar'02: 1887–90. There's evidence it'll soon reverse—*NewScientist* 13Apr'02: 11c & *Scientific American* Nov'02: 24. There's speculation that inverted mounts are formed of lighter materials below Earth's crust which periodically collapse disrupting Earth's magnetic field—*Discover* Mar'03: 13a. On the magnetosphere and its exploration see *NewScientist* 2Aug'03: 30–3.

61. Asteroids' 'bicentennial'—*Science News* Jul28'01: 61–3.

62. On asteroid impacts see Delsemme: 187–91, Leakey'95: 52–8, Poag thru-out, *NewScientist* 11Dec'99 Inside Science, ~29Apl.'00: 19d and ~4May'02: 28–31, *Science News* Jun15'02: 378–80 & 382, Discovery News Brief 11/29/99 and *Scientific American* Aug'03: 84–5.

63. The Tunguska devastation is now proposed to have been the result of a high-pressure gas explosion—*NewScientist* 7Sept'02: 14 and *Science* 13Sept'02: 1803.

64. On the Willamette Meteorite, the Museum and the Confederated Tribes of the Grand Ronde Community of Oregon agreed that the meteorite will stay at the Museum but that the tribes have access to it. See www.amnh.org/rose/meteorite.

65. Earth's destruction—Adams & Laughlin: 50. As described above, as our star, the Sun, ages it will swell into a red giant engulfing Earth. However some argue that in the process the mass the Sun loses will reduce its 'gravitational pull' on Earth so our planet's orbit will recede away from the red giant Sun; see *NewScientist* 19Jan'02: 24.

66. The two gases, hydrogen and oxygen molecules, when they combined would give off energy in the form of heat which initially would result in steam until cooled to liquid water. Still Emsley: 190 states "Nothing could be simpler than a water molecule, yet nothing is as complex in its behaviour." Horgan: 259 citing Philip Anderson, observes that "Particle physics cannot predict the behavior of water, let alone the behavior of humans."

67. In addition to the familiar three forms of matter, a fourth is plasma (as in fluorescent light tubes) and a fifth is Bose-Einstein condensate (recently produced at near absolute zero temperatures; see *Science* 23Mar'01: 2301–3).

68. For a comprehensive elucidation on water see Ball thru-out and *Nature* Science Update 28Jan'99, ~17Aug'01 & ~7Nov'01 by him. Also see McFadden: 99 & 121–2; *Science* 16Mar'01: 2043 (Water Workings), 2106, 2118ff & 2121ff;

~14Dec'01: 2305ff (Glassy Water); ~23Aug'02: 1288–9 (Water and Ice) and ~29Nov'02: 1722–3 (Water in Confinement); *Scientific American* Aug'01: 44–51 (amorphous ice in space) and *Science News* Feb10'01: 111a & ~Nov30'02: 340. On water's importance for Life see Audesirks: 28–32.

69. Anthropic principle quotes—Delsemme: 253–4 and Denton: 389. Also see Duve'02: 298–301 and *NewScientist* 10Jun'00: 32–5.

70. Arrogance—An anthropocentric conundrum (Does sound only exist if a human hears it?) attributed to Bishop George Berkeley (by Daniel N. Robinson) inspired a cartoon by Shel Silverstein: "Does a tree . falling . . alone . . . in a forest . . . . . make any sound?" He shows a huge old tree falling . . . hitting the ground . . . and saying "SHIT!" (*Different Dances* 1979, pages un-numbered)

71. Fine-tuned Universe—*Scientific American* Jan03: 35. Parallel Universes—*Scientific American* Apr'03: 40–51.

Chapter Six—Life's Beginnings

1. Brain-dead—*NewScientist* 7Jul'01: 38–41.

2. The bacteria *Escherichia coli* has at least two strains. The non-pathogenic laboratory strain is *E. coli* K-12. The DNA of the lethal *E. coli* O157:H7 was recently decoded; see *Nature* 25Jan'01. (E. coli is not to be confused with E-mail altho both have strains that can be disastrous.)

3. At this point Life's Beginnings is not addressing the moral or legal question of when human life begins in the womb.

4. For a thoughtful essay on 'Life' see *Science* 22Mar'02: 2215–6. Also see Mc-Fadden: 13–6 & 256–8 for a quantum approach to Life. Adams'02: 167 refers to Noam Lahav's *Biogenesis* listing "... forty-eight different definitions and characterizations of life, as put forth by scientists and philosophers over the last 150 years."

5. In 1952–3, Stanley Miller filled a flask with gases which he assumed were present in the Earth's primitive atmosphere, inundated it with simulated lightning and after a few days got a rich variety of amino acids, the building blocks of proteins, and components of nucleotides. See Fortey 38, Kauffman: 35–6, Margulis& Sagan'86: 49, Maynard Smith: 31, Rose: 262, Schopf: 122–8, Wills'00: 40–9 or *Science* 2May'03: 745–6.

6. For a comprehensive coverage of how life may have originated see Wills'00 thru-out.

7. On panspermia see Davies'99: 221ff or Rose: 256. On comets seeding life see *NewScientist* 22Jan'00: 4. But it seems to me this may just be a regression back to the old belief that Life came from God in Heaven. Even if life also emerged in the crusts of other planets (Gold: 194ff examines several candidates) an explanation is needed of how it got to Earth. Meteor impacts splashed material into space which eventually landed on neighboring planets, so there might have been such an exchange of life. Evidence of life in a Mars meteorite was reported by AT&T World-Net Feb26'01. Robotic exploration of Mars is ongoing.

8. On carbonaceous chondrites see Harwit: 428 & 562. Also experimenters have been able to simulate the conditions of outer space and "... get artificial cell membranes to form." Per AT&T WorldNet Jan30'01 on report in the *Proceedings of the National Academy of Sciences.* In addition two labs have produced amino acids by simulating conditions in icy, interstellar space—*Science News* Mar30'02: 195.

9. Earth accreted from very cold chondrites from out in space. They were somewhat warmed by release of their gravitational potential energy as they fell just as incoming meteors are today. Those near Earth's surface were vaporized by the impact energy of later incoming planetesimals and comets. Those nearer Earth's core were cooked by the gravitational energy released as the iron core sank. But those in between, if they weren't too close to rising magma, might have been spared and survived largely intact. Over time release of energy from radioactive decay would cause fractionalizing and migration of the chondrites' hydrocarbons toward the surface.

10. On the congeniality of Earth's crust to the emergence of Life see Gold: 168–70. For a scheme of how microbes in the deep crust might have come from the surface see Davies'99: 183–4. A recent experiment subjected bacteria to pressure equivalent to a 160 km column of water and found that 1% survived for 30 hours— *Science* 22Feb'02: 1444–5 & 1514–6.

11. On the deep hot biosphere see Gold thru-out, Adams'02: 173–6, Davies'99: 169–86, Dyson: 18 & 35, Gould'96: 192–5, Howland: 179–82 or Wills'00: 167–73. Most of the other references listed here don't mention Gold's theory. But see *Discover* Jul'99: 76–82 & Mar'02: 10 and *Nature* Science Update 17Jan'02. And the National Science Foundation has funded a five year project in South Africa's ultra deep mines #9978267. Objections—*Science* 14Jun'02: 1982–3.

12. Microbiology in Earth's crust—*Science* 10May'02: 1055–82. Below the ocean floor—*Nature* Science Update 4&9Dec'02, *Science News* Dec7'02: 363 and *NewScientist* 11Jan'03: 13.

13. The term 'cell' was adopted by Robert Hooke to describe plant cells which he discovered in the 1600s. *The World Book*, 1966, vol.3, page 250. See also Rensberger: 6.

14. "Water squeezed between two surfaces turns to jelly ... This behavior could affect proteins in cells ... and rocks moving deep in the earth." Reported in *Nature* Science Update 17Aug'01.

15. Template is used here not just in the sense of a flat pattern to guide your pencil in tracing that pattern, but more like 'jigs & fixtures' in the auto industry: these are devices designed to hold the various pieces in position while they're being assembled and fastened. On the utility of a surface for molecular assembly see Dawkins'87: 157, Dyson: 43–6, Maynard Smith: 32–4, McFadden: 90–2 or Wills'00: 101–2. Also see *Scientific American* Apr'01: 76–85 and *Nature* 21Nov'02: 340–3. A similar theory is Wächtershäuser's pyrite catalysts—Wills'00: 99–100.

16. How might heat and pressure induce molecules to go against entropy and combine into more complex molecules better able to withstand or absorb that heat and pressure? Recall that heat causes molecules to move faster or vibrated

more. Pressure is the resulting force of the molecules pressing against one another or their container walls. Given a template with a pattern that defines a more heat resistant macromolecule, the heat could cause the molecules to bump against the template randomly. As particular molecules just happen to hit their right places and stick, they would be assembled into the macromolecule. If that macromolecule were released somehow—maybe shaken loose by shockwaves—another could be assembled, then another and another replicated. See Loewenstein: 62–5. For recent experiments on the origin of life at high-pressure (rock depth of 7km) see *Science* 25Aug'00: 1307–8 & 1337–40. For a related alternative scenario see note 33 below on RNA forming by absorbing UV light.

17. On several finding the same solution, at the human level it's quite common for several inventors, totally isolated from one another, to come up with the same invention contemporaneously. It seems too common to always be 'just coincidence.' If there's some sort of communication that operates between human molecules, might it also work between macromolecules? In a later chapter we'll examine some 'far out' ideas such as Sheldrake's. For now let's just say this: Sheldrake proposes that there's somehow communication between related organisms (or proto-organisms?) such as yogurt?, plants? ... When one finds a viable solution, it somehow transmits that 'answer' to others, a 'morphic resonance.'

18. On the inevitability of Life emerging—Cech in Rolston: 31, Duve'95: 292 & ~'02: 184–5 and Wills'00: 260. But if Life was inevitable and emerged several times back then, why isn't it still emerging today? Well maybe it is, but it would face far more formidable adversaries now than then. Still with all the habitable volume in the Earth's crust, wouldn't there be somewhere it could hide out and evolve? Maybe there is but we haven't found it yet. (I obtained Conway Morris' *Life's Solution* too late to use here.)

19. On autocatalysis see Kauffman: 49ff—for example 64: "Increase the diversity and atomic complexity of the molecules, and more and more of the reactions among them become catalyzed by members of the system itself. As a threshold diversity is crossed, a giant web of catalyzed reactions crystallizes in a phase transition." It will have a component "... able to form itself by catalyzed reactions from a supply of food molecules. ... Life crystallizes at a critical molecular diversity because catalytic closure itself crystallizes." Also see Casti: 48–9, Loewenstein: 52–3, Lunine: 156–8, Maynard Smith: 6–7 or Margulis&Sagan'86: 53.

20. The Belosov-Zhabotinski reaction, made of some simple organic molecules, sets up two kinds of spatial patterns which oscillate in repeated cycles for long periods. See Goodwin: 45–56, Kauffman: 53–4 or Margulis'98: 78–9.

21. On self-organized criticality see Bak thru-out and Camazine &al thru-out on biological uses. Also see objections of McFadden: 94. Somewhat related is 'random noise'—*NewScientist* 23Nov'02: 19.

22. Quantum superposition—McFadden: 157–60, 167 & 266–70.

23. Microbes in deep biosphere—*Science* 10May'02: 1056–8.

24. For alternate scenarios of Life's origin see Drury: 225–7, Loewenstein: 79–110, Lunine: 156–63 and Wills'00 thru-out. Also see *NewScientist* 15Jul'00: 4–5, ~19Jan'02: 14 and ~11May'02: 7. A theory comparable to the deep hot biosphere is

midocean hydrothermal vents—*Science* 15Mar'02: 2006–7 & ~15Aug'03: 934 and *Science News* Apr26'03: 264–5.

25. On the definition of 'What is Life'? see Davies'99: 36. Dennett: 201 quotes Küppers: "The fact that we obviously are not in a position to give a comprehensive definition of the phenomenon 'life' speaks not against but indeed for the possibility of a completely physical explanation of life phenomena."

26. On the common ancestor view see Davies'99: 70–3, Delsemme: 127, Dennett: 86, Duve'02: 287–8, Eigen: 3, Gee: 82, Margulis&Sagan'86: 49, Mayr: 180 or Schopf: 108. Alternatively see Wills'00: 198–210.

27. Reticulated common ancestral community—Drury: 221–5, Ward: 73–81, Wills'00: 190–2, *Scientific American* Feb'00: 90–5 and *NewScientist* 22Jun'02: 10.

28. Symbiosis—Margulis'98: 5–9 & thru-out and Margulis&Sagan'02: 41, 55 & 98.

29. Protobionts—Wills'00: 139–42.

30. On rRNA as the initial portable template—Dennett: 156–63, Dyson: 38–42, Loewenstein: 106–9, Maynard Smith: 39, Margulis'98: 82, Schopf: 141, Steele: 52–7 or Ward: 65. However some believe an even better candidate than rRNA was PNA (*PeptideNucleic Acids*)—see Casti: 38, Wills'00: 132–6 and *NewScientist* 22Apr'00: 12. And for other alternatives, see *Science* 17Nov'00: 1306–7 and *Nature* Science Update 5Feb'02 & 19Dec'02.

31. RNA's instability at high temperatures—Schopf: 78.

32. Cell wall origin—Duve'02: 85–8 and Schopf: 142–4.

33. Recent evidence of a primordial RNA world—*Science* 11Aug'00: 878–9 and related reports in the same issue. Also see Maynard Smith & Szathmáry: 37–9. A recent computer model of early Earth, before the ozone layer formed to filter out 99% of the ultraviolet light, suggests that "... the secret of RNA's success is the ability of its bases to absorb the energy of the UV light."—*NewScientist* 7Jun'03: 22 (lending support to the above idea that proto-life grew by absorbing a threat's energy to bind molecules).

34. Mass of subterranean life—Gold: 86.

35. My 'zipper' analogy might be a little misleading. Zipper teeth intermesh alternately whereas DNA and RNA nucleotides abut one another 'joining hands.' On the evolution of RNA and DNA see Loewenstein: 82–7 & 107.

36. RNA to DNA—For a detailed scenario of how the evolution from RNA to DNA might have occurred—see Loewenstein: 81–7 & 104–8 and 117–21 for a graphic explanation of why DNA is so stable. However it's now being learned that DNA coils wriggle about constantly—see *Nature* Feature 6Feb'03.

37. Archaea—Howland thru-out. However Margulis&Sagan'02: 154 still group archaea with bacteria. For a review see *Science* 2Mar'01: 1707. "The domain Archaea is now subdivided into two kingdoms—Euryarchaeota and Crenarchaeota—and possibly a third, Korarchaeota."—*Science* 6Jul'01: 56–7. An extremely small parasitic microbe was recently discovered named 'Nanoachaeota'—*Nature* Science Update 2May'02.

38. Extinct domains—Davies'99: 182, Ward: 79–80, *Scientific American* Feb.'00: 94a and *NewScientist* 15Sept'01: 16 (chronocyte).

39. Viruses also spread genes but are not 'alive' since they depend on other cells for metabolism and reproduction—Margulis'98: 63–4 or Margulis&Sagan'02: 39–40. Dennett: 156ff suggests their ancestor might have been a step prior to 'living molecules.' See also Delsemme: 137–8 & 159–60 and *Science* 15Sept'00: 1866–7. It's only recently being realized that a type of viruses that attack bacteria, bacteriophages, are extremely abundant and diverse—*Science News* Jul12'03: 26–8.

40. Gene swapping—Margulis&Sagan'02: 41, 55 & 75 and *Science* 8Aug'03: 745–6.

41. Age of Life's first emergence—Davies'99: 186, Dyson: 31–2 and Schopf: 76–100. Schopf recently used new technology on his 'fossils' with controversial results—*Nature* Science Update 7Mar'02, *Science* 8Mar'02: 1812–3, *NewScientist* 22Feb'03: 28–31 & 31May'03: 20 (the oldest are thermophiles) and *Scientific American* Apr'03: 70–7. Note that these 'fossils' were all found in what is believed to be metamorphic sedimentary rock implying that this Life began on Earth's surface, still apparently it's not evidence from deep in Earth's crust.

42. Methane is "... 23 times as efficient as carbon-dioxide as a greenhouse gas" thus keeping temperatures above freezing in spite of 30% less sunlight back then. Moreover with little oxygen in the atmosphere, methane's resident time might have been 10,000 years then vs only 10 years today—*Science* 20Dec'02: 2341–2. Also see *Scientific American* Apr'03: 25.

43. Gold: 22 noted the structural resemblance between glucose $C_6H_{12}O_6$, a carbohydrate, and hexane C_6H_{14}, a hydrocarbon.

44. Actually they could use only some of the Sun's photons. Before atmospheric oxygen established the ozone screen, high-energy ultraviolet and X-ray photons were a deadly menace the bacteria had to 'learn' to cope with, see Margulis&Sagan'86: 80–1 and McFadden: 18. On the other hand these high-energy photons may have impelled mutations and evolution, see Loewenstein: 32.

45. Process: $6CO_2 + 6H_2O + photons \rightarrow C_6H_{12}O_6 + 6O_2$. On Cyanobacteria's emergence and pedigree—*Science* 3Aug'01: 819–20 and ~22Nov'02: 1538–9 & 1616–20.

46. This description of early metabolic processes is greatly oversimplified. For a more detailed elucidation including the role of ATP, see Drury: 187–95, Dyson: 16–7, Margulis&Sagan'86: 100–1, ~'02: 84, Schopf: 148–63 & 174–81 or Wills: 50–1 & 150–5. Also see *Science* 20Apr'01: 447–8.

47. Purple bacteria and proteobacteria—Drury: 225 and *Scientific American* Feb'00: 92b. See also Margulis&Sagan'86: 109–14 and Margulis & Schwartz: 49 & 66–73.

48. Oxidation of dissolved iron &c—Schopf: 171–3. It's also proposed that in addition Archaean volcanoes spewed oxygen-consuming gases until 2,450 or so million years ago (mya) when oxidized rock rose from the depths of the Earth allowing bacterial photosynthesis to gain the upper hand so that within about 100 million years they had created an oxygen-rich atmosphere—*Nature* Science Update 31Jan'01. Also see *Science* 3Aug'01: 819–20 and ~20Dec'02: 2341–2. However it's proposed that it took another billion years to permeate the oceans' depths—*Science* 16Aug'02: 1104–5.

49. On the timing of eukaryotes' emergence I find a wide range. Margulis& Sagan'86: 117 & 121 said 1.4 & 1½ billion years ago, then over 2 billion on 142 and on ~'02: 85. But more recently Ward: 113 says 2.5, and Schopf: 241 speculates as long ago as 2.8 billion. Then a find in Australia revealed that eukaryotes existed at least 2.7 billion years ago—*Science News* Aug28'99: 141a (per Aug13 *Science* report). Also see *Discover* Mar'03: 24–5. However it's proposed that the eukaryotes didn't really blossom until less than a billion years ago because of oxygen deficiency in the deep oceans—*Science* 16Aug'02: 1104–5 & 1137–42.

50. Known eukaryotes—"New data now indicate a huge potential diversity of extremely small eukaryotes including new major subgroups ... that overlap bacteria in size." *Science* 13Jun'03: 1704b.

51. For a somewhat dated but nonetheless instructive description of eukaryote origins, see *Scientific American* Apr'96: 50–7 updated ~Feb'00: 90–5. Also see Howland: 169–74, Lunine: 220–1 and *Science News* Apr26'03: 265b. Stewart & Cohen: 23 view this symbiosis to eukaryotes as an instance of emergence.

52. There is speculation that actin fibers came from a now extinct domain as noted above. Others speculate that the nucleus came from an invading virus—*NewScientist* 15Sept'01: 16.

53. Nucleus evolution—Margulis&Sagan'02: 145–61.

54. Mitochondria origin—Margulis&Sagan'86: 128–30.

55. Eukaryote evolution into plants and animals—*Science* 22Feb'02: 1482–5. Also see Margulis&Sagan'02: 88 for a chart.

56. Cloning—Schopf: 243–6.

57. Gene swapping disqualifies bacteria as having 'species' even though there are many types and strains of bacteria, or put another way, bacteria are all one species since they can all reproduce thru gene transfer according to Margulis&Sagan'86: 89; ~'02: 58, 65 & 83–5 and Margulis & Schwartz: 54.

58. The slow evolution of eukaryotes is blamed by some on low oxygen in the oceans—*Science* 16Aug'02: 1104–5.

59. Sex is more broadly defined by Margulis: 87–8 and Margulis&Sagan'02: 75 as any fusion of any remnants of genes from viruses, plasmids or other short pieces, by bacterial mating or hybridization.

60. For a detailed description and comparison of mitosis and meiosis see Audesirks: 180–96 or Schopf: 245–51. On "The Meiotic Ballet" see *Science* 8Aug'03: 785–9.

61. While the 'card decks' analogy aptly illustrates the gene 'shuffling' effect of meiosis, it poses a couple questions which will be addressed in the next chapter. Through sex the new composite cell gets two 'decks of blended cards' one from each parent, that is, two full sets of genes. As the cell divides again and again through mitosis, each new 'daughter' cell gets two sets of genes identical to the 'mother' cell's two sets. As the cells develop, a choice must be made of which 'deck' to 'draw' a 'card' from to 'put in play', that is, which parent's gene (allele) to express or activate. See Clayman: 220–1, Margulis & Schwartz: 14–5 or Schopf: 245–9. The other question concerns blending the genes on male mammals' X and Y chromosomes that carry the gender specific genes. Females have two Xs, but

males have an X and a Y so in meiosis the male can't very well shuffle the genes on these lone chromosomes; whichever one is passed on, is passed on mostly as-is entire—see Tyler-Smith in Crow: 218.

62. For an account of the rise and fall of the first sexually reproducing single-cell eukaryotic *microalgae* see Schopf: 252–8. Briefly, Schopf speculates that they increased rapidly then steadily declined as multi-celled eukaryotes *coelomics* emerged which buried organic carbon in fecal pellets thus reducing the larger microalgae's food supply.

63. Sex and death—Schopf: 261.

64. First multicelled organisms—Fossil evidence from southwest Australia suggests 2.0– to 1.2–mya, *Science* 10May'02: 1112–5 and *Nature* Science Update same date. Margulis&Sagan'02: 141 say "… many, if not most, bacteria in nature are multi-cellular organisms"—I assume they mean clusters of undifferentiated cells.

65. In addition to the sides of volcanoes, exotic vents have lately been reported on undersea mountains supporting some unidentified fish and larvae per ENN.com news 12/14/00. On vent and seep invertebrates see *Science* 15Feb'02: 1253–7. On the Snowball Earth and multicellular emergence, see *NewScientist* 12Apr'03: 30–4 vs an asteroid 580 mya ~3May'03: 17.

66. Life probable—R.Coren: 172–3.

67. Motivation—Eigen: 39 at least raised the issue altho I don't see that he fully answered it. "… a self-organizing system also needs, so to speak, to be 'motivated' to develop itself. Ultimately, it has no choice but to adapt itself to the given environmental conditions, for the creation of which it itself is partly responsible."

68. *Élan vital* was a term used by Henri-Louis Bergson (1859–1941)—a French philosopher, Nobel laureate and Catholic convert—variously translated as 'original impetus', 'vital impetus' or 'vital spirit'—Bergson'11: 53–4, 87 & 251–71; ~'35: 111–5 & 209 and Deleuze: 9 & 94–5. Bergson saw an "inadequacy of Darwinism," namely the lack of a motivating function. But his vitalism solution was analogous to the theory of 'phlogiston', a special substance thought to cause fire, mentioned in Chapter Two. I agree with Bergson's assessment of the 'inadequacy' but not with his solution. We're now quite sure there are no special substances, either for fire or Life. See also R.Coren: 83, Davies'99: 37–40, Duve'95: 287, Mayr: 8–16, Will'00: 110–1 and Wright: 3–4. (As an aside, a student of Bergson was Nikos Kazantzakis, author of *Zorba the Greek* and *The Last Temptation of Christ*—*free inquiry*, Spring'03: 63–4.)

69. Photons play a cardinal role in Loewenstein's: 3–110, conceptual scheme of Life's emergence. As I understand it some of the energy of the Sun's photons was converted into covalent bonds between carbon and other atoms such as hydrogen and oxygen to *form* ever more complex molecules. Thus photon energy was captured as 'information' rather than lost as entropy; it was used to build order rather than lost to disorder. When such molecules learned the stunt of making copies of themselves, by catalyzing themselves in feedback loops, proliferation ran wild as long as there was an unlimited supply of photons and source molecules, and until negative feedback loops evolved. Because the copying was imperfect, errors arose (mutations) which provided a variety of molecules to string together

into even more complex molecules. Loewenstein speculates how this led first to RNA, then proteins and later DNA. So recalling from Chapter Four's section on Light that photons reside in the microscopic quantum realm, when the Sun's photons strike organic molecules some of their electromagnetic energy can be converted into electromagnetic covalent bonds thus decohering and crossing the frontier into the macroscopic realm.

70. I got started on this line of thought by wondering, Why does a tree grow? I distinctly remember years ago when I first asked myself this dumb/profound question. We were visiting a friend in western Massachusetts and stopped at a restaurant because he, my wife and daughter were hungry. But I wasn't and didn't feel like sitting in a dark stuffy room while they discussed issues like peas vs. carrots. I waited outside, leaning against the car, idly looking at some scrub trees at the edge of the parking lot. And I began to marvel and ponder, Why does that tree grow? Not *how* but *why*? What motivates it to reach up against gravity toward the Sun, unrelentingly, against all odds, to find a way ... ? I was emboldened to ponder such a 'dumb' question having heard that Einstein asked himself, "What's it like to be a sunray traveling through space?" and "What's it like while falling through space?" (he's said to have asked a workman who'd just fallen from a building).

71. I'm reluctant to use a term, Life Urge, that smacks of vitalism, which implies a latent or inchoate life force which activates, morphs or decoheres. As an alternative to 'urge to life' I liked 'life impetus' but Chardin'59: 148ff used the term "The Impetus of Life" and while I admire him, I don't wish to support his theology. But then 'urge to life' could be conflated with 'demiurge', a Platonic or Gnostic deity who was believed to be the creator of the sensible/material world. Also see Duve'95: 286–90. Of course I don't really know whether there is a latent life force ('tho I doubt it) but we do know that somehow Life emerges that wasn't obviously there before, something more than just simple synergy (like my 'car' example), or at least several levels up the synergy hierarchy. (Some time after settling on the term 'Life Urge' I was pleased to discover that Damasio'99: 25 & 137–9 used it but, it seems to me, in a narrower sense as "... the urge to stay alive ...")

72. Probably some theists will seize on the concept of a Life Urge as God working in us: "Aha! That's how God 'out there' works 'in here'." I don't think so. That's a dualist mentality looking for the 'soul' and equating Life Urge with vitalism. As I understand it, *élan vital* was seen as a distinct life force imposed *on* matter to invigorate it whereas the Life Urge would be inherent *in* matter and emerge under the right circumstances (à la Loewenstein's scenario above?). I believe that Life emerges from 'inside', and was not imposed from 'outside'.

Chapter Seven—Animal Evolution

1. The complexity may be relieved by efforts to comprehend the big picture of Life's history viewing planetary biology as a whole—see *Science* 3May'02: 864–8.
2. Opinions vary on the timing of the multicellular eukaryotes' emergence

but this is a good enough consensus for our purposes— Ward: 105 (altho' there's fossil evidence for earlier, as noted above). 'Grand Climacteric' is the term Loewenstein: 35 uses for this event which I think has a nice ring to it.

3. On the eukaryotes' divergence into plants and animals see *Science* 22Feb'02: 1482–5. I found Margulis & Schwartz's *Five Kingdoms* an excellent resource for studying the forms of life. But there are quite a few less technical volumes such as Whitfield's *From So Simple a Beginning.*

4. Not just cataloging issues—I confess I haven't taken the time and made the effort to fully understand these issues but it's said "... that species concepts play an important role in furthering our understanding of biodiversity. These concepts can be appreciated as models that inspire questions about the nature of both boundaries and the internal structure of real evolutionary groups." from review of Jody Hey's book in *Science* 15Feb'02: 1238–9. Also see ~13Jun'03: 1692–7 "Modernizing the Tree of Life."

5. On the Cambrian 'explosion' and its animal phyla see Conway Morris: 141–7 & 169–70. Others suggest that the 'explosion' had a 'long fuse' preceding it— *Science* 20Jul'01: 438–9, ~16Aug'02: 1104–5 and ~22Nov'02: 1547.

6. Animals on land—There's tracks from 530 mya but not suggesting that they stayed, *Nature* Science Update 30Apr'02.

7. On liverworts' landing see *Nature* 13Aug'98: 671–4. But a year later at the International Botanical Congress the Deep Green project announced findings indicating many families of green plants living on land today descended from a single, green freshwater 'Eve' similar to today's *coleochaetes*; and that plants represent three kingdoms as noted above. To further confuse the origin of land multicelled organisms, more recently evidence of microbial mats on land 2.6 billion years ago has been reported—*Nature* 30Nov'00. Also see *Science* 10Aug'01: 1129–33 and ~14Dec'01: 2351–3.

8. Plants—Margulis & Schwartz: 370–81 and Margulis&Sagan'86: 169–75.

9. For a detailed illustrated description of photosynthesis see Audesirks: 112–9.

10. Some trivia: During the Carboniferous period 300 mya, the atmosphere's oxygen content rose to around 35% (now about 20%) and giant dragonflies evolved with 30" wingspans—Drury: 142–3, Lane: 76–7, Perkins: 17 and *NewScientist* 14Dec'02: 40–3. The rise in oxygen was the result of newly evolving and proliferating plants extracting the carbon from the carbon dioxide that had previously prevailed. By 380 mya leafless plants had dropped carbon dioxide by 90% and then leaves evolved releasing even more oxygen—*Nature* Science Update 15Mar'01 and ~10Aug'01.

11. Fungi—Margulis & Schwartz: 346–53 and Margulis&Sagan'86: 187–91. Fungal role in terrestrial life's start—*Science* 15Sept'00: 1884–5.

12. Whales' 'return' to the sea—*Scientific American* May'02: 70–9.

13. Animals—Conway Morris: 143–53, Margulis & Schwartz: 204–11 and Margulis&Sagan'86: 175–87. On placental mammals see *Science* 14Dec'01: 2266–8 & 2348–51.

14. From sea to land—another speculation is that as land masses were forced together by plate tectonics, the waterway between them closed forcing the sea animals to gradually adapt to land or perish.

15. Lewontin: 103 tells of a Vermont man who'd had the same axe in his family for 150 years; it'd had seven new handles and three new heads. And so it is with us—we're continually changing yet still the same.

16. Amino acids—Originally it was believed there were 20 amino acids but in recent years a 21st and 22nd have been found, and there may be more, see *Nature* Science Update 24May'02 reporting on *Science* 24May'02: 1459–62.

17. For a detailed illustrated description of protein production see Audesirks: 156–64.

18. For an introduction to human cells try Rensberger's book or Audesirks: 19ff. Recent research finds that translation also occurs in the nucleus of mammal cells—*Science* 10Aug'01: 1139–42.

19. Some of these basic rules are elucidated by Loewenstein: 88–104, 113–39 & 181–95 and Coen: 63ff.

20. On the number of distinct proteins in humans see Rose: 122.

21. Membrane functions—Audesirks: 70–82.

22. The term *stem* stems from plant growth. Stem cells are sometimes referred to as master cells which beget precursor cells, founder cells ... the field's moving rapidly. See *Science* 9Jun'00: 1778.

23. Therapeutic cloning—*Scientific American* Jan'02: 44–51.

24. The primacy of the regulatory proteins I surmise from Loewenstein: 162 & 208 although I found his glib style sometimes confusing (but amusing).

25. It was thought that once a stem cell differentiates it can't go back but 'plasticity' is being reexamined—*Science* 21Jun'02: 2126–9.

26. On the strategies for signal transmission see Loewenstein: 172–7 ff. For a concise, illustrated description see *Scientific American* Jun'00: 72–9. Potassium channels—*Nature* Science Update 1Nov'01.

27. Nerve cells—Audesirks: 656–65.

28. On such 'tools' see Dawkins' 1999 *Extended Phenotype*, a thought provoking book by the author of *The Selfish Gene*.

29. Creationists say Evolution is only a theory—there is no proof. But then by that criterion God is only a theory—so why do they choose to believe? For "15 Answers to Creationist Nonsense" see *Scientific American* Jul'02: 78–85.

30. Coen: 355–6 prefers the terms "alterations and assessment."

31. Darwin called this "descent with variation" or "natural selection" and his co-discoverer Alfred Wallace said "... the *fittest would survive.*" which Herbert Spenser popularized as "survival of the fittest" (that is, those whose traits best 'fit' their environment, not as in 'physically fit' meaning well conditioned—Browne: 313–4). However their ingenious paradigm fell out of favor because they had no mechanism to explain how variations could arise, since Mendel's 1865 paper was unread by Darwin (postmortem a German reprint was found in his library unopened even though he spoke a stilted German). Than again, since Darwin had "no facility with numbers" he probably wouldn't have understood Mendel. Mendel

had read German translations of Darwin's first two books. Not until 1900 was Mendel rediscovered and some began combining Mendel's genetics with Darwin's process dynamic of alternating variation and selection, but it was the mid-1900s before the evolutionary synthesis now called Neo-Darwinism was fully accepted. Ceccarelli: 15–29; Dawkins'99: 180; Henig: 114, 124–5, 143–4 & 157; Kohn: 34; Mc-Fadden: 57; Perkins: 13 and Rose: 187. As I was finalizing the manuscript I read Pennock's glowing review of Michael Ruse's *Darwin and Design: Does Evolution have a Purpose* in *Science* 22Aug'03: 1051.

32. More hair—it's even more confusing because northern mammals evolved to grow more hair in the fall and shed in spring.

33. Sex is defined very broadly by Margulis&Sagan'02: 191–9 & thru-out to include any combining of genes by whatever means. Also see *Science* 7Jun'02: 1792–5.

34. Recombination—for the most part male mammals can't cross-over the genes on their X and Y chromosomes since they have only one of each. Actually a few non-sex-determining regions recombine: "In all mammals, a small region of strict X-Y homology has been maintained in order to permit pairing and correct segregation of the sex chromosomes during male gametogenesis. This segment is known as the psuedoautosomal region (PAR)." Other segments of the Y chromosome undergo rearrangements without mix-up due to the small number of genes on Y—it has only about a tenth as many genes as the X. In Crow, see Tyler-Smith: 218–20 and Sargent &al: 231–2; and *NewScientist* 24Aug'02: 28–33. Most recently it's believed the Y chromosome has a 'mirror' palindrome sequence of genes at each end so that by folding on itself it can proofread the sequence—*Nature* Science Update 19Jun'03, AT&T Worldnet Jun18'03 and *NewScientist* 21Jun'03: 15.

35. Rather than just two sets of genes, there's a proposal that rare duplications may have produced four or even eight sets leading to major leaps in evolution such as from invertebrates to vertebrates—*Science* 21Dec'01: 2458–60. Also we humans are particularly prone to errors in our chromosomes—*Science* 21Jun'02: 2164–6. There are women who have only one X chromosome instead of two (XO: Turner's syndrome) and either gender can have an extra X (XXX or XXY: Klinefelter's syndrome)—Corballis in Crow: 143.

36. Alleles—Audesirks: 204–15. The catchphrase 'selfish gene' attributed to Dawkins'99: 180 might better be called the 'selfish allele' but either way it skirts over the issue of why it's selfish which, of course, I attribute to the Life Urge.

37. A fourth cause of mutations—termed adaptive, stationary-phase or stress-inducible mutation such as starvation—has recently been proposed and is being explored, see *Science* 30May'03: 1382–3.

38. DNA proofreading—McFadden: 65–6.

39. Early in the 1800s Jean Baptiste Lamarck's hypothesis that organisms evolve through the inheritance of acquired traits became widely accepted. Even Darwin tried to explain change with what he called *pangenesis*. Lamarck believed that traits developed prior to procreating are biologically passed on to progeny. Rather as I understand it, what may be passed on thru nurture is the disposition to those traits. Even so if innate traits aren't developed to give their owner a survival

advantage, their owner may not survive to pass on those traits. For example an individual may have traits to run fast but if they don't somehow train to develop into a fast runner, it may not out run a predator (or their less talented but better trained companions) and get killed before they can pass on those traits. See Coen: 350–1, Loewenstein: 151–3, McFadden: 56 and Steele &al: 2ff.

40. Steele &al analyze what they call retrogenes thoroughly and adamantly in their book.

41. Jumping genes—Avise: 117–23. For an explanation of how transposons 'jump' see *Science* 7Jul'00: 73–4 and ~18Aug'00: 1152–3. On retroviruses see *New-Scientist* 19Aug'00: 38–41.

42. Adaptive mutations—McFadden: 78 & 263–4.

43. Ozone layer damage 2–mya may have been caused by a nearby supernova's cosmic rays resulting in UV exposure that killed off plankton and thence the molluscs that lived off them; see *Nature* Science Update 12Feb'02.

44. In addition to magnetic flips, Earth's magnetosphere ripples—see *Science* 23Feb'01: 1466–7—so even without flips Earth's shield may be penetrated.

45. Hox genes—Audesirks: 747, Coen: 101 & 117–26 and Rose: 50–5. On regulatory controls see Avise: 45–9.

46. The concept of heterochrony is extensively covered thru-out McNamara and summarized on p.41 & 204. I first encountered the concept in Gould'77b. Also see Parker & McKinney: 240–9.

47. For an illustration of these homologous structures see Audesirks: 265.

48. On the role of the organism in selection, see Goodwin: 39–41.

49. On dying see Allman: 103 "Is Senescence Adaptive?"

50. It's suggested that the meteor's impact on Mexico spewed up debris blocking sunlight for a few years (questionable—*Science* 22Feb'02: 1445–6). This global 'winter' culled many cold-blooded dinosaurs without fur or feathers who couldn't keep warm. Moreover the 'winter' diminished plant growth so that dinosaur young probably couldn't forage food and starved, although some feathered birds survived. Mammals had had to avoid the dinosaurs so had stayed in underground dens during the day when dinosaurs were about and came out at night to forage. Thus mammals had adapted to low sunlight via warm-blooded temperature control, fur &c. It's argued that during the global 'winter' adult mammals were able to forage food and produce milk to feed their young until their young matured to forage on their own. But for the 'winter' to have lasted long enough for all the adult dinosaurs to have died off without progeny the sunlight must have been shaded for more than a few years. If the Mexican meteor's impact tremors reverberated around the globe shaking loose earthquakes and volcanoes, the volcanoes could have continued to spew their debris for decades while the dinosaurs went extinct. (A likely suspect: On the other side of the globe just opposite Mexico where the tremors in the Earth's crust radiating out from the impact would have all come back together and collided with one another, concurrently the Deccan Traps erupted. It produced a massive lava flood on what 65–mya was the Indian landmass long before it moved north closing the east Tethys Sea and colliding with Asia 40– to 50–mya pushing up the Himalayas; see Dixon &al: 228, Lunine: 242b,

Scientific American Mar'01: 19 and *Science* 6Apr'01: 93–5.) But with little plant growth for decades what did the mammals eat, dead dinosaurs? See Hrdy: 123 and Lunine: 121, 237 & 242. Starting in Jun'01 researchers from the U.of Alaska plan to drill 1½ miles down into the meteor's crater in Mexico to learn more about this and similar events. Moreover the Mexican meteor may have been only one of a swarm of meteors that hit Earth about that time based on findings in Ukraine and the North Sea, and there are probably others yet undiscovered—per a story in The Oakland Press (Mi) Nov5'02: A-12, copied from The New York Times. Also *Nature* Science Update, 10Apr'03.

51. It is proposed that a vast upwelling of methane, a "burp," from under the sea floor warmed the Earth's climate so that mammals from Asia could cross thawed polar lands—after the Beringa glacier receded but before the ocean rose(!?)—to usurp North America—*Science* 19Nov'99: 1465 and ~15Mar'02: 2028–9; but *NewScientist* 7Dec'02: 21 article on these methane bursts says there were no ice caps then! It's suspected that "... evidence of many other such methane burps lies hidden in the fossil record ..." per Jul29'00 Discovery.com News item on a Jul27'00 *Nature* report. Also see *Science* 18Aug'00: 1130–1. Another recent proposal is that 55 mya volcanoes increased carbon-dioxide levels and temperatures over a 60k yr span, per *NewScientist* 16Sept'00: 10.

52. On the Permian extinction see Delsemme: 185–6 & 193, and AT&Tdailynews Sept8'00 reporting on that day's *Science*: 1666–7. Evidence that the extinction was caused by a huge comet was reported by AT&T WorldNet Feb22'01, Discovery News Feb27'01, and in *Science* 23Feb'01: 1469–70, *Scientific American* May'01: 18–9 and *Nature* Science Update 18Sept'01. But *Nature* Science Update 7Jun'02 and *NewScientist* 26Apr'03: 38–41 suspect massive eruptions of lava in Siberia and *Nature* Science Update 22Aug'03 suggests a methane explosion. An older asteroid impact crater was recently discovered in west Australia dated 360 mya toward the end of the Devonian period when 85% of all species were wiped out—*NewScientist* 26Jan'02: 11. Evidence of even older asteroids is cited in *Science* 9May'03: 961–4 & ~13Jun'03: 1734–7 and *Nature* Science Update 13Jun'03.

53. The 200 mya catastrophe is suspected to be the impact at Manicouagan, Québec although the dating is problematic, see Discovery News May15'01, AT&T WorldNet Aug13'01 and *Nature* Science Update 17May'02 on Triassic-Jurassic extinction evidence. For a summary of impacts, eruptions and major mass extinctions see *Scientific American* Nov'01: 40–9 and ~Mar'02: 76–83. Two extinctions are being reclassified as 'mass depletions'—*Science* 7Dec'01: 2072–3.

54. Isthmus formation—Stanley: 179 and *Science* 7Jan'00: 13a.

55. Placentals vs marsupials—Gould'80: 294–5 argues that the North American predators' success was not due to an inherent superiority of placentals but to their evolution under greater stress having selected for superior traits. Also Conway Morris: 203–4.

56. Sexual selection—Miller: 33–67 & 70–2 and Zahavis thru-out.

57. Species—Mayr: 129. What may have happened is that gene alleles mutated into distinct genes that are no longer interchangeable.

58. On the Galápagos finches see Rose: 127–33 and Weiner: 86, 191–3, 196 & 209. What's not mentioned is that the finches and seeds may have co-evolved *pari passu* if the plants also had a short life span.

59. Punctuated equilibrium—Mayr: 195.

60. On the evolution of the horse 'bush' see Dixon &al: 281, Gould'96: 57–71 and Klein: 30–4.

61. Clades—Conway Morris: 177–80. To learn more about cladistics read Gee's book.

62. The whale-hippo link was reported in the Aug24'99 *Proceedings of the National Academy of Sciences* according to *The Associated Press*. However the whale-hippo link is not supported by fossil evidence; see *Nature* Science Update 20Sept'01.

63. On the reciprocal relation of genes, organisms and the environment see Lewontin: 100–1 & thru-out and Rose: 137–43. However the examples Lewontin cites are of micro-environments, niches, such as an animal burrowing and lining its burrow with grass, similar to Dawkins'82/'99. (A better example would be the beaver and its dammed ponds—Griffin: 99–112.) More compelling are instances of early photosynthesizers flooding Earth's atmosphere with their waste oxygen or we humans' affect on the world's environment. An intriguing possibility will be discussed in Ch.9 of a reciprocal relation in the brain between nerve impulses and neurons, like 'organisms' and their 'environment'.

64. On the next steps see Carol Ezzell "Beyond the Human Genome" *Scientific American* Jul'00: 64–9. Also see Rose: 18.

65. Morphic resonance—Sheldrake'95a: xix, ~'95b thru-out and ~'03: 9–10 & 16.

66. Systematics is under pressure for change from Linnaeus' pre-Darwin naming system; see *Science* 23Mar'01: 2304–7.

67. For a hierarchy of information, see Loewenstein: 108–9; for complexity, see Chaisson: 183–4, Gould'96: 202–12, Lewin thru-out and Parker & McKinney: 346–58; for synergy, see Corning: 99–102.

68. *Umwelt*—Stevens: 54–5. As I understand it in my example, eventho' UV light has deleterious affects on humans (so it's part of our world) since we don't sense it, it's not part of our *Umwelt* (purview?).

69. Smell's evolution—Allman: 76. The way I envision it, animals must move to take in food at their mouth so they evolved senses near their mouth to detect food and initiate a reaction to capture it. (Macrophages, single animal cells, basically do this.) Hence heads house the mouth, most sense organs and the brain.

70. Reptile and amphibian hearing range—Allman: 100–2.

71. Animal vibrations—ENN.com Jan25'01.

72. These animals detect magnetism with their iron-rich crystals. See ABCNews.com Science Jul23'99 and *Nature* 20Jul'00.

73. Electric eels and fish—ABCNews.com Science Jul14'99 reporting on *Nature* 15Jul'00. Also see Audesirks: 686–7.

74. Radio frequency reception has been anecdotally reported in dental braces but this was reception of man-made signals like the old crystal sets, not of natural origin.

75. UV light and 'visible' spectrum—*NewScientist* 29Apr'00, 12a and *Nature* Science Update 13May'02.

76. Polarized light sensing—Allman: 81 and ABCNews.com Science Sept29'99 reporting on that day's *Nature*.

77. Dogs' humans coming home—Sheldrake'99. Anticipating phone calls—Sheldrake'03: 95–106.

78. Ganglia—Audesirks: 421 & 665–8.

79. Competition vs cooperation—On the debate among ecologists see *Science* 31Jan'03: 644–6.

Chapter Eight—Human Evolution

1. Using Earth's beginning as 4,560 million years ago and the dinosaurs' extinction as 64.4 million years ago.

2. *Homo sapiens* emergence—Stringer in Crow: 27–8 says "more than 250,000 years ago" then he and Mellars in Crow: 42 raise it to 300,000—that's the earliest estimates I've come across.

3. Average tenure for species—Stock: 183 says 4 million years.

4. See Leakey's *The Sixth Extinction*. He fears that the next one will be like the previous five major extinctions.

5. Mammal emergence—220 mya is from Allman: 98 whereas Audesirks: 443 say 250 mya. Recent evidence however suggests a proto-mammal emerged 195 mya while true mammals first evolved 150 mya—*Science* 25May'01: 1535–40 reported by AT&T Worldnet May24'01. A proto-placental mammal fossil from 125 mya is reported in *Nature* Science Update 25Apr'02.

6. Today most mammals are placentals (other groups are marsupials and monotremes). It's recently proposed that placental mammals branched in four great groups; *Nature* Science Update 1Feb'01. See *Science* 26Apr'02: 637–8 and *Nature* & *Nature* Science Update both 25Apr'02 on a 'placental' from 125 mya.

7. Besides the mammary glands, other unique defining features of mammals are permanent teeth, the middle ear's malleus and incus bones (hammer and anvil) and the neocortex (other vertebrates have brain structures that correspond to neocortex, see LeDoux: 123; Allman: 114–5 compares bird's wulst to neocortex). But of course these are hidden inside the head so not as apparent as breasts. Mammal evolution was probably driven by a combination of factors. To avoid cold-blooded reptiles (dinosaurs) the mammals foraged at night, thus fur and warm-bloodedness evolved to keep them warm. The higher metabolism of warm-bloodedness, along with their small body-size's heat loss, required voracious feeding. Hunting success was enhanced by more flexible behavior enabled by the neocortex. Neocortical development required longer infancy enabled by maternal feeding, hence mammary glands. But mothers had to stash their infants while they hunted so from their reptilian jaw evolved the higher-frequency capability of the middle ear to better hear insect prey as well as their infants' cries which were inaudible to predatory reptiles lacking middle-ear bones. See Allman: 96–108 and Ramachandran: 210.

8. On primate's color vision, see Allman: 143–6, *NewScientist* 29Apr'00: 12a and *Science* 25Jan'02: 613–5.

9. On primates see Allman: 98–106 & 122ff, Attenborough: 267ff, Audesirks: 325–6, Delsemme: 198–9, Klein: 62ff or Whitfield: 42–5. On primate origins see *Science* 22Nov'02: 1564–5, *Scientific American* Mar'03: 28–30 and *Science News* Mar29'03: 198.

10. A colleague with SRI referred to such constructs as 'inverted pyramids'. An inverted pyramid rests its apex on very tenuous facts on which are stacked conjectures, ever wider and higher. If new facts shift the apex, the inverted pyramid starts to lean and has to be propped up with flimsy supporting qualifications. When the whole top-heavy construct threatens to topple over on whoever supports the theory, there's a mad scramble to get out of the way by disowning it. In paleoanthropology probably the most notorious example is Piltdown man: a hoax in 1912 England was not fully exposed until 1953; see Gould'80: 108–24, Kuper: 30–8 and Schwartz: 107–14. Though not hominid, a very recent hoax, *Archaeoraptor*, a composite primitive bird body and dinosaur tail, caught *National Geographic* off guard Nov'99; see *Science* 22Dec'00: 2221, AT&TWorldnet Nov20'02 and *Nature* ScienceUpdate 21Nov'02. Another hoax with stone tools is reported in *Science* 5Jan'01: 34–5.

11. On the proto-apes radiation see ABCNews.com-Science Aug27'99 article on a report in *Science* that same date. Also see Potts: 72 & 75 and *Scientific American* Aug'03: 74–83 on their return.

12. Ape/hominid split—Tyler-Smith in Crow: 221.

13. Chimps vs humans—Until recently it had been believed that the DNA of humans and chimps was at least 98.5% identical; now research finds a 1.4% + 3.4% difference—*NewScientist* 28Sept'02: 20 and *Science* 25Oct'02: 719–21. Chromosomal speciation in primates, *Science* 11Apr'03: 267 & 321–4, *NewScientist* 19Apr'03: 15 & ~24May'03: 15 and *Nature* Science Update 29Apr'03.

14. Earlier hominid fossils are being unearthed in the Rift Valley by a team from Kenya and France which are believed to be six million year old *Orrorin*; see AT&T WorldNet News Dec4'00, FoxNews.com Dec6'00, *Science News* Jul14'01: 20 and *Science* 15Feb'02: 1214–9. An even earlier 6– to 7–my old fossil skull from Chad *Sahelanthropus tchadensis*, nicknamed Toumaï is confounding paleoanthropologists as I write; see *Science* 12Jul'02: 171–3, ~29Nov'02: 1708–11 & ~28Mar'03: 1994–7 and *Scientific American* Jan'03: 54–63. For a comprehensive grading of the various human species as known in early 2002; see Collard in Crow: 61–100.

15. Though now dated I still find the Prologue of Johanson's *Lucy* an amazingly serendipitous and exciting story. However the Leakeys may have once again taken center stage with another species they're calling *Kenyanthropus platyops*, the Flat-faced Man of Kenya—see *Nature* 22Mar'01, but than again maybe not—see *Nature* Science Update 28Mar'03. Also see *Science* 25Apr'03: 562 & 607–12 on South African hominids.

16. Paranthropus is shown as a separate branch (genus) with three species on the chart in *Science* 15Feb'02: 1214. For sketches of their skulls see Klein w.Edgar: 40 & 58.

17. On scavenging meat see Drury: 336 and Ehrlich: 168. On fossil spears see Klein w.Edgar: 159. On dietary change driving human evolution see *Scientific American* Dec'02: 106–15.

18. Feeding and exercising brains didn't directly cause subsequent generations to have larger brains (Lamarckism). Rather this is an instance of The Baldwin Effect: Those who were endowed with slightly larger brains were enabled to develop them and obtain larger brains' advantages for survival of themselves and of their subsequent generations which also inherit their larger brains. See Calvin & Bickerton: 146–7, Donald'01: 210 & 260 and Wills thru-out.

19. Instead of calling this species *Homo erectus* some scientists call it *Homo ergaster* ('action man') from which they contend two species of *Homo erectus* later evolved along with *Homo sapiens* and Neanderthals—see Klein: 256–7, 273–5 & 293–5 and Klein w.Edgar: 96–101. A recently found fossil skull "... strongly suggests that *H. ergaster* is a misnomer ..."—*Nature* Science Update 20Mar'02; the abstract in *Nature* concludes "Its temporal and geographic position indicates that African *H. erectus* was the ancestor of *Homo sapiens*." Also reported by AT&T World Net that same date, *Science* 22Mar02: 2192–3 and *Science News* Mar23'02: 179. Also see *Science* 28Feb'03: 1293 & 1384–88 on a recent Java find, summarized in *Science News* Mar1'03: 162–3.

20. On brain-case sizes see Collard in Crow: 83–5, Klein: 580, R.D. Martin in Jablonski & Aiello: 51, McNamara: 293–4 and Parker & McKinney: 326. Recently small brained skulls apparently *Homo erectus* have been found in Africa and Georgia (Russia)—*Science* 5Jul'02: 26–7 & ~9May'03: 893.

21. On *Homo sapiens'* ancestry see Audesirks: 328a; Collard in Crow: 61–100; Drury: 333–59; Fortey: 289–315; Gee: 201–30; Klein thru-out & recapped: 574ff; Klein w.Edgar: 36, 78, 98 & 236; Mayr: 227–47; Swisher &al: 144; *Science* 23Feb'01: 1460–1 & ~15Feb'02: 1214–25 and *Discover* Mar'03: 54–9. Also see note 19 above.

22. The 'Mitochondrial Eve' or 'Out of Africa—2$^{nd'}$ theory gained prominence based on initially controversial analysis of mtDNA. Recall that only the female egg cell contains mitochondria (the male sperm cell loses its tail's mitochondrion when it fuses with the egg cell). It appeared that African women's mtDNA was more diverse than other women's throughout the world from which it was inferred that *Homo sapiens'* mtDNA evolved in Africa over 100,000 years ago and then radiated out of Africa. Instead the Multiregional theory relies more on fossils with 'modern' features, such as an up to 60,000 year old skeleton found in Australia; it seems unlikely that its ancestors emigrated from Africa in so short a time (see *Science* 12Jan'01: 230–1 & 293–7, *Discover* Aug'02: 52–7, eventho Noble & Davidson: 217 and Stringer in Crow: 29 believe *Homo sapiens* did, and Klein w.Edgar: 247–51; *Nature* Science Update 20Feb'03 and *NewScientist* 22Feb'03: 15 revise 60 to 50 kya). Moreover a southern China *Homo sapiens* skull and other bones have been re-dated to around 68,000, or more than 153,000 years ago—*Science News* Dec21&28'02: 387. Thus it's proposed that *Homo sapiens* evolved multiple times from *Homo erectus*, which migrated 'Out of Africa—1$^{st'}$ up to two million years ago, into multiple locations (to Russian Georgia by 1.75–mya—*Science* 5Jul'02: 26–7—

and to northern China by 1.36–mya—*Science* 28Sept'01: 2368–9) but interbred as they continued their wanderings thus mixing their genes (they didn't just go 'Out ... ' but went 'back and forth'—*ScienceNews* Mar9'02: 149c-50b). For my part I'm amenable to the Multiregional theory: As explained later in the chapter, if the australopithecine alleles that initially led to *Homo* continued to evolve endowing their owners with ever larger brains and the ensuing advantages, then it seems likely that advanced subspecies (races) would carry those alleles and so could evolve and prosper. Scientists who defend the 'mtEve' theory risk the dubious honor of finding themselves embraced by the Creationists. See Discovery.com Jun10'99; *Scientific American* Aug'99: 13–14; *Science* 12Jan'01: 230–1 & 293–7; *NewScientist* 13Jan'01: 6 & ~14Apr'01: 26–9; Avise: 40; Audesirks: 329b, 330 & 331; Ehrlich: 97–100; Klein: 586–95; Klein w.Edgar thru-out; Lieberman'98: 6–8 and Swisher &al thru-out (contending *Homo erectus* survived in Java until 27,000 years ago, p.228, thus making them contemporaries of the last Neanderthals in Spain). In addition to 'mtEve' there's a 'Y-guy' camp, see *Science News* Feb6'99: 88–90 & ~Nov4'00: 295. More recent studies of mtDNA and Y-chromosome DNA support the 'Out of Africa—2ⁿᵈ' theory—Cavalli-Sforza: 77–81, *Nature* 7Dec'00 reported Dec6'00 by AT&TWorldnet and *Science* 11May'01: 1051–2 & 1151–3 (bolstered by 160-kya *Homo sapiens* fossils from Ethiopia—*Nature* 11Jun'03). But recently it's claimed there was at least one other 'out of Africa' migration between the other two and that the migrants interbred—*Nature* Science Update 7Mar'02. For an overview of human movement see *Science* 2Mar'01: 1721–53 & ~20Dec'02: 2342. (Maybe there were more advanced male interlopers.)

23. On Neanderthal brains see Bickerton in Crow: 116–8, Klein: 377–8 & 390–1 and Klein w.Edgar: 175. Altho Neanderthals and *Homo sapiens* were contemporaries in Europe, apparently didn't interbreed—*NewScientist* 17May'03: 14c&d.

24. This scenario was drawn from an array of sources. *Time* magazine's Aug23'99: 50–8 cover article provides a well written overview. From ABCNews.com Science: 5/6/98 on *A.anamensis*, 6/11/98 on brain size (from *Science*), 12/9/98 on 3.5 mya fossil and 9/6/99 on *Homo erectus*, and from AT&T and Discovery.com 3/23/00 on knuckle-walkers (from *Nature*). Also see *Scientific American* Jan'00: 56–62, Dixon &al: 318–9, Klein: 144ff (notably 574ff), Klein w.Edgar: passim, Potts: 79ff, Stanley: 35ff, *Science* 15Feb'02: 1214–9 & ~21Feb'03: 1193–4 &1217–21 and *Discover* Sept'03: 33–43. (There are discrepancies such as dates and brain sizes, among these sources.)

25. Unpublished at this writing is *Ardipithecus ramidus* which the finding team's leader, Tim White, says will be the "Rosetta stone for understanding bipedalism." *Science* 15Feb'02: 1215–6. White also led a team that reported 160,000 year old fossils of *Homo sapiens* from Ethiopia—*Nature* Science Update & News and Views, and AT&T Worldnet all 11Jun'03; *Science* 13Jun'03: 1641, *NewScientist* 14Jun'03: 4–5, *Science News* Jun14'03: 371 and *Scientific American* Aug'03: 23–4.

26. Animal communication—Marler in Jablonski & Aiello: 1–15.

27. On the issue of which species is smartest, see Budiansky: 16.

28. The Sahara is only partially the result of the Tethys Sea closure and the Mediterranean desiccation. Today air flowing east from the Atlantic dumps its

water on the western rain forests as it crosses Africa, then divides and turns back west to cross over the Sahara and Kalahari Deserts before becoming the westerly trade winds. See Stanley: 105. On the Mediterranean see Agustí: 204, Dixon et al: 272–3, Potts: 75–7 & 92, Ryan & Pitman: 91–2 and Stanley: 54–5.

29. For a summary of the changes in Africa see Drury: 339–41 and Johanson & Shreeve: 257.

30. This Isthmus of Panama scenario is Stanley's: 180–7; also see Calvin & Bickerton: 186–7, Dixon &al: 294–301, *Science* 7Jan'00: 13 and ~22Dec'00: 2209 & 2288–91. But other scientists are not sure what caused the Ice Ages; see *Science* 15Sept'00: 1868 & 1897–1902; some argue that the closing of the Indonesian seaway was the cause, see *Nature* Science Update 10May'01. Whatever the initial cause, until 10,000 years ago the Ice Ages were reprieved with few-hundred-year-long warm spells every 1,500 years perhaps due to stochastic resonance—*Nature* Science Update 16Jan'02. On the huge Lake Agassiz that formed in what's now central Canada as the climate warmed melting the ice cap, see *Science News* Nov2'02: 283–4 and *Science* 6Jun'03: 1519–22.

31. Recent re-examination of fossils of Lucy's kin indicated their wrists locked to support knuckle-walking (see note 24 above).

32. Why didn't australopithecines evolve larger brains? It's likely that their genes periodically mutated, occasionally producing infants with slightly larger brains. Why didn't they survive, yet such *Homo* infants did? Because such infants are less developed and more dependent—Stanley: 52, 159, 167 & 216 suggests that such infant australopithecines would have been less able to cling to their mothers and/or, carrying them, their mothers impeded in tree climbing. If an infant fell it was vulnerable to predators. If a mother somehow lost an infant, she'd stop lactating, ovulate and soon bear another. Within a large population, infants were expendable. There's also the gruesome possibility that these large headed 'freaks' were disposed of, perhaps thrown to a predator so the rest of the troop could escape, 'sacrificed to the leopard god,' as will be explored further; see Ehrenreich: 59 & 69. Alternatively it's argued that *A. africanus* did evolve at least 50% larger brains if their female fossils are compared to great ape females; see R.D. Martin in Jablonski & Aiello: 52.

33. On sabertooths see Ehrenreich: 70, Klein: 253 and Stanley: 76–7 & 221.

34. An alternate, though not incompatible, theory is that *Homo* evolved in a partially aquatic environment: Many of the hominid fossils are found in Africa's Rift Valley which had more rivers and lakes, and a vast estuary when *Homo* first evolved. The theory argues that many *Homo* features can be explained as resulting from extended emersion in water: bipedalism, hairlessness, sweating, fat layers, breath control &c—Knight: 228–41 and Morgan'90 & ~'97 thru-out. It's true that whales and dolphins returned to water and lost their hair, but they don't leave the water as hippos do. Other mammals that spend their lives on land and in water didn't evolve these *Homo* features, for example seals, otters, beavers, muskrats, polar bears and moose (though none of these are equatorial). Others are good swimmers like caribou and wolves/dogs (chimps don't swim). So the 'aquatic ape' theory hasn't gained much acceptance, though it's interesting. As an aside, the em-

igration to Australia as long ago as 60,000 years might have been accomplished by a people adept at traversing open water—Diamond'99: 41–4 and Klein: 566–72. Also see *NewScientist* 25Nov'00: 28–33. Evidence of humans living along the Red Sea's African coast 125,000 years ago is reported in *Science News* May6'00: 292 (back then it was savanna). However Horrobin: 53 & 232–3 proposes that *Homo* evolved along the margins of lakes and rivers rather than in them as Morgan's aquatic hominids, which seems more plausible. Briefly, he argues 1) that hominids couldn't survive the heat and sparse water on the open savanna and 2) that a water-based diet is evidenced by fossils and by our inherited need for adequate water-grown nutrients—also see *Science* 3May'02: 835–6. (more on this below) They likely migrated during ice ages along seashores that are now submerged (such as the Bering and Indonesian corridors) but may be accessible to high-tech aqua-archeologists like Ballard.

35. Predation survival traits—*NewScientist* 13Apr'02: 34–7.

36. Around the time that the woodlands were shrinking and *Homo* evolved from australopithecines, there was a major reversal of Earth's magnetism, 2.6 mya (Klein: 52 & 158). As mentioned in the last two chapters, this may have allowed harmful Sun and cosmic rays to inundate Earth perhaps causing mutations in australopithecine's genes that produced *Homo*. A 'minor' mutation could have had major consequences: the mutation might not have been in a gene but only in where and/or when that gene is expressed, see *Science* 6Apr'01: 44–5 & ~15Feb'02: 1219–25. Interestingly the mutation rate of germline DNA is about five-times higher in hominoid males than females—*Nature* 11Apr'02. The abstract attributes the primary source to DNA replication errors. But since a female's sex cells are produced all at once before she's born whereas a male produces sex cells throughout his adult life, it seems to me the male's sex cells would be more vulnerable to radiation induced mutations.

37. For a scenario of how recurrent Ice Ages might have selected for brainy traits, see Calvin & Bickerton: 187–91, *Science* 15Feb'02: 1225 and *Science News* Jul5'03: 10–2. For an argument that problem solving fosters big brains, see *Science News* Mar16'02: 166 and *NewScientist* 16Mar'02: 11 both citing an upcoming report in *Proceedings of the National Academy of Sciences*.

38. While a walking stick may not seem like much of a weapon, consider the effectiveness of a shepherd's crook in fending off wolves. Instead of a crooked end, a long straight walking stick with a sharpened point becomes a rudimentary spear, effective in jabbing or impaling jackals or hyenas. However it would take great skill and more than courage, chutzpah, to go up against a lion with just a spear, much less a crudely sharpened stick. But presumably it can be done. The trick is to get a lone lion to charge directly at you, while with your rear foot you hold the butt of the spear in the ground at a low angle so that its point will enter the lion's neck low in the throat. The force of the charge should drive the spear into the lion's vitals, ideally its heart. If you succeed, you're a hero; if you miss, you may be a lion's dinner.

39. On *Homo erectus'* radiation out of Africa see Drury: 346–8 & 352–5 and 'Out of Africa' note 22 above. However Horrobin: 32–3 & thru-out argues that

Homo erectus didn't evolve on grasslands but along rivers, lakes and seas (see note 34 above).

40. On tool making and use fostering brains, see Horrobin: 34–7. Calvin: 169, Calvin & Bickerton: 163–5 and Winston: 84–5 argue throwing helped evolve *Homo's* brain which apparently Neanderthals didn't do—*NewScientist* 23Nov'02: 22–3. Ofek: 34–5 & 41 speculates that as tools became more refined by specialists they exchanged them for other goods so their deal-making further fostered brains' mathematical judgment. See a review of Ofek's book in *Science* 17May'02: 1243.

41. Evolution of the brain and pharynx are arguably the two most important modifications that led to *Homo*. But there were many others, a whole suite of complementary changes as mentioned earlier, such as: In deference to brain growth, the gut shrank by relying more on high-energy foods, like meat and fat, that were partially masticated from pulverizing (or partially digested from cooking after fire was domesticated). With less reliance on tree-climbing, hands and fingers broadened featuring refined opposable thumbs, arms shortened and shoulders turned more to the sides, and legs and feet lengthened while toes aligned and shortened (it'd be more accurate to say that these random changes were favored by their changing environment). We'll examine pelvic changes shortly. See Allman: 166–8; Aiello in Jablonski & Aiello: 21–31; Gould'77a: 64–5; Klein: 236; McNamara: 296–8; Mithen: 204–8 and F. Wilson: 21–34, 61–79 & 112–46.

42. Heterochrony also affected other aspects of human evolution, see Parker & McKinney: 249–57.

43. Brain growth—Recent research shows that a major difference between humans and chimps is in our brain's gene activity—five times greater—*Science* 12Apr'02: 233–5 & 340–3, *Science News* Apr13'02: 227c-8a and AT&T Worldnet News Apr11'02.

44. On mutated genes producing brainy 'freaks', Horrobin: 173–4, 206–7 & thru-out, posits that at least two, and perhaps four, mutated genes (alleles) had accumulated in our ancestors by 100+ kya before the second African diaspora. These brainy mutations probably occurred sequentially over 150,000, maybe even a million year time span so that each newly mutated allele in combination with earlier such alleles produced ever brainier 'freaks'. The downside is that today a small percentage of the world's population inherits all these alleles and can topple into madness if, Horrobin believes, they're deprived of essential nutrients common in humans' diet before industrialization. While inheriting all these alleles can lead to madness and low reproduction, inheriting only some can lead to higher intelligence and reproduction, so the alleles persist in the gene pool; see Stevens & Price: 193–5. Some believe one of these mutated genes was a 'language gene' and that it's now been found, see *Nature* Science Update: 4Oct'01 and *Science* 16Aug'02: 1105. Another "… gene thought by some scientists to foster bold, novelty-seeking personality, as well as attention-deficit hyperactivity disorder (ADHD), apparently spread substantially in human populations over roughly the past 40,000 years …" see *Science News* Jan19'02: 40. Also see *Science* 15Feb'02: 1219–25.

45. Next introduce a fanciful wrinkle: Say a few of those bigger-brained freaks were also nearsighted (quite common today) making them the first nerds

(without benefit of eyeglasses). Their nearsightedness made them less valuable in foraging parties but more valuable in tool-making. Thus their hand/eye coordination and developing know-how further exercised their oversized brains. And we nearsighted people don't lose our close vision as we age (as the aging, eagle-eyed hunters would have). So their tool-making skills could be refined on into later life—relatively sheltered in the less hazardous encampment—becoming a valuable asset to the troop. Else why didn't the nearsighted trait die out? (While the hunters were away, besides making tools were the 'nerds' also making babies?) The nerds probably became the innovators improving stone knapping and eventually binding stones to wood shafts, later inventing the spear-thrower (atlatl—*Nature Science Update*, 23Apr'03), sling, and bow and arrow to facilitate 'men's work.' 'Women's work' too saw improvised fish-nets, clothing, shelters and baskets. The trouble with this 'fanciful wrinkle' is that stone hand-axes (hand-held, without wood handles) didn't appear until more than a million years after the oldest Oldowan tools and then monotonously persisted little changed for another million years; see Potts: 139&188. But there is evidence of establishment of encampments or a 'home-base' by at least two million years ago. Certainly beginning at least fifty thousand years ago innovation blossomed; see Horrobin: 173–4 and Klein: 230 & 589–91.

46. On swallowing and breathing see Lieberman'91: 53–7, ~'98: 58–9 & 139 and Klein: 515–6.

47. Sound production—Benzon: 171–6 argues it was the imitation of animal sounds, both in hunting and defense, that favor the evolution of these organs.

48. On language evolution, see Lieberman'91: 53–63, 72–7 & thru-out. Benzon: 169–94 & elsewhere couples the evolution of language with music-making.

49. Baldwin effect—Dennett: 77–80, Donald'01: 210 & 260 and Wills thru-out. I obtained Weber's and Depew's *Evolution and Learning: The Baldwin Effect Reconsidered* too late to use here.

50. On Neanderthal speech see Klein: 391–2 & 516–7, and Lieberman'91: 63–72. Also see *Science News* Feb20'99: 118 on the hypoglossal canals controversy.

51. Neanderthal hands were stronger but less dexterous and thus less able to make and use tools as reported in *Nature* Science Update 6Feb'01 and *Science News* Feb10'01: 84b. But that theory is contested in *Nature* Science Update 27Mar03.

52. Based on Neanderthals' sloping forehead and extended rear skull, it appears that their brain expansion was not so much in the pre-frontal lobes as was *Homo sapiens* but in the rear brain. A wild thought on this will be posed at the end of Chapter Nine.

53. On humans' 'premature' (*altricial*) birth, see Gould'77b: 369, Noble & Davidson: 187 and Potts: 206.

54. On brain growth and pelvic adaptation, see Drury: 335–6; McNamara: 299; Parker & McKinney: 230, 321–2 & 326; Potts: 206 and *Scientific American* Nov'01: 72–77. For a counter argument, see Calvin & Bickerton: 204–5. Characterizing extended brain growth as 'retarded maturation' prompted some wag to observe something like "We're the most advanced because we're the most retarded" (I thought I read that in Gould'77b but couldn't find it later).

55. On human brains' energy use, see Allman: 175, Dunbar: 22–6, Horrobin: 55, Hrdy: 479, R.D. Martin in Jablonski & Aiello: 56 and Ofek: 66–9 & 73.

56. It seems that studying aborigines to understand our early ancestors would be problematical because the aborigines evolved cultures that stagnated whereas our ancestors continued to progress, albeit not necessarily to improve.

57. Australopithecines' philandering ways—Maybe they weren't. A recent study argues that *Australopithecus afarensis* males weren't much larger than females, unlike gorillas, orangutans and chimps who compete for females, so may have been monogamous. *Science News* Jul19'03: 45 and AT&T Worldnet Jul29'03 reporting on a study by Owen Lovejoy published in *Proceedings of the National Academy of Sciences.*

58. Bonobos, our closest living hominid species, have extended female receptivity, displaying swollen pink genitals; they "make love, not war." See DeWaal 99ff. *Homo* females evolved concealed ovulation and extended sexual receptivity through the usual reciprocal process; namely those females who were so inclined obtained support from their male partners thus enhancing success in raising offspring which perpetuated and enforced those traits in successive generations. However it seems unlikely that they were exclusively monogamous; it was better to have several 'fathers' for support and back-up; see Hrdy: 245–9.

59. Sexual 'dimorphism' reduced—that is, males lost some of their fighting characteristics such as extended canine teeth and much larger size than females. (Actually both genders' sizes increased but females more so; see Hrdy: 285 and Klein: 191.) Women have influenced the evolution of men by 'selecting' which men they mate with, that is which traits will be reproduced, and secondly by nurturing those traits in infants and children that grew to be men. At the same time the advent of tools which could be used as weapons reduced the advantage of dimorphic body characteristics instead favoring skill in handling weapons; see Boehm: 174–81.

60. Feed-as-you-go—Ofek: 71–2 & 131–2. The hunter-gatherers central encampments probably enabled an enlargement of the troop from a single extended family to multiple families—Ofek: 133–4.

61. Our western culture has a strong aversion to eating 'bugs' but primates started out eating insects and many still do including chimps. They're rich in protein and easier to get than meat. Amazonian Amerindians use insects to balance their cassava diet; see Horrobin: 95, Discovery.com News Nov9'00 on "Worms," AT&T WorldNet Jan16'01 "Ancient Bone Tools Suggest Apemen Ate Termites" and Discovery.com News "Termites Fueled Early Humans." (No, I don't plan to!)

62. Sharing in hunter-gatherer societies became an ethic so that a hunter's large kill wasn't his but the troop's, known as the 'own-kill' rule (it might soon spoil anyway or be scavenged). Free-riding and freeloading could be discouraged interpersonally within the troop; see Boehm: 212–7, Dunbar: 194–213 and Miller: 310–1. Others propose the emergence of exchange deals along with specialization wherein for instance a skilled hunter might exchange meat for a fine spear from a skilled spear-maker or for vegetables from a gatherer—Ofek: 134–7. But than lately the 'man the hunter' image of our early ancestors is being questioned—not only

were they meat scavenges but it's argued, relied mostly on 'gathering' by mothers and grandmothers—*NewScientist* 4Jan'03:16 and AT&TWorldnet Jan14'03.

63. On altruism and group selection see Boehm: 217–24 and Sober & Wilson: 192–4 & thru-out. Rather than see altruism as contrary to self-interest, if the image of oneself is enlarged to encompass not just kin but say the whole troop, an expanded Self, then 'altruism' becomes Self-interest—more on this in Ch. 10.

64. Diversifying the gene pool may have come about along with synchronizing women's ovulation cycles with the Moon and with each other. If the troop, or at least the young adults, 'partied' during the full moon and neighbors dropped by (say guys—and maybe gals—from a distant troop who traveled in the moonlight bringing fresh kill: bride-price) there'd naturally be some pairing. Those females who were ovulating would produce offspring with more viable mixed genes but also with the trait of synchronizing their menstrual cycles with the Moon. Those who weren't ovulating then may have inbred at another time with local males producing less viable offspring. Females who didn't synchronize with the Moon but with females who did (alphas?) would obtain the same benefits. (Women today synchronize with other women roommates apparently via pheromones; see Agosta: 153–4, and Hrdy: 220–1. Interestingly "Breastfeeding women and newborns give off odours that boost the sexual desire of other women."[sic]—*NewScientist* 27Apr'02: 11.) Men's underarm sweat relaxes women—*Nature* Science Update 28May'03.

65. Exchange—Ofek: 117–21 argues that, even though our hominid line radiated into geographic niches, we didn't diversify into multiple species because of the exchange of genes through the exchange of members with neighboring troops so that each generation spread the genes ever farther from troop to troop across great distances. Moreover the exchange of members was facilitated by the similar exchange of goods which maintained contact across long distances with remote sources of specialized goods such as prize flint.

66. On child-support, see Allman: 198–203, Cronk: 237–53 and Dunbar: 19–26. Some argue that females formed coalitions not only for mutual support in childcare ('alloparenting') but to coerce males into provisioning them, even using red body coloring as sham menstruation; see Knight for a Marxist scenario. It's also argued that at least as important as males for provisioning, were grandmothers who evolved to live long past childbearing age to help provision their grandchildren by foraging tubers, grubs &c—Hawkes &al in Cronk &al: 237–58 and Hrdy: 267 & 284–7 (for a profile of Hrdy see *Discover* Mar'03: 40–5). Such matrilocal societies (where daughters stay and sons go off to other troops) may have promoted social intelligence—Hrdy: 143–4 & 193.

67. Neocortex growth—Allman: 173–4 and Hrdy: 141. Cronk: 95 argues that tool fabrication and use indirectly fostered brain development because giving and receiving instruction exercised brains.

68. Theory of Mind—Dunbar: 6, 16 & 180–1; Mithen: 84 and Parker & McKinney: 135ff. However my experience is that other animals, particularly dogs can be very good at sensing people's feelings, a 'sixth sense'. For example I've seen a dog single out a fearful person and attack them. When jogging if I encounter a dog,

I take a positive enthusiastic attitude toward it and it's friendly. See Sheldrake'99 on dogs sensing their human's feelings.

69. Language and group size, both Kohn: 217 and Mithen: 111 cite Dunbar's idea that gossip superseded ape's grooming in that you can schmooze more troop members than you can groom. Parker & McKinney: 285–7 propose 'declarative planning' using symbols as a critical adaptation in *Homo sapiens* evolution as we'll explore toward the end of the next chapter. See Ofek: 118–21 on trade.

70. Egalitarianism—Boehm: 33 & 68–9 and Dunbar: 9.

71. Domestication of dogs—Allman: 204–7, Coren: 18–9 and Ofek: 17 & 50–4, and *Science* 22Nov'02: 1540–2, 1610–3 & 1634–6, *Science News* Nov23'02: 324–5 and *NewScientist* 30Nov'02: 16. However Coppingers instead argue that some 12 kya less skittish wolves began scavenging human settlements which lead to a symbiotic relation and the evolution of dogs. When food was scarce, dogs probably were eaten as in Asia today—indeed Caras: 76–8 speculates that 12–14 kya hunters brought wolf cubs back to their cave keeping them alive for future meals but some became pets. Cannibalism was probably rarer, see Discovery.com Sept30'99 article citing *Science* 1Oct'99, and *Nature* 7Sept'00, *Scientific American* Aug'01: 58–65, *Science* 11Apr'03: 227–8 and Klein: 360–1.

72. Goat domestication—Caras: 45–51 says 12–15 kya. Also see Ofek: 218–22.

73. Beginning herding and farming—Bronowski: 61–9.

74. Farming—Diamond'99: 105–6, 136, 142–3, 149–50 & 153–4; Mithen: 217–26; Ofek: 190–227 and *Science* 25Apr'03: 597–603.

75. Fire's influence—Pyne: 24, 102–6 & 119–26.

76. On the initial use of fire see Ofek: 153 & 162, Klein: 350–5 and Stanley: 81. Some argue for an earlier date of 1.7 mya, see *Science News* Apr29'00: 287a; others for even longer, 1.9 mya; or shorter, 0.5 to 0.2 mya; see ABCNews.go.com Aug10'99 (about veggie cooking). Noble & Davidson: 205–7 are skeptical.

77. Gazing into campfires—Oubré: 27.

78. Males' seed—It was 1827 before the human female's egg was recognized as an equal contributor to conception—Mayr: 153–5. Even so, just as a plant was not seen as alive until it sprouted, an embryo was not recognized as alive until it 'quickened', that is started moving—before then, abortion was acceptable.

79. Bonobo food/sex relation—Waal: 110–1.

80. Ocher claims are disputed by Noble & Davidson: 211. Yet it's not much of a stretch to think that this attraction to faked estrus signals evolved into an attraction to red lipstick and nail-polish.

81. We can't assume that gals inducing guys to go hunting was necessarily coercive; it may have been more like a children's game—first the red signal, then the hunt, feasting &c. Moreover guys I've known who hunted enjoyed it: getting out in nature (and away from their wives), the preparation, the quest, the comradeship ... and those who enjoy it often get good at it.

82. Some primate males will kill infants to bring the mother into estrus but not if they have bonded with her; see Hrdy: 34–5 &c.

83. Many writers speak of males and females having different 'reproductive strategies' as though their interest in sex was to produce children rather than just

for the fun of it (any more then, than now). They argue that males have a far greater ability to pass on their genes because females can produce fewer children in their lifetime. But this ignores the necessity of raising those children to adulthood for them to continue passing on those genes. Unless the female has support in child-rearing, her children are likely to die along with those genes. Admittedly males could raise their status among other males by producing children (back then they didn't have flashy cars and clothes as status symbols, only leopard hides).

84. For a synopsis of this 'battle of the sexes' see Knight's Preface vi-vii, and 138–47, 153, 167, 172–3, 187–9, 216–9, 340–1 & 345; Kohn: 200–9 and Power in Hurford &al: 118–25. On the menstrual link with the Moon see Ehrenreich: 105–6. See also *NewScientist* 13Oct'01: 42–5.

85. On displays in sexual selection the hand-axe is proposed as the hominid equivalent of the peacock's tail, see Kohn: 137–40 and Miller: 288–91. For over a million years hand-axes were made with little change and often then apparently discarded which supports the argument that they were for display and so required an obligatory standard design for comparison. But just as the peacock's tail signals vitality, McCrone: 281–2 suggests that the hand-axe fostered brain lateralization and so signaled mental ability. Also see Noble & Davidson: 169–70 & 190–205.

86. On runaway evolution of intelligence and language see Miller: 72ff especially 174–5. Miller's thesis is intriguing but I think he tries to explain too much with it. Nonetheless he has many thought provoking ideas so he's worth reading.

87. Proto-language may have originated in women's support klatches but I have a couple reservations. First, between close individuals, communication requires minimal language (my wife and I used to joke about how 'telepathic' our conversations were) so in a close-knit group word use may have been minimal. Second, the test of an innovation is its effectiveness in its environment: language facilitated both genders' hunting, foraging, planning, teaching &c facilitating survival in our ancestors' environment, not just in the klatch. If language hadn't been useful for survival outside the klatch, it wouldn't have survived.

88. *Homo sapiens'* radiation—Cavalli-Sforza, Nichols, Stringer & McKie and Sykes thru-out, *Discover* Mar'03: 54–9, and *National Geographic* Dec'00: 40–67 on the Americas. A recent study concludes that *Homo sapiens* radiated out of Africa at least twice and interbred with earlier migrants—*Nature* Science Update 7Mar'02. The invasion of Australia doomed many large marsupials and of North America doomed the mammoth and mastodon as reported by AT&T Worldnet: Jun7'01 citing *Science* of date and *NewScientist* 16Jun'01: 17. *Homo sapiens* invaded SE Europe at least 35 kya—*Science News* May10'03: 302. Ofek: 181–9 argues that during the ice-ages of 20– to 16–kya our ancestors—living in the ice-free corridor between the glaciers and the mountains of the Pyrenees and Alps all the way to the Himalayas—had a respite from predators which allowed freer movement, trade and the invention of money.

89. Animism and our prelingual ancestors—Freeman: 131.

90. On subvocal speaking by natural objects, see Jaynes: 84–91. Perhaps they

knew their subvocalization was from some 'person' they didn't know because of unfamiliar intonation, they didn't recognize this other 'person's' voice as theirs.

91. Besides inducing the full moon another illustration of aboriginal people confusing cause and effect was depicted in the 1985 movie "The Emerald Forest" based on a true story in which an Amazon rainforest tribe persuaded the frogs to begin their croaking which they believed brought on the rains.

92. The magic, myth and science ways of knowing I adapted from Georgia Nugent's first lecture of "Heroes, Heroines and the Wisdom of Myth" on the SuperStar Teachers' 1994 audiotape from The Teaching Company.

Chapter Nine—Un- to CONSCIOUSness

1. We all intuitively know what 'conscious' means until we try to define it. I'm using it here as more than just 'awake' or 'aware' of what's going on around us as are other animals. I'm using conscious as 'aware of oneself,' to 'know that you know,' reflexive and subjective. Closer to what Damasio'99: 16 calls 'extended consciousness' which "... provides the organism with an elaborate sense of self ..." than just his 'core consciousness' which only "... provides the organism with a sense of self about one moment—now—and about one place—here." His core consciousness might conceivably apply to a thermostat—though he wouldn't go that far—what some call *non*consciousness. But he sees its emergence as "... a new way for the *life urge* to press its claims ..." (p.25) [my italics]. Whereas Macphail: 2ff "... instead of making a forlorn attempt at a formal definition ... draw[s] attention to two features of human consciousness": self- and feeling-consciousness. I'll leave it there except to note that, just as we don't define a word using that word, we have difficulty defining consciousness using our consciousness; see Rowlands: 1 and thru-out. A good elucidation of consciousness is by Velmans thru-out. See also Donald'01: 117–9, Griffin: 4–5 & 14–7 and Taylor: 17–8 & 37–8.

2. Anthropomorphism, it's argued, is an extension of animals' survival strategy of assuming that ambiguous objects are alive on the basis that it's safer, for example, to assume a stick is a snake than to assume a snake is a stick. I'm less persuaded that our ancestors assumed that ambiguous objects were human, or at least possessed human characteristics, on the basis that it's "what matters most." Alternatively, 'until proven otherwise', ambiguous objects could be seen as gods or their relatives, or dead ancestors in a spirit world. See Guthrie in Andresen: 94–107. Later in this chapter I'll propose that anthropomorphism arises from our Life Urge.

3. On our 'connectedness' with animals and the heuristic uses of anthropomorphism, see Budiansky: 20 & 34–6 and Griffin: 27–8. Also see Parker & McKinney: 10–1 who note "... that some behaviors and abilities in great apes that are considered 'humanlike' are actually 'apelike' ... that derive from the common ancestry of apes and humans; to focus on these elements is to be apeocentric rather than anthropocentric." On 'mechanomorphic' see Griffin: 29.

4. On ganglia reflexes, vertebrates with severed spinal cords have reflexes of which the patients are unaware; see Macphail: 7. On the 'stretch reflex circuit' see Llinás: 28.

5. Animal tool use see Griffin: 113–26, Hauser: 35–6 and Parker & McKinney: 51–6.

6. Associations—Macphail: 104–5, 133 & 135. Also see Budiansky: xxii, 27–8 & 33 and Hauser: 232–3.

7. Brains emulate to predict—Llinás: 54–5.

8. Animal intelligence—Budiansky: 53, Macphail: 108–20 and Taylor: 21–6.

9. 'Most advanced' intelligence does not necessarily equate to the best adapted—adapted for what? Many less advanced animals are very well adapted for their niche environments; see Donald'01: 114. Also see Parker & McKinney: 347–58 on evolutionary progress.

10. Animals and language—Hauser: 194 & 208, Lieberman'98: 31–48, Macphail: 120–25 and Parker & McKinney: 187–9.

11. Language as indicator of consciousness—Macphail: 219–23. He argues that because no other animals evolved language they didn't evolve consciousness. He overlooks the fact that they didn't concurrently evolve the necessary vocal components—they didn't evolve the 'hardware' to implement the 'software'. So I find his argument inconclusive, which he acknowledges. The jury's still out on cetacean's 'language'; see Griffin: 230–1, ABC News Science Aug17'99 on dolphin research in Sweden and Fox News.com Aug24'00 reporting on *Science* 25Aug'00: 1310–1 & 1355–7. Also see Discovery.com News Aug10'00 on bird brain research reported in *Nature* then.

12. Animal consciousness and the mirror test, see Budiansky: 161–71, Griffin: 275–6, Hauser: 101–3, Jaynes: 459–60, Macphail: 178–81 & 185, Parker & McKinney: 154–5, AT&TWorldnet Apr30'01, Discovery.com News Aug29'00, *Scientific American* Jul'01: 29 and *NewScientist* 16Nov'02: 26–9.

13. Energetic expense and cognition—Parker & McKinney: 275.

14. "About subjects and predicates" see Macphail: 221–7.

15. "... cause-and-effect ..."—Pinker in Jablonski & Aiello: 124.

16. Beginning of consciousness, see Damasio'99: 25–31.

17. Consciousness' emergence vs. language, see Damasio'99: 107–8 & 184–9 and Donald'01: 156 & 276–7, plus ~146–7 on the 'executive brain' and ~254 on 'cognitive communities'.

18. Immune system self/nonself—*Science* 12Apr'02: 298–300.

19. Brain's self-representational capacities—*Science* 12Apr'02: 308–10.

20. Distinct self—as infants we began Life as part of our mother in her womb and at her breasts, but by the 'terrible twos' begin to assert our selfhood by saying 'NO!' to most everything. More later.

21. On 'reading' others' minds, see Budiansky: 161–4 and Hurford: 180. That language evolved in order to deceive and manipulate rather than communicate is countered by Pinker in Jablonski & Aiello: 125.

22. Niccoló Machiavelli may have tried to write a satire (disguised as a scholarly treatise to avoid *The Prince*'s wrath) but today most everyone takes him seriously; see Viroli: 156.

23. On the emergence of Self, Jaynes: 261 & thru-out, contends that consciousness of Self didn't become prevalent until c700BC when our ancestors realized that the voice in their head wasn't a god speaking to them but was their own thoughts. Macphail: 226–7 interlocks the concept of Self with the evolution of language and hippocampal systems without speculating when that occurred.

24. On human's implicit and explicit cognitive systems, see Macphail: 141–58.

25. Some contend as children and adults we have no conscious recollection of our infant experiences before we began to talk, see Macphail: 170–3.

26. Preconscious processes, see Velmans: 210–1.

27. On the performance of nonverbal cognitive tasks, see Budiansky: 18.

28. Hippocampal studies—LeDoux'96: 198–208 and Macphail: 153–5.

29. On the 'interpreter' see Gazzaniga: 24, and on the basal ganglia's functions see Lieberman'00: thru-out.

30. Mind-body or bodymind—Pert thru-out. Benson: 71–3 includes the brain, and central and peripheral nervous systems, but not the somatic cells. Whether our brain or whatever is somehow linked with a 'cosmic consciousness' (as Jung believed) will be explored toward the end of this chapter and in the next.

31. Analysis of projection, see Velmans: 114–27 & 226–33.

32. My own experience of consciousness has several more or less simultaneous 'dramas' unfolding which seem largely unrelated. For example on my daily jog through a nearby park, I'm first of all aware of my body: breathing, effort level, any twinges and so forth. I'm also remotely aware of the surrounding panorama my body's moving through including the paving underfoot; any traffic; the sky, trees, birds, adjoining pond &c including related sounds and the wind. (Sometimes the wind and scents will trigger feelings from canoe trips in Ontario's Algonquin Park.) I'll briefly focus on an interesting bird, or a bottle that needs picking-up and the ensuing motions of my body. Another 'drama' is the tune or song that's likely playing in my head (no earphones). But along with these 'dramas' I carry on a continuous rambling subvocal monologue which I can rarely suppress only briefly by concentrating on my footfall or breathing. Damasio'99: 185 believes that we compulsively compose verbal stories about what we observe and experience. How do you experience your stream of consciousness?

33. Neural Darwinism—Edelman&Tononi: 83–6; Calvin: 82–3.

34. Organism vs. object, see Damasio'99: 133–41.

35. The centrosome is speculated to be an animal cell's 'brain' which, among other things, controls its movement via its cytoskeleton made of microtubules—Rensberger: 56–61. Intriguingly the microtubules resemble nanotubes now being researched for miniature computers—*Nature* Science Update 29Jan'02.

36. The cranial nerves' pathways bypass the spinal cord, see Clayman: 72.

37. Brains' predictive function, Llinás: 13–51.

38. Exoskeletal brains, see Llinás: 4–5. Exoskeletal animals such as arthropods not only have their brains and nerves but all their viscera and muscles encased in the skeletal shells of their body.

39. Concise history of neuroscience—*Science* 10Nov'00: 1113–20.

40. Edelman & Tononi: 54 assign a much larger role to what they call the *reticular activating system* as does Austin: 159.

41. Smells are picked up in the nose by the odor receptors which send nerve impulses through the olfactory bulbs and tracts to the cortices thus bypassing the thalamus; see Freeman: 7 & 20 and Nolte: 118. Pheromones are odorless and so affect us unconsciously. They are picked up near the nasal cavity by the vomeronasal organ (aka Jacobson's Organ) which sends nerve impulses to the accessory olfactory bulbs and which, it seems, also go directly to the cortices (cingulate? after the hypothalamus?); see Agosta: 113–4, Austin: 263, Llinás: 166, Watson: 8–9 & 31, *Nature* 15Jun'00 & ~12 Jul'01, Discovery.com News Sept29'00 and *Science* 21Feb'03: 1163 & 1196–1201. Dr. Joyce Brothers, in answer to a question about perfume Jan29'02, stated "The amount of the human brain devoted to our sense of smell is very large, much larger than that devoted to vision." However I'm unable to corroborate her claim altho Steriade: 9 identifies olfactory brain areas.

42. Thalamus—Austin: 263–74, Crick: 83–5 and Edelman & Tononi: 38. However Freeman: 96–114 argues that the limbic system performs many of the functions ascribed by others to the thalamus.

43. Primitive brain structures are concisely described by Goldberg: 30–1.

44. The limbic system is now believed to be only one of the sources of emotions; 'information substances' (neuromodulators, peptides, hormones, factors and protein ligands) are believed to be produced thru-out the body and transported into the brain via internal fluids' circulation, like plants—Pert: 133–45 & 350.

45. The enlarged hippocampus of the black-capped chickadee, for example, enables them to remember the locations of the thousands of seeds that they stored; see Hauser: 86 and Macphail: 130.

46. The cerebellum is proportionately small in frogs but large in birds to control flight; see Audesirks: 670. Across mammalian species the proportional size of the cerebellum remains largely the same except in humans and in those using echolocation such as dolphins and bats; see *Nature* Science Update 10May'01, *Science News* May19'01: 312b and *Scientific American* Aug'03: 50–7. For the cerebellum's origin see Allman: 77. As an interesting aside the cerebellum discriminates sensations induced by oneself from non-self thus explaining why we can't tickle ourselves; see AT&T WorldNet Sept10'00.

47. Primitive brain—Clayman: 76–7. Life regulation—Damasio'99: 55 & 60ff.

48. Reptilian brain. For a sketch of MacLean's reptilian, old- or paleomammalian and neomammalian brain areas, see Stevens: 263.

49. FAPs, see Llinás: 133ff.

50. On the internal milieu, see Rose: 17–8 wherein he also uses the terms *homeodynamics* and *autopoiesis* which are fancier words for the Life Urge. Also Damasio'99: 136–41 on "… the urge to stay alive …"

51. Limbic system, see Johnston: 110–1. But LeDoux'96: 98–103 argues against the idea that it's the emotional brain; also see Damasio'99: 60–1, *Science* 8Nov'02: 1191–4 and Pert note 44 above.

52. Brain's clocks—see *Scientific American* Sept'02: 58–65 & 66–73.

53. Amygdala's responses—Austin: 175–9, LeDoux'96: 157–174, Restak: 114–8, *Discover* Mar'03: 32–9 and *Science* 25Apr'03: 568–9. Uncontrolled violence is attributed to the cortex' failure to control the amygdala as reported in AT&T Worldnet Jul27'00 citing *Science* Jul28'00: 569ff. Preliminary research cited in *Nature* Science Update 1Aug'02 suggests flooding the amygdala with brain chemicals similar to those in cannabis dampens its action (no "Reefer Madness"). AT&T Worldnet Sept27'02 citing a recent report in the *Journal of the Cerebral Cortex* stated that "Women's Brains Better at Handling Anger" because generally their orbital frontal cortex is larger than men's eventho' their amygdala is the same size.

54. Primitive brain activates—Benzon: 31–2. But indirectly the neocortex can influence the primitive brain by facial expression, song/music and dance—Benzon: 40 & 104. Chapter Ten will more fully explore methods of affecting the primitive brain's emotions.

55. Brain structures and functioning of the proto-self, see Damasio'99: 22–3, 153–6, 170 & thru-out. On a more basic level the immune system learns to distinguish self from non-self.

56. Brain as computer—see Crick: 16–9; Edelman & Tononi: 47–50; Horrobin: 80–3 and McCrone: 106–10, 153, 187 & 291. Future computers may use quantum memories to mimic ours, see *Nature* Science Update 6Aug'01. However Gazzaniga: 48 & 54 takes issue with characterizing the neocortex as 'plastic' and 'rewiring' itself. Goldberg: 217–8 sees the evolution from a strictly modular brain to one also utilizing cortical structures as not only greatly increasing flexible capacity but also requiring an executive component, namely the prefrontal lobes.

57. Primitive brain's importance—Freeman: 35.

58. Primitive brain anatomy—Clayman: 76 and Nolte: 37–9.

59. Vertebrate brains are crowned by the cerebrum—also called the *telencephalon* which evolved as the *pallium* in reptiles, the *wulst* in birds and the neocortex in mammals—Allman: 113–5 and Jerison in Wallin &al: 187–93.

60. Human's frontal and temporal lobes' expansion, see Deacon: 186 & 217, Donald'01: 164–7, Freeman: 106 & 139 and McCrone: 201 & 292. However Parker & McKinney: 328 cite data showing proportionate expansion of the frontal lobe as the whole hemisphere expands among existing primates and *NewScientist* 23Feb'02: 15 quotes Passingham for a similar conclusion.

61. The mammalian brain has many components that are formed of cortices, especially in the primitive brain, but those cortices have one- to three-layers whereas the evolutionarily newest, the neocortex, has six-layers—Freeman: 113.

62. Women's corpus callosum is thicker per Candace Pert: 247, "... they are able to switch back and forth from the rational, or left brain, to the intuitive, or right brain, with relative ease." Hum ... Goldberg: 94–8 has studied women's and men's hemispheres and finds differences in shapes which he correlates with dif-

ferences in behavior, decision making and functions. (Goldberg escaped from the Soviet Union in his mid-twenties so he's not intimidated by 'political correctness'; see p.93.)

63. For a more detailed brain description, see Audesirks: 666–87.

64. Calvin's metaphor is described in *Scientific American* Oct.'94: 100–7, Calvin'96 thru-out and Calvin & Bickerton: 55–91. He uses many 'cartoons' and analogies to help describe his proposal.

65. Dendrites—*Science* 27Oct'00: 735–58.

66. On the area of our flattened neocortex Calvin'96: 52 says four sheets of typing paper which is $4 \times 8\frac{1}{2}'' \times 11'' = 374$-sq.in.=2.6-sq.ft., but McCrone: 87 only says over $1\frac{1}{2}$-sq.ft. Our neocortex is divided into two hemispheres as noted earlier, so it'd be more analogous to two rainforests separated by a divide (the Amazon and West African back when the Atlantic first opened?). Also the neocortex 'shell' is not just on top under the skull but wraps around down into the fissures and crevices. Whereas the neocortex has some six layers, in addition our brain has other more ancestral cortices with only one, two or three layers, akin to less dense 'woodlands' and 'brush' adjoining the 'forest'; see Freeman: 113.

67. Glial cells, aka astrocytes, may perform other critical functions; see Rose: 148–9, *Science News* Apr7'01: 222–3, ~Nov17'01: 309, *Nature* 17May'01 and *Science* 4May'01: 872–3 & ~18Oct'02: 556–62. Also "... glial cells ... account for about half of the human brain's weight." per AT&T WorldNet Jul26'01 citing *Science* 27Jul'01: 567 notice of a study on-line. There's speculation that "... glial cells might be turned into new neurons"—*NewScientist* 24Nov'01: 16–7.

68. Neuron vs. plant growth—Coen: 224–5.

69. My description here of our visual system is shamefully oversimplified in order to focus on neural Darwinism. A little more detail would explain how the lens of each eye focuses light on the rear inner surface of the eyeball's sphere producing what is essentially a hemispherical two-dimensional image there. The image in each eye is split vertically in two so that the view on the right side of the head is focused on the left side of the inner hemisphere and visa versa. The rods and cones there, the retina, transduce photons into nerve impulses which are sent down the optic nerve fibers. The optic nerves lead to the optic chiasm where the halves from each eye are paired so the inputs from both views to the right go to the left brain and visa versa. The nerve impulses go through the thalamus LGN (Lateral Geniculate Nucleus), then to the primary visual areas (V1&V2) in the rear of the brain (the occipital lobes) as described in the main text. (Some of the noncolor nerve impulses from the eyes bypass all this and go directly to the superior colliculus on the brainstem where it reacts rapidly to sudden changes thereby redirecting eye movement and other primitive functions—Austin: 241–4.) For a more comprehensive description, see Crick: 76–7, 121–38 & thru-out (his book's title is misleading, I think); Llinás: 96–109; Ramachandran: 70–4; Zeki: 13–21 & 78–9 and *Scientific American* Nov'99: 69–75.

70. Specialized visual areas, see Crick: 150 & 156, McCrone: 94–5 and Zeki: 58–68.

71. Waves to pulses = analog to digital? For a slightly different explanation of what happens in neurons, see Freeman: 37–63. He believes the nerve impulses act in ensembles. Moreover Pert: 139–40 contends that neurotransmitters (information substances) are picked up by receptors all along the nerve-cell's membrane not just across from synapses: parasynaptic.

72. Spontaneous nerve cycling, idling or firing—McCrone: 153–5.

73. Dendrite growth forming memories, see Horrobin: 99.

74. Visual areas' maps, see Crick: 147–59 and *Scientific American* Nov'99: 72. On distributed maps in the ventral temporal cortex for recognition of faces &c— *Science* 13May'01: 196–8 and ~28Sept'01: 2405–7, 2425–30 & 2470–3.

75. Nerve impulse bursts—Crick: 211–2 and Freeman: 88.

76. Nerve impulse frequency—Crick: 92, 210 & 244–5; Llinás: 120–31 and Taylor: 289–90. Freeman: 58 reports the gamma range between 20 and 100Hz; he also refers to nerve impulses in dendrites as 'waves' and in axons as 'pulses': 41–3; also see 110–2. On synchronizing see *Science* 23Feb'01: 1506–7 and ~22Jun'01: 2233 & 2295–9. Edelman & Tononi: 106–7 & 113–8 explain the binding problem with what they call 'reentry'.

77. Neural transients—McCrone: 116–9. Apparently this is what Edelman & Tononi: 69–70 call 'coherence'.

78. Regarding multisensory integration or convergence in mammal's entorhinal cortex, see Freeman: 7, 97 & 101. On the parietal cortex, see Restak: 13.

79. Connections from the sensory areas are relatively sparse so nerve impulse patterns apparently are condensed into categories (gists?) before being sent on, see Lakoff & Johnson: 18.

80. Binding electromagnetic fields—Pockett: 107–8.

81. Auditory defers to visual cues in judging direction, hence the ventriloquism effect—*Nature* 14Mar'02.

82. Abstract art, see Zeki: 205–8.

83. For drawings of vase/faces as well as a Necker cube, see Calvin: 67 or Crick: 30 & 40. Also see Edelman & Tononi: 25.

84. Completing the gestalt (amodal completion)—Crick: 36 & 38 and *Nature* 15Mar'01.

85. Consciousness, see Edelman & Tononi thru-out. However I found Edelman challenging to understand (I haven't read his previous books). For example on page 74: "These empirical observations suggest that underlying consciousness are distributed neural processes that, through reentrant interactions, are at once highly integrated but continually changing and thus are highly differentiated." ('integrated yet differentiated' = synergistic complexity?) His use of terms seems unusual. For example he's opposed to the term 'representation' which he seems to equate with 'symbol' and instead uses the term 'map' even though a map is a representation of a territory (see Damasio'99: 320–1; but Freeman: 15 &103 is also troubled with 'representation' preferring 'meaning' and 'field'). Edelman uses the term 'degeneracy' by which I understand him to mean 'redundancy'. Even so I found his book worth the struggle of reading several times because he provides valuable

information and insights. (Crick: 284, Calvin: 82–3 and Rose: 172 also had trouble following Edelman so I don't feel too dumb. But Damasio'99 praises Edelman on the dust jacket and Donald'01 cites him.) Freeman's book isn't any easier but just as rewarding.

86. Authors sometimes conflate reverberations of neurons with those of impulses, see Crick: 207 versus 251–2.

87. The hard problem of consciousness, see Chalmers: xi–xiii, McCrone: 302–5, Stewart & Cohen: 205 and Taylor: 48–53. However Peter Carruthers in Walsh: 82 concludes that "The 'hard problem' of phenomenal consciousness ... is not so *very* hard after all." And Rowlands: 25 states "The problem of phenomenal consciousness, the problem of *explaining* how phenomenal consciousness can come from what is not conscious, has no solution. We know consciousness is produced by what is not conscious, but we can never understand how." [his italic] and elaborates p.216–9.

88. Gordian knot, if your memory needs refreshing: Gordius was a peasant in Phrygia (now northwestern Turkey) who happened to drive his wagon into town just after an oracle had proclaimed that the next man driving a wagon into town should be proclaimed king. So in gratitude to Zeus he tied the yoke securely to the wagon and left it in the temple grove where it stayed many years while his intricate knot weathered and tightened. A legend grew that whoever could untie the knot would rule all Asia. Many tried unsuccessfully until Alexander of Macedon in frustration took his sword and sliced through it with a single stroke. He went on conquering all the way beyond the Indus river (now in Pakistan) until his exhausted, homesick troops threatened mutiny. Gordius fathered Midas famous for his golden touch. Per Microsoft Encarta Encyclopedia 2001.

89. The 'world knot' was Schopenhauer's term for the 'hard problem' as described by Edelman: 2, 3 & 163.

90. On the subjective experience of consciousness, see Deacon: 458. What allows the brain to create "subjective neural activities," according to Feinberg: 147, is that *"The conscious brain has no sensation of itself."* [his italics] "... sticking a pin in the cortex itself evokes no pain that is referable to the brain itself. The brain has no sensory apparatus directed toward itself." But he doesn't explain further as though its significance is obvious. Is he implying that the brain's sensory apparatus is instead directed toward its own neural activities which thus create subjectivity? That it 'senses' emergent synergy? However Freeman: 94 says it's "... wrongly believed that you cannot feel stimuli given directly to your brain."

91. Cem-field—McFadden: 295–314 and his "Synchronous firing and its influence on the brain's electromagnetic field: evidence for an electromagnetic field theory of consciousness" published in: *Journal of Consciousness Studies* (2002) 9: 23–50 intriguingly offers explanations for many intractable aspects of consciousness. Also see Pockett: 105–13 & 115–25.

92. Subjective feeling—Cook in Crow:187–9.

93. Quantum consciousness—Penrose'94 & ~'97 proposes that conscious-

ness might arise from wave-like quantum-mechanical effects involving protein filaments called microtubules in nerve cells. Also see *Nature* Science Update 5Sept'03.

94. Core- and extended-consciousness are terms coined by Damasio'99: 16, 168ff, 195ff & 338n10. Edelman & Tononi: 102ff use the terms 'primary' and 'higher-order' consciousness for similar states. Stewart & Cohen: 202 call core-consciousness 'awareness' and reserve 'consciousness' for "... a kind of introspective awareness in which the possessor has a definite feeling of individuality." Rowlands: 2–3 and others use the term 'phenomenal consciousness' for experiential, subjective states that have a qualitative feel (he also refers to 'monitoring' or 'introspective' consciousness, p.16–22.) Also see Freeman: 126 and Horgan: 238 & 244.

95. Brain structures that correlate with core-consciousness are centrally located in the brain, are of old evolutionary vintage, are present in numerous non-human species and mature early in each human's development—Damasio'99: 106 & 270–1. JA Hobson: 176–9 also includes the forebrain (neocortex) whereas Hobson & Leonard: 88–94 see the thalamus as the central player in consciousness.

96. Core-consciousness essential—Damasio'99: 121.

97. Qualia—Stewart & Cohen: 206 explain as virtual experience and on 189 as 'figments of reality' in our inner world that we project out onto what we perceive as the outer world of reality.

98. On the effect of ambient light, see Lakoff & Johnson: 23–4 and Zeki: 183–91. Also see Deacon: 117–9 on color perception and naming.

99. Sound: as mentioned above, air pressure vibrating at a frequency of 440Hz is perceived as the musical note A above middle C (if you have 'perfect pitch', the rest of us resort to 'relative pitch'—see Jourdain: 111–7; altho we may have been born with perfect pitch but relinquished it—AT&T Apr.11'01 on Feb.23 HealthScout report citing Jan'01 issue of *Developmental Psychology*). Our individual neocortex has learned ways to convert these natural phenomena into unique conscious qualities, hence the term 'qualia'. As an aside, whereas light and sound have their own nerve pathways that finally terminate in dedicated visual and auditory regions in our and other mammals' neocortex, no region dedicated to 'pain' or 'pleasure' has been found in the cortex. This raises the question: Does an animal without consciousness experience pain if it has no pain qualia?—see Macphail: 186–201. On the necessity of qualia, see Velmans: 82–7.

100. Initial consciousness—Damasio'99: 169–70.

101. Animal 'feelings', see Macphail: 5–7, 15–7, 186–7 & 228. Damasio'99: 73, believes that consciousness is required to feel pain.

102. 'Concept' is defined a little more basically by Edelman & Tononi: 104–5.

103. The distinction between qualia and concepts can be confused when we apply scientific understanding to our experiences. The qualia of colors we can conceive of as light frequencies but that drains the experience of its richness, its 'color'. But in Chapter Four the quale of 'gravity' we conceived of as the compaction of space, of Earth pushing up, without diminishing the experience; to my mind, it enriches it. And the thesis of this book is that the quale 'God' should be conceived of

as the Life Urge which, I believe, can be a richer experience once you think it through, get used to the idea, feel it and let it permeate your being, namely, assimilate it so it becomes a quale, which some may call 'faith'.

104. On our brain's synthesis, see Freeman: 90.

105. Quote 'unified conscious state' from Edelman & Tononi: 146.

106. Multitasking, see Donald'01: 80, 130–4 & 258–9 and Damasio'99: 201.

107. However recent research indicates that "Spatial awareness is a function of the temporal not the posterior parietal lobe"—Letters to *Nature* 21Jun01.

108. Probably the 'where?' nerve impulses don't go directly to the somatosensory region but via the thalamus and/or the limbic system's entrorhinal cortex—Edelman & Tononi: 42 and Freeman: 101–2. By the way Ramachandran: 74, calls the 'where', 'how'.

109. On the somatosensory band, you may have seen drawings of a distorted man, a homunculus, laid out along the band with his feet at the crest, his body draped down the side and his head at the bottom. Certain body parts such as his hands and mouth are exaggerated to depict their greater sensitivity. More accurately there should be a half-man on each side of the brain to depict the left hemisphere sensing the right side of the body and vice versa. Moreover his toes wouldn't be at the crest but down in the fissure and his legs would come up over the crest. See Glynn:179, Llinás: 205, Ramachandran: 26, Taylor: 70 and Velmans: 129.

110. On the 'what?' and 'where?' pathways in the brain, see Austin: 244–8, McCrone: 171–3 and *Science* 12Jan'01: 260–3. Yet these are only two of the six questions newspaper editors told cub-reporters to search out: what, where, who, when, how and why. 'Who?', that is facial recognition, is processed in the so-called 'face area' (at the occipito-temporal junction)—Damasio'99: 165–6, *Science News* Jul7'01: 10–2 and *Science* 28Sept'01: 2405–7. 'When?', may be tracked by our 8–12 Hz "central timing mechanism"—Llinás: 30 & 48. (Our circadian clock is in our *suprachiasmatic nucleus* (SCN) and elsewhere—Hirsch: 144 and *Science* 20Jul'01: 437–8, ~8Feb'02: 955–7 & ~18Jul'03: 319–20.) 'How?' is addressed in the pre- and motor regions. 'Why?', probably in the prefrontal.

111. On the differences between the hemispheres, brain lateralization, there's speculation that it's largely unique to humans (maybe not—*NewScientist* 17May '03: 20) and that it evolved over the couple million years our ancestors spent first learning to make and use tools. For example to make a hand-axe a right-handed person holds the raw stone with their left hand while grasping a striking stone with their right hand to flake pieces off the raw stone. Their left hand positions the raw stone observing it with the right halves of their eyes' retinas, thus those visual nerve impulses are fed to the occipital lobe of their right hemisphere (as described in note 69 and Ch. 8's note 85). Similarly their right hand aims the striking stone observing it with the left halves of the eyes' retinas, thus feeding those nerve impulses into their left hemisphere's occipital lobe. Consequently the right hemisphere evolved to concentrate on the overall picture and the left on the fine detail. Kohn: 139–40 & 155 and Miller: 288–91 argue that gals selected guys for their hand-axe skill thus reproducing the trait. But inadvertently the gals may have been se-

lecting for other capabilities too such as proto-language. Adapting this division for language, the right brain guides the conversation while the left selects and chains words together; see McCrone: 174–7 & 281–2. Crow &al pursue the notion that there were mutations or transpositions on hominids' X and/or Y chromosomes which led to brain lateralization, language and speciation. (Gazzaniga: 151 & thru-out believes our left brain has an 'interpreter' which "... seeks to understand the world" and will fabricate explanations and memories if need be; also see *Scientific American* Jul'98: 50–5 and *Science* 18Jul'03: 384–6.)

112. On processing in the frontal cortex, see Austin: 253–9, Goldberg: 23–6 & 70ff and McCrone: 194–202. On the location of cognitive and interpersonal functions in the prefrontal cortex, see Freeman: 106–7 "The dorsal and lateral areas of the frontal lobe are concerned with cognitive functions, such as logic and reasoning in prediction, and the medial and ventral areas are concerned with social skills and the capacity for interpersonal empathy." For more detail, see Passingham: 37, 122–3, 236–7 & thru-out. Donald'01: 194–7 and Passingham: 191, 220–1 & 251 see a larger role for the *neo*cerebellum, namely to store the sequence of movements once the frontal cortex has worked them out—see *Science* 14Jun'02: 1979–80, and Lieberman'00: 119–20 cites other roles. (Apparently the cerebellum controls the same side of the body, whereas the cerebral hemisphere is 'wired' to its opposite side, as noted above, so the pathways between them are crossed—Deacon: 295.) However Llinás: 136–44 & 170 argues that fixed action patterns, FAPs, are stored in the basal ganglia. Recent research on aborted human fetal tissue found development of neurons between the thalamus and frontal lobes that appears to be unique to humans—*Science* 7Sept'01: 1746–7.

113. Motor region—Just as the somatosensory band has a homunculus that receives signals *from* thru-out the body, the motor band does too, but instead sends signals *to* particular muscle groups. Recent research found that, whereas a brief stimulus makes the respective muscle twitch, a longer stimulus induces a sequence of actions toward a particular position—*Science* 3May'02: 1587–8.

114. Proto-self to Self, see Damasio'99: 22, 153–5, 168–82 & thru-out and Llinás: 23–4.

115. Theory of mind—*Science* 16May'03: 1079–80.

116. Knowing one's own thoughts is not essential, perhaps even an impediment, to knowing another's thoughts especially if one is completely dominated, subsumed, by the other so that one has little perception of their own Self. This condition Jaynes: 75 believes existed before consciousness emerged (also Armstrong'01: 10–12 citing Karl Jaspers' 'Axial Age'). As a frivolous aside, I'm reminded of the line in the song "When I was a Lad" from Gilbert & Sullivan's *H.M.S. Pinafore,* ♪"... I always voted at my party's call and I never thought of thinking for myself at all." Humorous but pathetic and perhaps all too common as one struggles between dependence on authority figures and one's Self. Who hasn't found themselves in situations where their opinion not only didn't matter but was taken as insubordination; see Freeman: 150–1 on entrainment and brain washing. On the other hand if you truly want to understand another person, your opinion

shouldn't matter, you should just try to hear them and empathize, but without necessarily agreeing with them, in effect accepting them without abandoning your own Self.

117. Language metaphors, spoken or written, not only evolved long after conceptual metaphors but are derived from conceptual metaphors.

118. Conceptual metaphors, see Fauconnier: 9–13, Lakoff & Johnson: 45–59 and Lakoff & Núñez: 39–49.

119. Primary and complex metaphors—Lakoff & Johnson: 45–73.

120. Calvin'96 cites his comb example thru-out.

121. Rewire our brain—"*Neuroplasticity* refers to the ability of neurons to forge new connections, to blaze new paths through the cortex, even to assume new roles. In shorthand, neuroplasticity means rewiring the brain." Schwartz & Begley: 15–6.

122. Lakoff & Johnson: 19 contend "... that the peculiar nature of our bodies shapes our very possibilities for conceptualization and categorization." which perhaps explains our inability, cited in Chapter Four, 'to make the shift to the quantum realm'.

123. Authorities' influence on our judgment of causality, see Macphail: 146 and the above note 116 on knowing one's thoughts.

124. Learning and consciousness—Mandler's dictum states "that consciousness is essential for learning and memory"—Donald'01: 228 & 231—but *Nature* Science Update 25Oct'01 counters that "Subliminal sights educate brain."

125. Lessening of attention with learning, see McCrone: 135. On automatization, see Donald'01: 57–8 & 176 and Passingham: 221 & 250–1. Llinás: 174–5 & thru-out uses the term FAPs (fixed action patterns).

126. Memory duration, see Crick: 83 and Taylor: 131–4 & 203–4. Also *Science News* Nov10'01: 294 and *New Scientist* 3May'03: 26–9.

127. Memory—Donald'01: 49ff, McCrone: 194–216, *Nature* 17May'01 and *NewScientist* 17May'03 Inside Science #160. If the hippocampus is destroyed, new memories can no longer be stored but previous memories can be recalled; see Donald'01: 163 and Freeman: 104. Depicted in the 2000 movie "Memento."

128. Memory conversion during sleep, see Taylor: 298–9, *Science* 13Oct'00: 247–9 & 350–3, ~2Nov'01: 1047–63, *Nature* Science Update 22Feb'02 and *Neuron* Jan25'01 as reported in AT&T WorldNet 10/12/00 & 1/25/01 and Discovery.com News 1/26/01. On the importance of non-dream sleep to learning, see *Nature* Science Update 26Apr'01 and AT&T WorldNet 4/25/01.

129. Childhood development of neocortex, see Donald'01: 209 & 281, Freeman: 38–40, Greenfield: 61–3, Lieberman'98: 122–3 and Restak: 22–6, and also *Science* 2Nov'01: 1011–2. Donald'01: 232–50 also cites the amazing feats of Helen Keller, blind and deaf from $18\frac{1}{2}$ months old.

130. Each brain unique—Freeman in Wallin &al: 412–7.

131. Of memory recall my brother use to say that he had an excellent memory: everything he'd ever seen, heard, read &c was stored in his memory. But he said his recall was weak.

132. Another personal anecdote about memory recall: While driving with my oldest son and this then fiancée to visit her family, she reminded him to give her aunt, a nun, the five dollars he'd pledged to the Poor Souls in Purgatory. Well, I had an inkling what that was about but I asked anyway. They explained that it was the practice in her family when you lost something, the Poor Souls would help you find it if you made an offering to them. My son had misplaced an item and after a vain search pledged five dollars to the Poor Souls and shortly thereafter he remembered where he'd left it. So I mischievously asked two questions: How does the nun get the money to Purgatory? and What do the Poor Souls do with it—are there vending machines in Purgatory? Then I offered my interpretation: Since our egos are entangled with money, we can get our ego out of our unconscious mind's way by sending a token of it away with the money. The recollection of where he'd left the lost item was back in his mind somewhere but was blocked; letting go of his ego unblocked it. It was quiet in the car for a while after.

133. Remembering only the gists—Schacter: 192–3.

134. Memory classification, see Donald'01: 51–2 plus 161 on 'autocuing'.

135. Autobiographic memory—Damasio'99: 17–8, 173–5 & 199–200, and on episodic memory, see Donald'01: 200–2 & 282.

136. Definition of intent from Freeman: 8.

137. Neural Darwinism—Edelman & Tononi: 79 & 83–6.

138. Proactive sensory neurons, Freeman: 29 called it the 'unidirectionality of perception'.

139. Attractor landscapes, see Freeman: 80, 104 & 133 and McCrone: 62–70.

140. Neuromodulators—Freeman: 107–8 & 152.

141. Chaotic processes in the brain, see Freeman: 86–7 & 133–5, McCrone: 59–73 and NewScientist 25Aug'01: 7.

142. Reentrance—Edelman & Tononi: 36, 44 & 48–9.

143. Feedback and anticipation, see Freeman: 120–1 and McCrone: 157–64. On the same neurons' involvement in both perceiving and imagining, see Nature 16Nov'00 and AT&T Worldnet Nov1'00 & Nov15'00. For recent research on how our brain anticipates object perception see Science News Nov2'02: 275–6.

144. Delay from brain activity to awareness (Libet's research), see Donald'01: 53; Edelman&Tononi: 68–9; Freeman: 124, 135–6 & 139; McCrone: 120–44; Taylor: 273–80 and Velmans: 195–7 & 211–2. A half-second is a nominal time; if caught unawares it can be longer than a second but even an athlete anticipating and concentrating on a simple trained reaction requires at least 0.1 to 0.2 second. A tenth-second may be the minimum due to the 8–12 Hz periodicity of voluntary movement—see Llinás: 30 & 55–6.

145. Brain's head-start and freewill, Horgan: 234 quotes Libet "… we may exert free will not by initiating intentions but by vetoing, acceding, or otherwise responding to them after they well up from our unconscious."

146. Anticipation—McCrone: 145ff.

147. Executive guidance: CEO—Edelman & Tononi: 58.

148. Influencing brain action is what I believe Freeman: 104–5, 125–6 & 135–9 means by 'brain state transitions' and "... a sequence of global states of awareness."

149. Cem-field and free will—see McFadden (cited above note 91): 31–9. He seems to use a narrowed definition of 'free will'.

150. Quantum Zeno Effect—Schwartz & Begley: 357, also 342 & 350–4. I find their explanations unconvincing, you can tell.

151. On the thalamus as 'spotlight', see Crick: 62 & 245–50 and Edelman& Tononi: 139ff on their 'dynamic core' generated within the thalamo-cortical system. On the limbic system (entrorhinal cortex) see Freeman: 97, 101–2, 104–5 & 139–40.

152. Metacognition, the executive function and intermediate-term governance, see Donald'01: 47, 59, 70, 75, 84, 90 & thru-out. He speculates, p.196–9, that the multiple expansion of the prefrontal cortex, hippocampus and neocerebellum, and their interconnections during human evolution provided reentrant circuits for prolonged slow looping of nerve impulse patterns enabling 'keeping thoughts in mind' running 'round your brain' and automating skills.

153. Modular and innate vs. general purpose brain—Goldberg: 55–8 & 215–9, Kohn: 159–62 & 254 and Parker & McKinney: 231–2. On the prefrontal and religion see McNamara in Andresen: 237ff.

154. I once asked an eminent philosophy professor if we humans have instincts; without hesitation he flatly answered: No. He was from my alma mater, the local Jesuit university (though not a Jesuit) speaking to a men's group at the parish I belonged to back around 1960. But the more I thought about it, the more it seemed to me that if we evolved from animals, why wouldn't we too have instincts? He displayed the intellectual arrogance typical of the Church then which gradually turned me away.

155. Instincts—see Winston's survey of human instincts, thru-out.

156. Instinct/archetype—Stevens'83: 49, 52 & thru-out.

157. Shadow and guilt—Stevens'83: 210–43. As I understand it, one's unconscious 'shadow' is also called one's doppelgänger.

158. True restraint—I thought I'd seen this years ago in reading Kahlil Gibran but I haven't found it. Maybe I coined it myself!?

159. Idling neurons' impulse generation—Freeman: 41–3 and *Science* 20Jan '01: 443–4. Recently it's suggested that "... with billions of neurons constantly sending signals ... the chattering actually boosts the brain's processing power" aka noise or stochastic resonance—*ScienceNews* Jun'03: 20–1.

160. Association cortex role in creativity—Pfenninger & Shubik: 66–7, 96 & 235. Zeki in *Science* 6Jul'01: 51–2 describes the visual brain's role in artistic creativity.

161. Sleep on it—see Hartmann: 161–7 on artistic and scientific thinking, and dreams.

162. Recall the apocryphal story of Archimedes in mid200s BC who cried "Eureka!" (I've found it!) as he ran naked through the streets of Syracuse Sicily after emerging from the baths with the solution to a vexing problem. He'd been

wrestling with the problem but his mind had drifted as he gently bobbed in the water. When it suddenly dawned on him that his body was buoyed up by the weight of water it displaced (this varies from Perkins: 7). (The story goes that Archimedes was killed by an irascible soldier of the Roman general Marcellus when, as ordered, Archimedes didn't immediately get up from the ground where he was tracing out a problem in the dirt. Sagan'80: 52n and *Science* 1Nov'02: 967–8.) I've heard that when the Beatles first got the musical inspiration for "Yesterday" the only words that came were "scrambled eggs" which pretty well captures the sentiment of the song (try it). In a Jan11'02 Peter Jennings ABC-TV show interviewing Harvey Schmidt about his composing the song "Try to Remember" for the "Fantasticks" musical, Schmidt tells a similar tale of inspiration from 'out of nowhere' while exhausted from futile trying. Poincaré's experiences are described by Pirsig: 266–9 and Penrose's by Horgan: 240.

163. By 'fertile mind' is meant a brain that from childhood has been exposed to enriching experiences and has developed skills in the field of interest as per Karl Popper cited in Coen: 226–7 & 358. Also see Damasio's list of requirements for creativity in Pfenninger & Shubik: 63–6.

164. A nifty story I heard years ago of how structure can foster creativity is from a radio interview with Meredith Willson about composing his musical "The Music Man." Over the years touring with his choral group as ideas for songs came to mind he'd jot them down and toss them in his 'old wardrobe trunk'. So when he came to compose "The Music Man" he was confident knowing he had all those ideas to draw from. But as he worked on each song in the musical nothing he had was quite right so he'd compose something from scratch. This happened time and again. When he had completed the musical he found he hadn't used a single idea from his trunk. But he said if he hadn't had all those ideas in his 'old wardrobe trunk' he never would've had the courage to start.

165. On getting ideas out so they can be examined, Einstein's special relativity theory gestated for a decade followed by a fruitless year of struggle. One day in Bern he visited his friend Besso, talked a lot about the problem and "... suddenly comprehended the matter. Next day I visited him again and said ... 'Thank you. I've completely solved the problem.'" See Pais: 139. Also see Donald'01: 278–9.

166. Reality check—While a strong imagination is an asset for creative thinking, Horrobin: 205–8 describes how the very genes (alleles) that foster 'genius', foster schizophrenia—an imagination so strong that it overpowers the mind's ability to discriminate reality. The 2001 movie "A Beautiful Mind" uses Nobel laureate John Nash's struggles to show how real his imaginings seemed. His ability to sustain thoughts in his mind and relentlessly manipulate them enabled his genius but, when combined with his other problems, this same ability fabricated his delusions.

167. Pre-conscious processing is believed to be prolonged in savants enabling their powers—*NewScientist* 9Oct'99: 30–4.

168. The distinction between reasoning and rationalizing is rarely so precise; we're often blind to our own biases. As an aside, when I was with Edsel Product

Planning, the guys in market research facetiously wanted to put on the first page of their assigned reports, "These are the conclusions on which I based my facts."

169. Interpreter—Gazzaniga: 24, 133 & 174–5.

170. Paradigmatic thinking—Donald'01: 260.

171. Causality in human's mind—Freeman: 126–33.

172. Language likened to species—Hurford &al: 1–2. Also see Donald'01: 284–5.

173. Human brain relative size—Lieberman'00: 150–1. Donald'01: 293–4 lists brain expansion that coincided with language capacity.

174. Hybrid mind—Donald'01: 153–7, 202 & 252ff. Also see NewScientist 17May'03: 40–1.

175. On the distinction between a sign and a symbol, see Passingham: 240—he seems to say that a symbol is a sign we humans use for communication. On animal communication see Griffin: 187–211 and Marler in Jablonski & Aiello: 1–15.

176. Reading—Eventho writing/reading developed only a few millennia ago, human brains can become very adept at reading. But the human brain couldn't have evolved the capacity that quickly. How come? A proposed answer has two parts: First the symbols used in writing were selected from natural images, minimized and stylized so the evolved human brain was pre-adapted to recognize them and make appropriate associations. Second the various pre-adapted areas of the brain are taught to complete their adaptation to reading thru 're-wiring'. See NewScientist 5Jul'03: 30–3.

177. Infant brain growth—Restak: xiii, 1–5 & 11–18. Early development of synapse—Science 25Oct'02: 770–6. 'When do babies develop memories?'—AT&TWorldnet Nov1'02.

178. 'Informavore' is attributed to George Miller by Pinker in Jablonski and Aiello: 124.

179. Assimilation—Freeman: 9, 14–5, 29 & 120.

180. Mammals require play early on to develop their neocortex and cerebellum—NewScientist 9Jun'01: 28–31 and Paul Harris thru-out. ("Children have to interrupt their education to go to school." Sidney Harris in the 1960s) Brain development goes through a second bout of growth and pruning in adolescence—Restak: 72–7 and NewScientist 19Oct'02: 16.

181. Solipsistic minds—see Donald'01: 149–50, 250–4 & 286–7; and Freeman: 90, 120 & 141ff and in Wallin &al: 414–5 where he calls it epistemological solipsism rather than metaphysical solipsism.

182. Birds and whales sing—see Discovery.com News Jan5'01 citing Science 5Jan'01: 52–4.

183. Lateralization—in Crow see Ploog:132, Corballis: 141 & 146–8, Steele: 158–63, Cook: 172, Crow: 197–212 and Tyler-Smith: 223–4. Also see Science 15Feb '02: 1219–25.

184. Maternal/infant behavior and symbol evolution—see Parker & McKinney: 284–5. Imitation—Science News May24'03: 330–2.

185. Grooming vs. gossip—Aiello: 28 in Jablonski & Aiello and Power: 111–5 in Hurford &al. Eric Berne: 15 used the term 'stroking' for a range of human inter-

actions. But note that as the contact shifts from tactile to cerebral (face-to-face, phone, e-mail ...) the emotional content diminishes as the information content increases; see McLuhan'95: 161–2.

186. Hand-axe unchanged—Kohn: 63, 141 & 158 and Mithen: 123.

187. Holistic scene to lineal sequence—McLuhen somewhere describes how we have to break the scene into some sequence in order to describe it verbally—"a picture's worth a thousand words."

188. On the relation of finger movements to verbal areas in the brain, see Passingham: 249–50. There's speculation that watching another handle something activates 'mirroring' in Broca's (speech) area of the observer's brain—*NewScientist* 27Jan'01: 22–6.

189. Other changes—Lieberman'01: 142–56 suggests that walking may have pre-adapted our ancestor's basal ganglia for cognition. Benzon: 171–6 argues that our early ancestors imitated animal sounds so that by 300 kya they had evolved the tongue, throat and breath control that enabled language and song/music.

190. How language evolved—*NewScientist* 30Mar'02: 24–7 describes work with robots to find the answer.

191. Mimesis—Donald'91: 168–200, ~'01: 240 & 261–9 and in Hurford &al: 49. Not to be confused with memetics, the study of memes cited in note 227 below and described in its antecedent text.

192. Written symbols—many generations after vocal symbols had evolved, visual symbols evolved and were also linked directly to the gists or were linked indirectly to mental sounds which then linked to their respective gists. (This concerns the esoteric issue of whether for instance when you see the word 'dog' do you think of the idea of dog as you would if you saw a picture of a dog or do you mentally sound the word 'dog' which then makes you think of the idea of dog.) Literacy involves massive restructuring of our brain—Donald'01: 302–4.

193. Stepping-stones vs leaps—pursuing this analogy, in crossing a creek that's too broad to leap, we use stepping-stones until we run out, then we have to leap from a stable stone across to the far bank (I've a beautiful photo of my son John doing this at age fifteen in Colorado). Similarly our ancestors used preadaption: prelingual 'stones' such as natural sounds and gestures to position themselves for the 'leap' to language—see Aitchison in Hurford &al: 20–1. Donald'91: 183 cites 'limbic speech' produced in primate's limbic system and cingulate gyrus, and restricted to "emotional utterances" such as expletives (implicated in Tourette's syndrome?) as an early step to prosody. Noble & Davidson: 218–26 & thru-out trace a speculative chain of capabilities leading to language. Also see Benzon: 181–2 on what he calls a 'Gestalt switch'. There's a recent mathematical model which indicates that language had to have evolved in a leap—*Nature* Science Update 22Jan'03.

194. Internal dialog—Jaynes: 75 & 85–91. Seeing and conversing with gods, see Fox: 102ff and Jaynes: 72–5 & thru-out. Also see Bentall in Cardeña &al: 99–101 on misattribution of inner speech.

195. Language evolution was perhaps far more complex than I've described it here—see *Science* 22Nov'02: 1565–7 & 1569–79.

196. Prosody absent in writing—When reading I subvocalize thus partially filling in what I imagine the prosody might be. How about you?

197. Music—Donald'91: 34, 38–40 & 80; Ehrenreich: 184 and Powers in Hurford &al: 125. On the left brain's musical involvement see *Nature* Science Update 23Apr'01 & ~13Aug'01. For recent work on musical minds see *Science* 13Dec'02: 2138–9 & 2167–70.

198. Musilanguage—Brown in Wallin &al: 271–300. Also see Brown &al in Wallin &al: 8–14 [no, that's not a typo]. Falk, also in Wallin &al: 214, suggests hominid brain lateralization began 2–mya (altho' 2.6–my old fossils were associated with tool-making as cited early in Ch.8) and wasn't fully evolved until several hundred kya. Frayer & Nicolay also in Wallin &al: 232 suggest that by 1.5–mya our ancestors had the capacity to sing.

199. Language vs music—Tone languages like Chinese Mandarin use pitch to distinguish different meanings for the same word sound—Brown &al in Wallin &al: 8–9—and thus use both sides of their brain—AT&T Worldnet Jun30'03 citing findings to be presented that week at the Royal Society in London.

200. Imitating—Benzon: 173–4 and Molino in Wallin &al: 173–5.

201. Mother/infant—in Wallin &al, Dissanayake: 394–9 and Trehub: 438–41. Babies recognize mom's voice from the womb—AT&T Worldnet May23'03.

202. Child ditties—Dissanayake in Wallin &al: 403.

203. Dance to trance—Freeman in Wallin &al: 417–20.

204. Chorusing—Merker in Wallin &al: 317–20.

205. Group formation—in Wallin &al, Freeman: 419–22 and Geissmann: 119. Also rhythmic shouting and stamping in formation may have driven off predators—Ehrenreich: 82 and Ofek: 110–14.

206. Words that are based on primary metaphors from the somatosensory and motor regions can activate their emotional content as does mimesis, for example literal vs. metaphorical words such as "These colors are similar." vs. "These colors are close." or "He achieved his objective." vs. "He got what he wanted most." see Lakoff & Johnson: 58.

207. Cultural evolution of course includes language evolution. From an original ur-language there eventually evolved as many as 100,000 languages, now down to 6,000 and by 2100 down to 500 according to one estimate—McWhorter: 257–9, and thru-out he congenially illustrates how language evolves and goes extinct.

208. Mythic stage—Donald'91: 210ff and ~'01: 259–62 & 274–300. As cited in note 69 to the previous chapter, Parker & McKinney: 285–7 coin the term 'declarative planning' which utilizes symbols to jointly plan and anticipate outcomes. As I understand it instead of telling stories of past episodes, they tried to compose stories of desired future episodes, like scripts, in order to enact them together. Just as the prefrontal cortex stores memories of past images, actions, events, sequences ... which are retrieved to imagine and re*enact* them, it can also speculate about the future by similarly imagining images, actions, events, sequences in order to *enact* them. A kind of virtual *déjà vu*.

209. Theoretic—Donald'91: 333 and ~'01: 260, 262 & 305–20. Omnès'99a: 253 seems to make a distinction between theory and paradigm by equating 'paradigm' to a mental concept that can be envisioned in our mind whereas he includes in 'theory' formal or mathematical formulas that work but seem beyond our mind's ability to envision, such as in quantum physics.

210. "... the subjective difficulty of [humans learning] a concept is directly proportional to its Boolean complexity (the length of the shortest logically equivalent propositional formula)—that is, to its logical incompressibility." *Nature* 5Oct'00 'letters to nature' abstract.

211. Cultural base to build on—*Science* 15Feb'02: 1223c quotes Owen Lovejoy, "Early hominids ... 'may well have been every bit as intelligent as we are today, but they lacked the shoulders of giant on which to perch.'" In other words, each generation's mind extensions (language, writing, drawing ...) allow the next generation to have increased mind, to be 'smarter'—*NewScientist* 17May'03: 40–1.

212. In studying for this chapter I purchased and read (more or less) the following authors listed in the Bibliography: Austin, Benzon, Budiansky, Calvin, Chalmers, Cole, Coren, Crick, Damasio, Deacon, Donald, Edelman (tough reading but worthwhile), Fauconnier, Feinberg, Freeman (also tough), Glynn, Goldberg, Greenfield, Griffin, Harris, Hauser, Hirsch, Hobson, Horgan, Horrobin, Hurford, Jablonski, Jaynes, Johnston, Jourdain, Juslin, Kohn, Kors, La Cerra, Lakoff, LeDoux, Lieberman, Llinás, Macphail, McCrone (an easy read after I'd struggled with Edelman, Freeman &al), McWhorter, Miller, Mindell, Mithen, Noble, Nolte, Parker, Passingham, Penrose, Pert, Pfenninger, Pockett, Quartz, Radin, Ramachandran, Regan, Restak, Rowlands, J.M.Schartz, Sheldrake, Steriade, Stevens, Stewart, Taylor, Velmans, Walker, Wallin, Walsh and Zeki.

213. Cartesian—René Descartes (1596–1650) believed that God created two classes of substance: mind and body. Also known for his *"Cogito, ergo sum,"* "I think, therefore I am" and his coordinates, now familiar graphs for plotting one variable against another. Also see *NewScientist* 24May'03: 38.

214. Platonists include many mathematicians like Penrose'94: 50 & 412–7 who envision a "Platonic world of mathematical forms" out of which mysteriously [his word] emerges the physical world and which our mental world seeks to discover (the Logos). Bergson: 42–3 & 321–2 also was a Platonist, hence it seems his *élan vital* is a property that is imposed *on* matter from outside rather than emerging *from* matter as the Life Urge.

215. For a history and analysis of dualism, see Macphail: 23–47 & 204–7 and Velmans: 9–20 & thru-out. Also Hobson & Leonard: 76–8.

216. Morphic resonance—Sheldrake'95a: xix.

217. Mental radio—Radin: 16, 66–7 & 159.

218. Radio—Our skull and meninges create an effective 'Faraday cage' that shields our brain from most exogenous electric fields (like insulation on an electric wire) but not from magnetic fields such as magnetic resonance imaging (MRI) scanning. See McFadden: 299 and his "Synchronous Firing and its Influence on the Brain's Electromagnetic Field: Evidence for an Electromagnetic Field Theory of

Consciousness" in *Journal of Consciousness Studies* (2002) 9: 23–50, p.25–6, Prediction 6.

219. Morphogenetic fields—Sheldrake'95b has proposed seven experiments to test his theory but most scientists have dismissed him as a New Age crank, see Kayzer: 141–75.

220. Low frequency—Pockett: xvi-ii. However she says "... waves of this frequency do not propagate well and are therefore not particularly useful for transmitting information over long distances." This is not my understanding.

221. 'Brain waves'—Pockett: 129–31.

222. Radin: 59ff has assembled an impressive array of evidence to corroborate his psi claims which at times seems to be reaching. For a nonpartisan assessment see Targ &al in Cardeña &al: 219–52. Shermer in *Scientific American* Feb'03: 31 says "... there is no theory for how psi works." He must not have read some of these authors.

223. Consciousness/quantum physics connection—Lindley: 82–3 disparages this approach.

224. Microtubules and consciousness—Penrose'94: 369–77, ~'97: 128–34 and Radin: 284–5.

225. Hidden domain—Friedman thru-out.

226. There's much speculation about the Neanderthals—see Klein, Kohn, Mithen, Shreeve, Tattersall and Wills thru-out or passim; Bickerton in Crow: 116–8, Klein w.Edgar: 169–229 and *Science* 14Sept'01: 1980–1 and ~7Mar'03: 1525–7; and www.neanderthal-modern.com. But, aside from Friedman's: 193 allusion to "earlier peoples", the only references to psychic abilities I came across were fictional—William Golding's 1955 *The Inheritors* (cited by Kohn: 183) and Wiley Miller's Oct.26'97 *Non Sequitur* cartoon, about the Børks' (Neanderthals') telepathic abilities, which he said was just his imagination (in personal communication).

227. Memes—Aunger: 4, 12–3, 16, 22–3, 329 & 331–4.

228. Trying to 'steer' the evolution of 'our runaway material culture' can be likened to trying to steer an elephant by the tail: Its tail's not only a lousy helm but it's hard to see where you're going from back there. And back there you have to put up with a lot of nasty things, dust in your face being the least of them. But if you can get the elephant going in the direction you want, you can make incredible progress. It's even better if you can climb up to sit behind its head where you can see farther as well as nudge and talk to it (and get away from its rear's nastiness). The 'elephant' of course is evolution. Hopefully a fresh demythologized comprehension of evolution's trajectory will help put us up on top.

229. On animals' sensing of Life, see Houser: 224–5.

230. Supposed Life Urge primitive brain structure—There's some support for my supposition. The limbic system of the primitive brain is believed to become unusually active during intense religious experience—*NewScientist* 21Apr'01: 24–8. "... some have indicated that the limbic system is the 'seat of the soul'"— Newberg &al: 189. Altho' the title of Alper's book *The "God" Part of the Brain* implies a structure, I only find discussion of a function.

Chapter Ten—'Religion'

1. For recent overviews see *Science News* Feb17'01: 104–6 and *Newsweek* May7'01: 52–8. The term 'spiritual experience' instead of 'religion' is employed by Varela in Andresen: 207. On 'mystical experience' see Wulff in Cardeña &al: 397ff.

2. Animism—in Andresen, Pyysiäinen: 77 and Guthrie: 103.

3. Sun explained—Until just early in the past century, the Sun was thought to be fire but they couldn't explain how it could keep burning, until nuclear fusion was understood. Also recall that at first Constantine believed the Sun-god and Christ were the same.

4. Persistence of 'God'—Newberg &al: 129.

5. Life Urge vs God—If you're up for it, let's get a little more specific. Both external and internal sensory data are mostly channeled to the thalamus in the primitive brain which parcels them to dedicated areas of the neocortex. The neurons in the neocortical areas have been shaped both by previous inputs and by chance so that they're biased in the way they process the data. The various areas attempt to fit the data to recognizable characteristics such as qualia which then are assembled into percepts or gestalts. In turn the percepts are forwarded into the frontal lobes of the neocortex where those neurons too have been shaped by previous activity and where they try to fit the percepts into recognizable concepts. Using our 'red ball in the sky' once again, the 'red' quale with the 'round' shape in the 'far' distance fits their 'Sun' percept. And the Sun separating from the horizon fits their 'sunrise' concept. So where's Life Urge come in? The notion is that the Life Urge compels the neocortex to seek out Life, to look initially for signs of Life in everything until it learns which are lifeless, then 'scratches those off its list'. So until proven otherwise, it interprets the Sun as alive which humans did for millennia, not only the Sun but virtually everything else. And if their projections infused that object with other signs of Life, say a voice, well that settled it. At least until they acquired new ideas that undermined those earlier concepts. So given their Life Urge's predilection for Life, early hominids saw gods in everything until they gradually winnowed down their 'list' using knowledge and reason. Alternatively, Alper: 153–4 argues that "The human brain consists of an interactive network of separate and individual mechanisms or processors often referred to as cognitive functions" including mating, language, musical &c, and spirituality. "... the majority of our species is physiologically 'hard-wired' to perceive spiritual reality ..." That's not my understanding of how our brain operates as described in the previous chapter. Also see Alper: 137–9.

6. Faith—I confess I don't recall ever having 'faith'; belief yes, but faith no. I've always been a skeptic deep-down so faith is a feeling that's foreign to me, tho' I don't dispute that others may have 'faith'. In this regard I find Damasio'03: 29–38, 79–80 & 85–6 instructive. He says emotion precedes feeling and seems to say that only feelings emerge into consciousness. Then if one hasn't a percept/concept (like 'God') to hang a particular emotion (the Life Urge?) on, perhaps it's unable to emerge into consciousness as a feeling (such as faith). Apparently my belief was too skeptical a 'peg' to hang my most fundamental emotion on, my Life Urge. Per-

haps by conceptualizing my Life Urge *as such*, instead of as 'God', in time it could emerge as itself instead of as 'faith'. Than again maybe as adults we require a life-threatening catastrophe such as John Newton's near shipwreck to experience faith in the Lord's "Amazing Grace"—Granfield (pages unnumbered). But rather than credit our great-good-fortune to 'the Lord', credit luck and our Life Urge's resilience—to take advantage of luck requires courage and striving, and we just might succeed.

7. What I'm calling 'numinous' is extensively described by Austin: 14–30 as 'mystical' which to me has theistic connotations undoubtedly stemming from my Catholic upbringing. Presuming some readers may react similarly, I've chosen the less charged term used by both Rudolph Otto and Carl Jung, per Stevens & Price: 42, 179–80 & 220. An alternative is Cosmic Consciousness coined by Richard Maurice Bucke over a century ago but he too attached theistic connotations.

8. "Don't just do something, stand there!"—It seems to me one of the Barringer brothers used this twist in the 1970s.

9. Self vis-à-vis world—Since both hemispheres have parietal and somatosensory cortical lobules, both are juxtaposing the body and its surroundings. But perhaps the left is taking the body's perspective and the right the surroundings', that is, the left 'looks' at the surroundings from the body's viewpoint (the self) and the right 'looks' at the body from the surroundings' viewpoint (the world). See Newberg &al: 28.

10. Zen Buddhism and self—Austin: 22–3 & 34–43. It's my understanding that Eastern cultures put a premium on society and discourage individualism so it's consistent to devalue the self.

11. Capitalized 'Self'—Jungians use Self to integrate the conscious with the unconscious; see Stevens'82: 300 (Jung'90: 147ff didn't). Benzon: 184 uses Self for Vygotski's Self, "... the internalized Other" (akin to Jaynes' idea? Ch. 9 note 23)

12. Spontaneous numinous experiences have been interpreted as revelations like Moses' burning bush or Paul's epiphany on the road to Damascus as mentioned in the early chapters.

13. Primitive brain components implicated in numinous consciousness—Austin: 159–281. Also see the conjecture about a 'Life Urge brain structure' on p. 153 above.

14. Autonomic nervous system—Newberg &al: 38–46.

15. Testosterone/estrogen, beta-endorphin—Austin: 195, 218–9.

16. Consciousness of percept—J.Taylor: 268–70 & 275 has a somewhat different theory of how our mind can be aware of percepts (phenomena) without involving the self (perspectival).

17. Passive and active approaches—Newberg &al: 117–23 and Austin: 287–8.

18. Ritual—Newberg &al: 80 & 86–90. For a review/critique of Newberg and d'Aquili's ideas see Andresen in Andresen &al: 260–5.

19. Ecstasy and orgasm—Newberg &al: 125.

20. Altruism—If the self expands beyond one's body to include the whole troop or nation or humanity, or all living things within the Self, then while altru-

ism might be at the expense of the narrow self, it could be serving the enlarged Self and it's Life Urge. So while in the extreme the self may perish, the Self prospers (without the life-after-death rewards of martyrdom or self-sacrifice).

21. Common convictions—Stevens & Price:183–5 propose that a charismatic leader's numinous experience, whether induced or spontaneous, could found a belief system for his followers.

22. Symbolic thinking—Oubré: 121–23 & thru-out. I only came across Oubré after I'd completed a working draft of the whole book else I would have cited her more. Her book's extensively researched but quite speculative covering human evolution from the beginning.

23. Entrancing experiences—Maslow'64: 59–68 lists aspects of what he calls 'peak-experiences' which sound much like numinous consciousness. But also on pages xiv–xvi he describes less intense, longer lasting 'plateau-experiences' like I've described. Also in Kogel & Katz, Maslow: 214–8.

24. Self—My capitalized 'Self' is probably similar to Jung's usage, but he sees the Self as unconscious out of which the ego emerges—see Stevens'82: 141–2.

25. Great Self—Austin: 18 & 52.

26. Attributed to God—The difficulty may be more fundamental. Recall that our brain, from the data it receives, tries to form gestalts that are creditable, are plausible. For example with the vase-vs-faces drawing, it alternately tries one then the other. But if it can't make sense of the data from previous percepts it recognizes, it's at a loss to come up with a plausible gestalt and so makes a bad guess. Our brain's gestalt or image of our self may be too narrow, inhibiting. For instance if you think you can't dance, or speak in public, you'll have difficulty doing it (tho' you can fantasize doing it, like a Walter Mitty). Our brain/mind distinguishes self from non-self, so what isn't self must be non-self. What's not plausible as *my* self must be some other self; a spirit, saint, god or God.

27. Evolution's long trajectory—Not like a bullet's predictable trajectory but in Merriam-Webster's second meaning: "a path, progression, or line of development resembling a physical trajectory." Evolution's progress is something like the ascent of a mountain: traversing back and forth seeking a way to higher ground, sometimes going back down in a setback or to find a way around an obstacle, but ever pressing onward and upward to higher levels of synergistic complexity. Life will find a way, sooner or later.

28. Others see themselves as kin to all living (animal) beings, notably Buddhists and Hindus, but they see the world as stagnant and cyclical, not evolving.

29. Evolution's eyes—Joseph Campbell: 32 said something that appears similar but perhaps not as broad: "... we are the earth, we are the consciousness of the earth. These are the eyes of the earth. And this is the voice of the earth."

30. Evolution's executors—*Science* 7Sept'01: 1786–90 describes how our antibiotics, herbicides and pesticides are inducing evolution of bacteria, plants and insects as an 'unintended consequence' we must take responsibility for. But I'm saying more: I'm considering our bodily extensions—tools like cars and computers—as extending evolution in an extra-biological sense as I'll elaborate in Ch.11.

31. Unique capabilities—Goodenough: 172 quotes her father's favorite metaphor: "'Life is a coral reef. We each leave behind the best, the strongest deposit we can so that the reef can grow. But what's important is the reef.'" I'm not quite so humble and altruistic.

32. "We are all the beneficiaries of all who've gone before us" is the way David McCullough put it in a Sept30'02 PBS show "Statue of Liberty" one of Ken Burns' American Stories. But that doesn't explicitly credit all the non-human organisms nor suggest our obligation to all who'll come after us.

33. Self as individual vs group-member—This is an age-old dilemma. To function in society we must participate in various groups—family, work, play, social, community, nation or what have you—yet we strive to retain our individuality. We start out in our mother's womb as part of her, then strive for years to 'cut the cord', to gradually become less dependent on our natal family—physically and psychologically—a process Jung called 'individuation'. Jung'90: 147–8 and Stevens'82: 141–2. Bly and Campbell use myths to explain the process. Yet thru-out life we're drawn to merge with others—playmates, classmates, lovers, families, military, work ...

34. Liminal state—Stevens & Price: 195 & 219. Think of it as the *sub*liminal tentatively emerging into consciousness. (from Latin *limen* = threshold)

35. Gender rôles are instilled by society accentuating one's own gender stereotype while suppressing the opposite. But since we're all somewhat androgynous, our opposite traits are thus driven into our unconscious only to be projected onto an appropriate target of the opposite gender, what Jung'90: 162–85 called the anima/animus principle. So we fall in love with our projection of our denied self, then later when it wears off wonder what happened to the girl/guy we married. (♪"The girl of my dreams is the only girl in all the world to me ..." The composer of "The Sweetheart of Sigma Chi" never married but lived out his life as the organist at Detroit's Metropolitan Methodist, per my mother.) Also see Franz: 123 & elsewhere and Stevens'82: 67 & elsewhere.

36. A young (now ex-)priest I used to know who'd entered the seminary in his early teens told me that he had the terrifying feeling that there was no real person beneath all the rôles he'd put on.

37. Nondirective method—Rogers'61: thru-out.

38. The RC network used to publish pamphlets and newsletters authored by Harvey Jackins and his staff some of which are since published and in print, but I haven't read them.

39. Encounter groups—Rogers'70: thru-out.

40. Split personality—Nor am I suggesting having an 'out of body experience', see Alvarado in Cardeña &al: 183ff. Also see the note 103 below on the concept of 'soul'.

41. Bioenergetics—Lowen'71: thru-out. He has several other books still in print that may be more reader friendly. However I ran across the term 'bioenergetic psychics' in a Dec'02 *Wired* article which I take to be something different (no explanation was given).

42. Stigma of psychotherapy—Eagleton running with McGovern in 1972 had his therapy exposed as one of Nixon's 'dirty tricks'. And when I inquired about insurance coverage of my psychotherapy, a company personnel flunky couldn't wait to call the top executive.

43. Freud vs Jung—Specifically Freud believed "... the contents of the unconscious are reducible to infantile tendencies which are repressed because of their incompatible character." Whereas Jung includes not only everything a person has in some way ever experienced but also what might be called instinctual knowledge inherited from their ancestors (instincts/archetypes)—the personal and the collective unconscious. See Jung'90: 57, 111, 115 & 377–93. Also see Hartmann: 170–93.

44. Circadian clock—JA Hobson: 133–40. An intriguing consideration is that the mammalian circadian clock's primary function is to regulate body and brain temperature while we're awake and in non-REM sleep, but not in REM sleep during which we're essentially cold-blooded, that is, our reptilian brain partially reverts us back to reptiles! See Hartmann: 202.

45. Dorsolateral prefrontal cortex—JA Hobson: 126–7.

46. Neuromodulators—JA Hobson: 38–47, 70–1, 124–7, 142–7, 151–2 & thruout and Hobson & Leonard: 108, 110–4 & 120–2.

47. Consciousness—JA Hobson: 175–81.

48. REM sleep—Hartmann: 195–7; JA Hobson: 50–5, 182, 184, 186 & 193–5 and Hobson & Leonard: 104. All mammals (except monotremes) and probably birds experience REM sleep—Hartmann: 210–1. Also see *NewScientist* 28Jun'03: 28–35.

49. Sleep patterns—JA Hobson: 120. Why this mammalian sleep pattern was favored by evolution puzzles me. It evolved long before our species had fire to light the night and ward off predators, and of course other mammals never had fire. The unlighted night is some twelve hours long (plus or minus, depending on latitude and season) yet we humans nominally require only eight hours' sleep. What happened during the other third of a moonless night? Somewhere I read that primitives wake during the night and talk, make love or whatever. They may have posted a guard and slept in shifts, but so what? Perhaps the limbic system was hyperactive to compensate for the diminished vigilance of the sleeping body (pertinent noises are incorporated into dreams). Or perhaps the brain was exercising those emotions to maintain hair-trigger conditioning. Both help survival. See JA Hobson: 77, 117 & 128–9. However Hartmann: 119–9, 202–6 & 209 suggests that our early ancestors were under constant stress with little time to assimilate, make connections and abreact so they did it at night in prolonged REM sleep. Whereas Benzon: 162–4 seems to suggest that because mammals' reptilian brain can't act directly in the world, it acts virtually in neocortex.

50. Memory storage during non-REM sleep—JA Hobson: 122–4 and Hobson & Leonard: 103.

51. Rapid eye movement initiated by superior colliculus on the brainstem pons—Crick: 126–8; however JA Hobson: 139–41 sites only the PGO (Pons-Geniculate-Occipital).

52. Primary visual cortex—JA Hobson: 58–9.

53. Hallucination—JA Hobson: 154.

54. Dream memory—JA Hobson: 79.

55. Amygdala—JA Hobson: 61.

56. Disguised meanings—JA Hobson: 72.

57. Prefrontal not forming basins of attraction in sleep—but something must be happening, else why, when we have a problem, do we say 'I'll sleep on it' and frequently it works?! So somehow associations and concepts must be forming somewhere in our brain—where else but in the prefrontal cortex? Perhaps in a different area of the prefrontal than the dorsolateral that's differently affected by the neuromodulators. See Hartmann: 151–8.

58. Jung's dreams are reported in his 1965 'autobiography', but Noll: 13 claims Jung's descriptions were not written by him.

59. In Fritz Perls' 1969 *Gestalt Therapy Verbatim* he describes sessions where he has his patient visualize and talk to every item in their dream to bring each into consciousness and expose it.

60. Universals—Campbell, Franz'80a, Jung'90 and Stevens'82. Also see Hartmann: 240–1.

61. Contextualize—Hartmann: 8, 14, 28–9, 62 & 116.

62. On The Threshold Of A Dream—title of a Moody Blues' CD.

63. Sleep images—Hartmann: 239–41.

64. For a survey of Hobson's and others' alternative theories see *Science News* Aug11'01: 90–2.

65. Non-dreamers—Some people function on minimal sleep and thus little REM sleep and dreaming. They may also be highly intellectual, not intuitive nor inclined to daydreaming and reverie. See Hartmann: 157, 219–29 & 276–7.

66. Lucid dreaming—JA Hobson: 32, 93–8 & 102; Bosnak: 163ff and Godwin thru-out. Also see Austin: 311–27 & 422 and LaBerge & Gackenbach in Cardeña: 151–82.

67. Sleep deprivation—JA Hobson: 5, 50 & 284

68. For Huxley's 'adventures' see JA Hobson : 105–11.

69. Long-term effects—JA Hobson: 149–50. Marijuana, unlike other illegal drugs and alcohol, doesn't cause permanent brain damage—AT&T Worldnet Jun27'03 citing a U.of Calif.-San Diego study by Igor Grant of that date.

70. LSD/dreaming analogy—JA Hobson: 26–7; also see ~251–8. On the affects of other drugs see ~287–303.

71. LSD in psychotherapy—JA Hobson: 82–4.

72. Psychedelic drug affects—Austin: 418–43. On marijuana see *Science* 26Apr'02: 678–82 and *NewScientist* 7Sept'02: 6. On cocaine see AT&T Worldnet News reporting on *Science* 11May'01: 1039 & 1175–8. On ecstasy see *NewScientist* 20Apr'02: 26–33.

73. Stop the world—Carlos Castañeda attributed this phrase to his apocryphal mentor, the sorcerer Don Juan.

74. Opening those 'doors' wider—Other than Huxley, I've only read Carlos Castañeda's books, but that was enough. I'm not that brave or venturesome!

75. Artists were employed by the Church back then to sell religion; today they're employed by advertisers to sell everything.

76. Cave paintings—Why they were painted and how they were viewed is speculative, as was their dating until recently (see *NewScientist* 19Apr'03: 8). The art work of putatively 30–kya at Chauvet is as sophisticated as that of 12– to 17–kya at Lascaux and Niaux which suggests that artistic abilities evolved much earlier. (For west European sites see Klein w.Edgar: 259 and Lewis-Williams thru-out, and worldwide see Clottes & Lewis-Williams thru-out.) Indeed engraved stones found in a South African cave are dated 77–kya. See AT&T Worldnet 10/3/01 citing a report in *Nature* of that date and *Science* 11Jan'02: 247–9 cited in *Nature* Science Update of that date. Also see Horrobin: 5–7 on the derision that the Altamira cave painting's discoverer suffered in the 1880s. But 100 years later it was noted that the chambers with the most artwork were the most resonant suggesting "... that caves were the sites of religious ceremonies involving music."—Jourdain: 305. Bone flutes have been found from as much as 53–kya—*Science* 5Jan'01: 54 and Kunej & Turk in Wallin &al: 235–68. On the 'lion man' from 30-kya see *Nature* Science Update 4Sept'03.

77. Hang on our walls—I have four of Barbara Ragalyi's serigraphs—Vesper'90, Red Snapper'91, Freckled Violet'92 and Quiet Morn'95—which 'speak to me' but I'm not yet sure what each is trying to say. I also have four of Hiromu Oda's minimalist water colors he did for me years ago depicting quiet Japanese scenes. My favorite tho' is a painting my granddaughter Chora did when she was five (in her maternal grandmother's studio) which resembles a stellar nebula—I had it framed of course.

78. Uninhibited—While visiting Chora and family on their return from New Zealand, her grandmother offered to show me how to do spontaneous painting. But then she begged off when she 'got a headache'. I was somewhat relieved, coward that I am.

79. A psychotherapist friend uses crayons, water-paints, sand &c especially with children to help them deal with their feelings.

80. Fresh eyes—Years ago I heard the term 'soft eyes' which I understand to mean not staring, not foveating, using a broad encompassing peripheral view, a relaxed gaze instead of a hard look. When driving in light traffic, sometimes I'll keep my eyes looking ahead but try to see as much as I can to the sides, even try to see what's behind in the rear-view mirror without looking directly at it.

81. Music, "... the language of the emotions"—Scherer's Forward in Juslin & Sloboda: x. Yet apes have emotions but they don't sing or dance—Benzon: 28. But Geissmann in Wallin &al: 103–23 analyses Gibbon (lesser apes) songs. See Donald'01: 270–1 and Oubré thru-out on the evolution from apes' to humans' brains.

82. Active emotions (in the original sense of e-motion) as opposed to passive emotions or moods like sadness. See Sloboda & Juslin in Juslin & Sloboda: 87–8. I suppose the Life Urge is in all emotions if we see it as a continuum from intense elation/striving to shutdown sadness/depression—it's not gone 'til you're dead.

83. Evolution of song/music—There are at least four compatible theories: Imitation of animal sounds, mothers lullabying their babies, guys courting gals

and group chanting/dancing. See Benzon: 171–6 & 182–3. Also in this volume see Ch.9's section on Early Development under Music & Language.

84. Unifying the troop—Benzon: 41–4, 82, 178, 188–9 & 207–9 argues that rhythmic rituals with chanting, singing and dancing aligned neurons in each member's neocortex so that they shared in common patterns thus coupling their behavior and attitudes. Also see Donald'91: 38–43, Oubré thru-out, and Sloboda and Inge in Astley &al: 124 & 172–84.

85. Monks' chants—An intriguing thought: Tibetan monks chant *Om, Mani Padme Hum* at around 40Hz in a resonant room. Might it be that they're resonating the gamma frequency in their brains and thus inducing synchronization of nerve impulse patterns thereby producing more intense percepts as described in the sections on Binding and Emerging Consciousness in Ch.9? On *Om* ... see Matthiessen: 104.

86. Brain structures processing music—See Benzon: 46; Falk in Wallin &al: 203–4; Jourdain: 9–10, 25–7 & 51–7; *Science* 5Jan'01: 54–6 and ~13Dec'02: 2138–9. There's evidence that men and women process music differently—Falk in Wallin &al: 208–9.

87. Music's roots—*Science* 5Jan'01: 52–4.

88. Music's ineffability—in Astley &al, Sadgrove: xv, xx & xxvii; Hone &al: 89–90 and Ground & Sloboda: 116–20.

89. Sad music—Benzon: 115.

90. Hank Williams, sr.—"Long Gone Lonesome Blues" *Lonesome Blues* CD, Polygram Records, 1992.

91. Bach's St.Matthew Passion—I bought a CD and first played it during Lent. I couldn't stand it! I put it away until the next Lent when I played it again. This time it wasn't quite as bad but I put it away again. After several years and several listenings I came to enjoy it very much. The same thing happened with Schubert's C Major Quintet (D.956) and other music. So I told my kids that CDs need to age before they're good, like wine (no, they didn't believe me). Joking aside, I find I need a gestation period for my brain/mind to adapt to an unfamiliar style of music which means I'll sometimes listen to a piece over and over (my kids threatened to disable the 'repeat' button on my CD player).

92. Sadness to joy—Gabrielsson in Juslin & Sloboda: 435–41 in his SEM (strong experiences of music) project reported that almost all the 300 respondents' moods improved as the result of their experiences—they went from dread or depression to joy and hope.

93. Beethoven's Ninth—The wild-abandon frenzy of the 2nd movement exhausts itself and dissolves into the 3rd's lonely despairing struggle to resolutely 'press on regardless' until finally in the 4th it burst into Schiller's "Ode to Joy" (albeit with a theistic theme). My resonating with the 3rd movement's strains betrays my repressed feelings of an unavailing lonely struggle which I strive to rise above, to maintain my 'eternal optimism' while eschewing Panglossizm. And it works, like a good bowel movement.

94. Severe depression usually requires professional help to extricate one from the well of negativity.

95. Amazing Grace—On a Saturday in the summer of 1988 I took my wife to the train to visit her sister in California. I had plans the following Saturday to drive to Ontario's Algonquin Park to meet my canoe buddy for our weeklong 'expedition'. That Friday noon at my office I was stunned to be served with my wife's divorce papers. Even so, by Sunday morning I was resolutely driving down along the Ottawa River and then onto the long rugged trail to our Cedar Lake rendezvous, listening to the radio. The disc jockey told the story of John Newton and how he came to write "Amazing Grace" interspersed with various renditions including on bagpipes. I was blown away, in tears the whole time. It was just a wonderful catharsis, with no theological connotations.

96. Thoreau—E.Porter selected Thoreau quotations juxtaposed with stunning photos of nature from the northeastern states. Matre & Weiler's is an anthology of renowned naturalists. Sigurd F. Olson captures the feel of northern wilderness as E.O.Wilson'84 does of the tropics. (A brother-in-law suggested some of Thomas Berry's books but I haven't read any.) I use such pictures and description to hone my sensitivity, then go out into nature to find my own sanctums.

97. Biophilia—E.O.Wilson'84: 1 "... the innate tendency to focus on life and lifelike processes." altho' Erich Fromm used the term earlier per Kellert: 1–5.

98. Kids 'grounded in nature'—Nabhan & Trimble thru-out. By tagging along with my young children on their adventures, exercising minimal parental restraint, I rediscovered my own childhood sense of wonder and exploration.

99. Nature—Some writers instead use the term 'creation' which to me implies a creator, for instance Kellert & Farnham: xiii, and a stagnant rather than an evolving ecology which must be preserved as discussed by the contributors thru-out their book.

100. Fail to notice—I remember as a teenager on a summer vacation to my father's family's homestead in Québec, standing on the road with my dad in front of the farmhouse. To the west just beyond the farmhouse and outbuildings was Lac Aylmer glistening with sunlight. To the east beyond the flowering bright-green fields was the dark-green forest and beyond the forest, the purple hills. The broad sky was azure with puffy white clouds. My dad kept looking around and finally volunteered "You know, as a kid growing up here, I never noticed all this!"

101. You may already be conflicted about mowing your lawn. Where we used to live we had a half-acre of lawn which I mowed like a good neighbor. But when a patch of daisies came up, I mowed around them telling my neighbors I was changing its name from lawn to meadow. Joking aside, we Americans squander our time (mowing, fertilizing, patching &c), our money (for the lawnmower, gasoline, fertilizer, spreader &c) and our resources (water and run-off, and air pollution from the exhaust and cut grass) on our penchant for lawns. Maybe we *should* change them to meadows—a few have, to their neighbor's consternation. See Bormann &al thru-out.

102. Paragon of animals—Even though 'paragon' is a bit overwrought, I couldn't write a respectable book, now could I, without quoting Shakespeare at least once. *Hamlet* act 2, sc.2, l.297.

103. Concept of a 'soul'—Frattaroli: 6, 8 & 17–20 reinterprets Descartes' dualism not as divorcing the mind from the body but the soul from the brain/body, "... considering the soul as a complex entity, the center of the whole person, the experiencing self." ('Sounds a little like Jung's concept of Self.) "... *listening to the soul* ... a richer, more engaged awareness of the soul as authentic self—an ineffable mixture of pure consciousness and personal passion—captured in the full experiencing of conflicted emotion." (his italics)

104. Seeing 'God' in them—I'm speaking figuratively but I suspect some who intellectually agree with my logic but aren't emotionally ready to abandon theism may grasp at this to preserve their belief in a 'God'. They should ask themselves why—why the necessity of positing a god at all? Let it go! Set it aside and try living without it. Initially it may produce angst but if you can stay with your anxiety and emptiness, you should become comfortable as you get down into your Self and begin to fill the void.

105. Sex stimulates some of the same areas of brains as do mind altering drugs—see *NewScientist* 23Nov'02: 38–40.

106. Near death experience—Greyson in Cardeña &al: 315ff. Also see Berman thru-out and Schlagel: 326–34. In the final chapter of this volume I discuss the issue of suicide.

107. Sorcerer's Apprentice—Recall in Disney's 1940 movie "Fantasia" how Mickey Mouse, enacting Goethe's story to Dukas' music, tried to get out of hauling buckets of water by casting a spell on the broom only to have it all get calamitously out-of-hand?

108. Expanded Self—see Oubré: 190–1 on transcendence.

109. Theistic science writers—A few I've pursued are Alexander, Denton, Peacocke and Ruse. Non-science writers are Brasher, Cimino & Lattin, Frankl: 137ff, West, N.T. Wright and Spong. But if you've digested my ideas you may see theirs differently.

110. Buddhism—Eerdmans': 222–42 altho' be forewarned this is clearly Christian apologetics. See Armstrong'01: 107–13 on the Self and incarnation.

111. Zen Buddhism—Austin: 11–4 & 127. Also Metthiessen's *Snow Leopard* describes his experience of Zen and is a great read. Pirsig's Zen &c is also a good read but has little to do with Zen, as I recall.

112. Great Self—Austin: 18. The years of intensive training required for Zen are perhaps comparable to what's required to become a world class athlete—training the mind vs the body.

113. There's concern that Buddhism is being subverted by what James William Coleman calls "The New Buddhism: ..." in the title of his book as reported by Stephen Prothero on Salon.com 2/26/01.

114. TM—Maharishi thru-out.

115. UU name—Two communions were merged in 1961. Unitarians believed in the unity of God, not the trinity. Universalism affirms salvation for all people, not just 'the chosen'. Buehrens & Church: 42.

116. UU agnostics & atheists—At least one member feels UU has drifted away from skepticism, see *Free Inquiry* Fall'02: 48–9.

117. Deeds not creeds—Buehrens & Church: 50.

118. Common faith—Buehrens & Church: xxiv–v & 193–4.

119. God—Buehrens & Church: 84.

120. Creator—Buehrens & Church: 192.

121. Life—Buehrens & Church: 15–6.

122. My exposure to UU—In doing research for this book I attended only one Sunday service at the Birmingham Unitarian Church (Mi). But for twenty years I ran circles around it—literally. The group I ran with met every Sunday morning at a parking lot adjoining their property. We had a ten-mile (+/−) out-around-and-back route that widely circumambulated the church. But because of the time conflict I didn't bother exploring it then. I've since been attending some week-day historic/scientific talks there by Rabbi Sherwin Wine. UU's Website is www.uua.org.

123. Today's Humanism shouldn't be confused with Renaissance humanism which referred to 'the humanities', notably the study of Latin and Greek classics—Gould'03: 38–9 who says on 36 that "... for the Renaissance, the *recovery* of ancient wisdom, not the *discovery* of novel data, became the primary task of scholarship."

124. The Affirmations of Humanism: A Statement of Principles—Available from: Free Inquiry, P.O. Box 664, Amherst, New York 14226–0664. Their website is http://www.secularhumanism.org. Also see Humanist Manifesto III, www.americanhumanist.org.

125. Intuition—Lamont'97: 210–3 believed that people have peak experience but that mystics misinterpret them as supernatural, and that closely related is in-tuition which scientists depend on to suggest new hypotheses. Additionally Faith Lagay's article in *Free Inquiry* Winter'02/03: 34–7 stresses the importance of emo-tions in seeking consensus on issues.

126. Humanists personable—To explore Humanism I attended the American Humanist Association 2003 conference in Washington DC May 8–11. The many hu-manists I met were mostly outgoing, positive and fun.

127. Non-theistic religion—another is Humanistic Judaism (see Appendix B). It's not clear to me whether Scientology is non-theistic but even if it is, their be-lief in past lives and immortality (per MS Encarta) turns-off any interest I might have had in it.

128. Online—Brasher: 142–3, 154–8 & 185–7 explores how the Web is chal-lenging the role of traditional religions to generate understanding of what it means to be human and is providing alternative prospective avenues to the sacred.

129. Gay movement—See Clendinen & Nagourney thru-out.

130. Quakers—Microsoft Encarta Encyclopedia.

131. "How do you pray?"—Spong addresses this in his Chapter Nine, espe-cially pages 142–3.

132. Answer from unconscious mind—A similar effect may explain the workings of Ouija boards, tarot cards, ink-blots &c by getting our conscious mind out of the way, our unconscious may conceivably be less hindered and can answer thru non-verbal channels. Calvin: 129 cites John Maynard Smith's idea that we re-fuse to accept them as meaningless.

133. Getting stuff out—Recall in the 2000 movie "Cast Away" Tom Hanks' character talked to 'Wilson', the volleyball he'd drawn a face on. Prayer is like that but the volleyball can be a crucifix, statue or just our imagination. Still, we're talking to ourself, like Hanks' character.

134. Suppliant—Apparently a common idea of prayer is asking something from a higher power according to a multi-book author being interviewed on NPR 5/2/99pm (a phone call prevented my getting his name). It sounded like the pagan view of gods in Ch.3. On postures see Oubré: 124–5.

135. Saying 'I'll pray for you' can be a way of avoiding actually doing something real for that person yet avoiding feeling guilty for not doing anything. Why not do both?

136. Placebo effect—"Expectation ... increase[s] the release of the brain chemical dopamine ..."—Nature Science Update 10Aug'01. But the placebo effect remains controversial—Scientific American Jan'98: 90–5 and ~Oct'01: 16; Science News Feb3'01: 74–5&78 and AT&T Worldnet News May23'01, Jan1'02 & Feb7'02. On 'anomalous healing experiences'—Krippner & Achterberg in Cardeña &al: 353ff.

137. Prayer—Sheldrake's morphic resonance, mentioned toward the end of the previous chapter, or attuned Cem-fields mentioned earlier in that chapter, conceivably could link people with each other—but not in my view, with non-existent gods or the dead. An attempt to scientifically test non-theistic prayer is interestingly described in Wired Dec'02 "A Prayer Before Dying."

138. Mother Mary—The Lennon-McCartney/ Beatles' song Let It Be comes to mind: ♪"When I find myself in times of trouble Mother Mary comes to me, speaking words of wisdom, Let it be ..." It's a beautiful song and sage advice but obsolescent theology. Yet maybe it's useful to conjure one's mother image for reassurance as long as one realizes it comes from within themselves and owns it. Alternatively, I'm told 'Mother Mary' means 'marijuana'.

139. Our own best friend—Children use a security blanket, teddy-bear or doll (see Margery Williams' The Velveteen Rabbit Doubleday or listen to Meryl Streep read it on CD, but you'll need to interpret the animate ending). Could it be a surrogate of themselves until they're mature enuf to internalize their self? Or are they taught to project their Self out onto Jesus &al?

140. Imagination—Harris: 172–3, 183 & thru-out.

141. Others' religiosity—In the 2001 movie "The Pledge" Nicholson's character tells his 'step daughter', after a Christian minister has attempted to proselytize her: Some people believe, but others think the stories are like the make-believe stories he's been reading to her (fairy-tales &c). His comfort with his own unbelief reassures her.

142. What we do speaks louder—If we tell them one thing but do another, it not only discredits what we say, but discredits us and betrays our hypocrisy. Thus what we think we're teaching them may not be what they're learning.

143. Drugs—Hallucinogenic drugs are currently illegal, but seventy-some years ago alcohol was too until society realized not only that it couldn't, and shouldn't try to control it (as now with drugs) but that attempting to was a waste

of money (and spawned crime, as drugs do) and that legalized alcohol was a source of tax revenue (turn a loss into a gain). (Somewhere I heard that coffee and tea were once illegal in places—Turkey?) Wouldn't it be better to find ways of making some benign drugs legal and concentrate on eradicating the truly dangerous ones? Many states make a legal distinction between hard liquor and beer & wine— why not between hard- and soft-drugs? But both organized crime and anti-crime organizations have a mutual vested interest in keeping drugs illegal. And the traditional religions' lobby also has a vested interest in opposing competition to their religions. (The alcohol lobby probably does too—was the 1930s movie "Reefer Madness" sponsored by them?) Legalization or de-criminalization is not currently a priority of mine but de-demonization could be. (After his death it was disclosed that "... Carl Sagan was a secret but avid marijuana smoker, crediting it with inspiring essays and scientific insights, according to Sagan's biographer ... Sagan died of pneumonia ... He was 62." Per foxnews 8/22/99) *Science* 16Jun'00: 1972 on the Science of Marijuana. On LSD—Austin 581-3.

144. Applying science to theology—Peacocke thru-out and Ruse thru-out, and Sadgrove in Astley &al: xii-xiii, for example all seem to, satisfactorily enough to their minds anyway.

145. Short-circuit your brain—Freeman: 149-53 explores unlearning processes.

146. What confession's for—By making sex sinful, even sometimes for married couples, the Church guarantees that all normal people will feel guilty and in need of the Church's forgiveness. Before reliable contraceptive technology, abstinence was the only dependable birth control method but with dubious ovulation monitoring, abstinence had to be nearly perpetual.

147. Low birth rate—*NewScientist* 20Jul'02: 38-41 reports that the fertility rates in 2000 were 2.0 children per woman in the US and 1.2 in Italy, the home of the Catholic Church. The rates in Brazil and Mexico have dropped to half their 1980's rates.

148. Very upsetting—When a parent leaves a young child, say at a daycare, it can be very upsetting for the child. The feelings of abandonment are awful, bringing on crying, anger or rage. Likewise the thought of losing the ultimate parent figures, "Father in Heaven" and Holy Mother of God, could restimulate (abreact) latent feelings of abandonment bringing on anger or rage against whoever threatens to take them away.

149. Watch my back—Some religious fundamentalists—Christian, Jewish or Muslim—may feel threatened and a few even justify assault or a more devious retribution, so I don't try to impose prototheistic ideas on them.

Chapter Eleven—Tools

1. Lamarck believed that what a parent learns, they pass on to their offspring through their 'genes' (see page 303 note 39). But a body extension or tool is not a

living organism so strictly speaking a tool doesn't pass on its design improvements to the next generation of that tool via neither a Lamarckian nor a Darwinian process. Rather human innovators learn how to improve the tool and 'mutate' the tool's design for its next generation.

2. On tool evolution and stagnation see Klein: 406–24; Klein w.Edgar: 71, 103–4, 142 & 232; Kohn: 77, 94 & 180–1; McNamara: 304–5; Parker & McKinney: 201–3 and Stanley: 230–1 (not the Stanley® brand of tools). However Kohn: 117–49 proposes that the hand-axe also prevailed for sexual selection as a 'standardized' display of male fitness as is the peacock's tail—Zahavis' Handicap Principle. But an alternative (compatible) explanation seems more plausible, namely that tool handling favored lateralization of the brain as described in Ch.9 note 111; see McCrone: 281–2.

3. Embracing change—Norman: 33 delineates the spectrum of customer adoption of new technology.

4. Extension vs prosthesis—eye glasses correct a deficiency rather than extend eyes' capability.

5. Functioning better—As I paddle my solo canoe from my local millpond, up the river and out onto the adjoining lake, its near shores are lined with docked speedboats and pontoon motorboats. They're bigger and faster than my little canoe but are they better? As they bob idly their owners are probably working to pay for them while I enjoy the quiet lake and get some exercise paddling across over to the wildlife marshes on the farther side.

6. Uneven acceleration—The medieval Dark Ages have a stigma as a time of little innovation but that's disputed by Gies thru-out.

7. Hunter raiding herd—In the 1980 movie "The Gods Must Be Crazy" a hungry bushman leader who's ventured out of the Kalahari uses his bow & arrow to kill a goat but has no conception that the herd might be owned by someone.

8. Hitler and Stalin rationalized their policies in the name of 'higher causes', Hitler: the Third Reich and Aryan purity (the master race), and Stalin: world communism. Alexander spread Greek culture thru-out the known world and the conquistadors brought their Spanish God and technology to the new world.

9. Corporate raider—In the 1991 movie "Other People's Money" Danny DeVito plays an over-the-top ruthless raider but, as I recall, it turns out the firm is at the end of its life-cycle in a small town.

10. Worse to have to steal—In the 1948 movie "The Red Shoes" the impresario tells the young composer whose symphony has been plagiarized by his professor "You're young and talented. He's an old man who's never composed anything. It's far worse to have to steal than to be stolen from." Or words to that effect.

11. Innovative entrepreneur I'm distinguishing from a 'cookie-cutter' start-up entrepreneur such as a franchised donut-shop or even an auto plant in an untried location. Many things can go wrong with a start-up but at least the product/service, market, production know-how &c are all proven. All of the same things can go wrong for an innovative entrepreneur but in addition there's at least one major element that's unproven, anywhere from product (plasma TV, DVD players) to distribution system (Dominos pizza delivery, FedEx, Amazon.com). A

start-up entrepreneur is like a successful species invading a new territory but an innovative entrepreneur is like a new species.

12. What can go wrong?—It's hard to anticipate everything. As Pontiac's economic development advisor* a couple firms I helped start crashed unexpectedly on the brink of success. Diolight was a long-life light-bulb that used a diode to convert AC to DC. The diode size was initially miscalculated too small but the supplier for the test bulbs furnished larger diodes unbeknownst. The test bulbs worked great, but after Diolight geared up and produced 100,000 with the specified undersize diode they all failed. Vixen was a state-of-the-art motor-home planned, when OPEC drove up oil prices, to get high-mileage by using a BMW diesel engine among other things. But General Motors converted gasoline engines to diesel with disastrous results tarnishing diesels' reputation. After the new Vixen plant was in production, OPEC fell apart and fuel prices dropped, moreover the US/Austrian exchange rate drove up the BMW engine price. (*I used to joke that an 'advisor' was a guy who knew many ways to make love but didn't know any women.)

13. Venture capitalists are sometimes called vulture capitalists because the disreputable ones will hang on until the entrepreneur is exhausted but on the brink of success, then oust him and take over. They're like hunter-gatherers who help-out until the herder's goats are fat or the farmer's crop is ripe, then raid.

14. Just to get rich?—When aspiring entrepreneurs came to me for the city's assistance I'd caution them that success was very iffy and even if they succeeded it might be stolen from them. So I'd ask, Even if they don't get rich will the adventure have been worth it? Then I'd illustrate with the probably apocryphal story of Daniel Boone—how he borrowed money and left his family in West Virginia while he went off to the Kentucky-Tennessee territory where he was almost killed by the Indians before he negotiated a treaty. But then the surveyors told him the land he'd staked out for himself was wrong and that he had nothing. So he went off to Oklahoma to trap in order to pay off his debts. But he had the adventure—all the surveyors got was the land.

15. In retrospect I ask myself if the projects I've been involved with thru-out my career advanced or hindered the evolution of Life —'an examination of conscience'. Of course I know more now than I did back then, but they'll illustrate what I mean. Even if the Edsel had succeeded it was just another entry in a crowded segment of the car market so it had a negative impact on Life's evolution (wasted resources) tho' it's planning was an exciting learning experience for me (what not to do). But I didn't put it on my résumé (a personnel guy jokingly said it'd be better to say I was in jail during that time). My two inventions never went beyond the patent stage because I wasn't coming up with solutions to key design problems and they were taking too much time away from fathering my kids (a proud accomplishment). If I'd succeeded they would have made marginal improvements to heating-cooling and bicycles—big deal! SRI tried to put together a multi-client housing study of all the elements that should make up the housing industry. It made me realize that a gas utility had many of those elements, so when I left SRI I joined the local gas company. They had to get an SEC waiver and

launched a major initiative in inner-city housing. But then the SEC reversed itself and they had to divest eventho' it was improving many people's lives and the community. With the City of Pontiac, neighborhood improvements, industrial parks, downtown projects &c helped reverse the city's image and its decline so I'd say it advanced Life's evolution (tho' not all projects did). And hopefully this book will too. (I'm somewhat amused by those who smugly feel superior because they never failed, but of course they never tried. And they missed out on the fun!)

16. Angel investors—The Oakland Press (Mi.) Oct25'02: C-1&2 where Marsha Stopa reported on a speech by Rick Inatome, founder in 1970 of Inacomp. He "... tied widespread disaffection with the current business climate to the aging of the ... population, with 5,000 reaching 65 daily. Roughly 80 percent of baby boomers, called 'zoomers' want to continue working ... their longer productive years, $1 trillion in net worth, understanding of how business works and their disappointment with traditional investments, and you have a huge group—from 250,000 to 2.5 million—of potential angel investors" which "... will eventually result in a resurgence of interest and investment in innovative entrepreneurial ventures ..."

17. Greedy man—Neil Young's *Harvest Moon* "Natural Beauty."

18. Excitement of science—Feynman: 9.

19. A dedicated nurse with 40+ years experience in intensive-care and 'stepdown' units is becoming disheartened. She now finds that most of her patients have ailments that are 'self-inflicted'—smoker, sedentary, obese—and now expect the medical profession to take over responsibility for their irresponsibility.

20. Proteomics—*Scientific American* Apr'02: 40–7.

21. Humanity's adolescence—Stock'02: 17.

22. Cloning—Bronowski'73: 401 on Eve, and on slippery-slope Stock'02: 3–7, 155 & 151 and *Free Inquiry* Winter'02/03: 34–7. Mule cloned—*Science* 30May'03: 1354 and *Nature* Science Update 30May'03. DNA re-write allay fears—*Nature* Science Update 29Apr'03.

23. Interfacing with nerves and brains—Kaku: 112–7, Dertouzos: 77–80, Stock'02: 21–4 & 31 and *NewScientist* 1Feb'03: 38–9. However Pockett:109–10 raises an interesting speculation—if consciousness is due to electromagnetic fields in our brain might it be theoretically possible to tune into an individual's patterns and thereby communicate directly?

24. In the next decades—Stock'02: 176–7. On gender selection see *NewScientist* 16Nov'02: 23 and *Nature* Science Update 11Aug'03. Also see "The designer baby myth" by Stephen Pinker in *The Guardian* Jun5'03.

25. *In vitro* fertilization—Stock'02: 52–6. Disposal of unwanted eggs is the current practice eventho' they're fertilized. Thus conception has occurred. By Pope Pius IX's 1869 declaration they're "ensouled" and a person. The Church needs to update its definition. Stock'02: 134.

26. Auxiliary chromosomes—Stock'02: 65–8, 71, 77 & 186.

27. *In vitro* and cloning—*Scientific American* Jun'03: 62–7 and AT&T Worldnet Jul17'03.

28. Changing attitudes—Stock'02: 39, 53 & 199–201. Crude genetic programming has been practiced for centuries, and still is in many culture, wherein parents (fathers?) select their children's marriage partners not only to control property but 'genetic purity'.

29. Germinal choice technology—by Stock'02: 110–1 & thru-out. Also see Buchanan &al: 156–203, Duve'02: 242–9 & 259–65 and Kaku: 229–38.

30. Choice of children—Adoptions could decline as affluent couples can use technology not only to have their own 'flesh and blood' but the best in their gene pool, as opposed to the less certain stock of an adoptee. Given the tremendous expense, time and energy needed to raise a child, ambitious parents would want to start with the best odds they can.

31. China—Stock'02: 159–61 & 164. Also Buchanan &al: 333–45.

32. Eugenics—Buchanan &al: 27–60, Kaku: 256–7 and Stock'02: 198 & 244. Also see Microsoft Encarta on Social Darwinism.

33. Gifted vs non-gifted—Stock'02: 176–85 & 190–6.

34. Under-caste—Kaku: 126–8.

35. Infanticide—Alexander: 463–4.

36. Selecting human traits—see *Free Inquiry* Winter'02/03: 34–7.

37. Determinism—Buchanan &al: 23–6 and Sober in ~: 347–70.

38. Aging—Stock'02: 86–9 & 96. In pre-literate cultures sages had a long-view of their unchanging history—they might be the only one old enuf to remember the last tsunami and know how to survive it. In the future, sages will have an even longer view of our rapidly changing history—the 1929 crash and the depression, the rise of Hitler and the plight of the Jews. "Those who refuse to learn from history are doomed to repeat it." (Russian proverb?)

39. Stone Age biology—Dertouzos: 295–8 & 300–2 describes what he sees as our limitations vis-à-vis emerging technology. A couple of factors may enable continued expansion of our biological mental faculties. Altho even larger newborn's heads would be unable to pass thru the mother's pelvic area, cesarean sections are becoming more prevalent—due in part to more older mothers—obviating the impediment. Secondly by off-loading more routine tasks from the brain to computers or whatever, those areas of the brain might be taken-over by functions that only human minds could perform. See Oubré: 165.

40. X-ray, CAT, PET and MRI—Kaku: 198–9.

41. Speech recognition—Kaku: 58–65.

42. Hindu-Arabic numerals—Seife: 78–80 credits Fibonacci's *Liber Abaci* in 1202 for introducing Islamic mathematics to Europe.

43. Ubiquitous and invisible—Kaku: 24–8 and Norman: thru-out.

44. 2– & 3–D—With further thought we realize that our eyes are basically two-dimensional as described in Ch.9—our retina is a hemispherical inside-surface on which each eye's lens projects scenes. The lens adjusts to focus on near or far objects plus the two eyes point at the objects. Our brain interprets these data as three-dimensional representations. See Crick: 76–7, 206–7, 236 & 246–7.

45. Virtual reality—Dertouzos: 55–77 and Kaku: 40.

46. Virtual emotions—Dertouzos: 299–302.

47. Thru the looking-glass—Turkle: 9–18. The 'looking-glass' refers to Lewis Carroll's sequel to his *Alice in Wonderland*.

48. Computers emulate brains—Goonatilake: 58–70 and *NewScientist* 19Jul'03: 40–3.

49. Posthuman—Hayles: 283–91 concludes "Although some current versions of the posthuman point toward the anti-human and the apocalyptic, we can craft others that will be conducive to the long-range survival of humans and of the other life-forms, biological and artificial, with whom we share the planet and ourselves."

50. Merged evolution—Goonatilake thru-out.

51. Industrial revolutions—Dertouzos: 8–9 cites two, first with the steam engine starting in the mid-18th century and the second with the IC engine, electricity and synthetic chemicals in the 20th.

52. Third revolution—Dertouzos: 306–7 counts from the first two industrial revolutions. But we could cite some others. Certainly the switch from hunter-gatherer to herder-farmer, and the move to towns and cities count. Gutenberg is often cited also.

53. Programmed robots—Kaku: 76–98 & 130–3.

54. Progress—Gould'96: 171 & thru-out on bacteria's prevalence and 197ff on complexity and non-progress (altho in his last serious book Gould'03: 103, bottom, concedes "... validating the claim that science, in some meaningful sense, 'progresses.'"). Also R.Wright: 257–76. Gould famously argued that if evolution's 'tape' were rerun the outcome would be far different. But Conway Morris disagrees— *NewScientist* 16Nov'01: 26–9—because of ubiquitous evolutionary convergence, the emergence of the same patterns over and over again. (Conway Morris's just published *Life's Solution: Inevitable Humans in a Lonely Universe* I received too late to utilize. In his *Crucible of Creation* he also disagreed with Gould's ideas in *Wonderful Life* about the Burgess Shale.) Chaisson: 182 also urges caution in regarding evolution as progress because overall "... disorder rises in the Earth-Sun environment" but on 197 acknowledges human cultural evolution's progress.

55. Culture that we build on—Diamond'99: 22 asks "Why is it that Europeans, despite their likely genetic disadvantage and (in modern times) their undoubted developmental disadvantage, ended up with much more of the cargo? Why did New Guineans wind up technologically primitive, despite what I believe to be superior intelligence?" and on pp. 26, 29–30 & thru-out describes the natural and cultural advantages he believes led to our 'superior' culture ('cargo' is a New Guinean term for imported technology and luxuries).

56. Smarts—Smarter folks tend to 'intermarry' and eventho' they may have fewer kids, it seems they afford them more educational advantages. So perhaps we are selecting for smarts both biologically and culturally, tho' I've no statistics on it.

57. Evolution's trajectory—R.Coren: 102–10, 146–51 & thru-out does a masterful job of tracing the trajectory from the past and into the future, but I think he underrates consciousness, p.193 & 196. Chaisson: 205 traces evolution's trajectory but on 218–9 cautions the difficulty of projecting where the rising curve of com-

plexity is headed. Corning'03: 306–8 & 316–9 suggest that rather than try to make forecasts instead we make strategic plans including contingent plans. In Bruce Stutz's review in *Discover* Oct'02: 78 of Browne's biography of Darwin, Stutz says that even Darwin's most ardent supporters did not appreciate "... that evolution has no direction, for the good or toward the best." But in my careful perusal of Browne I found no such statement or even reference.

58. Both the horse-collar and stirrup originated in Asia and were introduced into Europe in the Middle Ages—Gies: 45–7 & 55–6.

59. Play—Some years ago a local outfitter (Benchmark: canoes, camping stuff, fly-fishing gear &c, no guns or power) told about a prankster in a small town who had a billboard painted of a hearse with bicycles and kayaks on top pulling a trailer loaded with a snowmobile, jet-ski, motorcycle, canoe &c. The then chic caption read "Whoever has the most toys when he dies, wins." Local preachers were outraged so he told them he'd have it painted over shortly but then asked "Why do you object to it?" He never got an answer—apparently they didn't appreciate satire.

60. Speculators—Back about 1970 when I worked for a gas company I had a discussion with the controller about stockholder loyalty. He claimed our sole responsibility was to the stockholders because they owned the company. I said why should we feel loyal to them if they're not loyal to us?—they may have bought the stock yesterday and will sell it tomorrow if the price is right. I argued what I'd learned at SRI that we owed responsibility to all the *stake*holders, all who had a stake in the success of the company—not only loyal stockholders and bond holders, but the employees, customers, suppliers and community who should all be responsibly represented on the board of directors.

61. Infectious greed—Federal Reserve Chairman Alan Greenspan's term used in his July'02 report to Congress on the reason for the then current business crisis. He blamed greed for causing business executives to embellish balance sheets and artificially inflate stock values. I would also implicate the stock market speculators whose greed not only emboldened executives to pander to them but who punished corporations that didn't by dumping their stocks in favor of those whose executives did. (In Dec'96 after the first two years of a rapid rise in stock prices, Greenspan had questioned whether the markets were in the grip of "irrational exuberance"—stocks were way over-priced even then.)

62. Inner gratification—I wonder if self aggrandizement is due to an impoverished Self. They may feel empty as the result of projecting their Self out onto 'God' and futilely try to fill the resultant void with stuff. Some devout Christian neighbors of mine own expensive cars and stuff—if they're truly Christian, shouldn't they instead invest in good works?

63. Know the price, vs. value—Oscar Wilde in *The Oxford Dictionary of Quotations*: 818:12.

64. Profit—Businessmen I've known seem to be of two types: Those that produce a product take joy and pride in their product and are less caught up in just making money, altho' they use it wisely. Those that are engaged in trade seem more interested in 'doing deals', buying stuff at a good price and selling it for a better price, they like to 'turn a profit'.

65. Saving the World—How to: *Scientific American* Jan'03: 36–7. How not to: *NewScientist* 28Sept'02: 24.

66. Islamic militants see us as evil—I was told it's not just a resentment of our affluence. After WWI the way the West divided the Ottoman Empire into despotic kingdoms (which the US favor), we deny them the freedom we enjoy—Answer to my question after a 3/2/03 talk by Ismail Ahmed, Director of the Center of Arab Social Services in Dearborn Michigan.

67. "There is grandeur in this view of life"—Darwin 1859 *On the Origin of Species*, ch.14.

68. No longer support plants—Ward & Brownlee'02: 106–16 argue that CO_2 levels will drop below what plants need to grow.

Chapter Twelve—Society

1. Sweet Old World—on Emmylou Harris' "Wrecking Ball" CD. Lucinda Williams' words are to a friend who committed suicide, "See what you lost when you left this world/ This sweet old world."

2. Bergson's parents were Jewish but purportedly he was converted to Roman Catholicism in his 60s and published *The Two Sources of Morality and Religion* in 1932 (trans. 1935) "... in which he aligned his own philosophy with Christianity"/Encarta. Also see the Index for earlier notes.

3. Heaven—The myth the IHM nuns taught us was that "After Lucifer and his rebellious angels were driven out of Heaven down to hell God created man to replace them. But men and women had to prove their worthiness for Heaven by serving Him on Earth, else they went to hell. Once there are enough human 'saints' in Heaven to replace Lucifer's fallen angels, the world will end."

4. Preemies—Out of 4004 such births during a ten month period in Ireland and the UK, by age $2\frac{1}{2}$ only 155 had no apparent physical or mental problems yet—Story in the Aug18'00 Oakland Press (Mi) page D-5 by Bruce Hilton of Scripps Howard News Service about a report in the New England Journal of Medicine. However another study by Yale U. School of Medicine reported by AT&TWorldnet Feb11'03 (citing the AMA Journal) stated "Premature infants with very low birth weights suffer learning and other mental problems early on, but most improve by age 8 ..." (adjusted to full term) 'Most' = 66% who were borderline and 49% who were retarded (excluding those that suffered a brain bleeding problem).

5. Abortion—Catholics believe that unless a fetus is baptized, which presumably it's not if aborted, it can't go to Heaven but instead goes to Limbo for eternity. Maybe they could devise a way of baptizing the embryo or fetus *in utero* before abortion, but that seems even more absurd.

6. Abstinence—It took our ancestors two-million years to evolve a perpetual state of female sexual receptivity which for the past two millennia the Church has tried to suppress. Their alternative to perpetual abstinence was abstinence during presumed ovulation, dubbed 'Vatican roulette'.

7. Married priests—Until around 1100 married clergy were common tho' discouraged, but to get their undivided loyalty Pope Gregory VII invalidated them. Küng: 86 & 92.

8. 'Only God can decide when you die'—The Church teaches that if you're not in the 'state of grace' (have committed an un-confessed mortal sin) when you die, you'll go to hell. So you'd best be in the state of grace as much of the time as possible because you never can be sure when you'll die, when 'God will take you'. Like musical chairs—when the music stops if you don't have a chair, you're done.

9. Capital punishment—During President George W. Bush's Jul23'01 visit with Pope JohnPaul II, the Pope spoke out against the death penalty. During Bush's six years as governor of Texas, that state carried out 152 executions, the highest rate in the US, and under his presidency US federal authorities resumed executions after a 38 year hiatus.

10. Terminal patients—The man who arguably did the most to force this issue into the public's consciousness, Dr. Jack Kevorkian, worked here in southeast Michigan. During the 1990s he helped 130 terminal patients end their suffering in defiance of Michigan law. But no jury would convict him until the last when hubris made him dismiss his attorney and defend himself before a biased judge (witness her reprimand and disallowance of the deceased's relatives testifying). Kevorkian tried to continue his publicity from prison but the governor imposed a gag-order. Appeals drag on—he's 75 in May'03. See Jack Lessenberry in The Oakland Press, Feb23'03: A-7.

11. Can't stand the heat—Harry S. Truman, 1952.

12. Choose your death—I first confronted my Catholic 'morals' and open-mindedly considered this issue on seeing the 1971 movie "Harold and Maude" wherein on her eightieth birthday Ruth Gordon's character, Maude, deliberately overdoses. While I thought she had plenty of life left in her and thus was premature, I came to respect her right to make that decision. The 19–year-old 'Harold' was perplexed by her suicide eventho' he'd staged several sham suicides himself in vain attempts to shock his egocentric mother.

13. Rage—from Dylan Thomas' 1952 poem "Do Not Go Gentle into that Good Night" reportedly written for his dying father.

14. Near death phenomena—Berman thru-out and Greyson in Cardeña &al: 315ff.

15. About to die anyway—On September 11, 2001 when NYC's Twin Towers were impacted by jet planes commandeered by Al Qaeda terrorists, some occupants trapped above the inferno facing certain death instead jumped from windows to their certain death (self defenestration). Were these acts of despair and desperation, or their last great adventure: skydiving sans parachute? Were they able to override their amygdala and take control of their behavior, rather than be overcome with terror and desperation?

16. Fear of dying—Like the old-man in the musical "Show Boat" who sings Jerome Kern's "Old Man River" ♪"... I'm tired of living and feared of dying ..."

17. Selling indulgences—When I was a kid at Gesu, a Jesuit parish across from a Jesuit university, the priests would accept a 'donation' of $2 or $5 (worth a lot more back then during the Depression) to say a deceased person's name at mass in order to help shorten their time in purgatory. Gesu's church had five altars to accommodate the many Jesuits saying their daily masses.

18. If not for them, that value wouldn't exist—This argument is most persuasive for intellectual property—literature, music, computer code—where there's no substrate, but less so the greater the rôle of the substrate. For example a creator of a chair say, used wood but where'd they get the wood? How'd a developer of land get the land? Was it stolen or defrauded from earlier 'owners'—say going all the way back to the Indians—and what about the non-human animals that live and depend on that land? The 'value added' is attributable to the creator, but what that value is added to, may not be.

19. *Atlas Shrugged*—Ayn Rand's 1957 novel of a society that virtually enslaved its creative people only to have their creativity dry-up. (Rand had fled the Soviet Union in 1926.) But part of the reward for creating is the sheer joy of creating, aside from any monetary or recognition rewards, yet if these latter are denied or expropriated, resentment can stifle creativity. The Beatles wrote a song "Taxman" and Ingmar Bergman briefly left Sweden, as I recall.

20. Obesity—What Is To Be Done? *Science* 7Feb'03: 845–60. Are fat and sugar addictive? *NewScientist* 1Feb'03: 26–9.

21. Higher insurance premium for high-risk lifestyles—With car insurance, if you're not adequately insured your insurer won't pay to fix your car. But would society let people die who don't have adequate coverage? In Michigan I'm told hospitals are required to accept and fully treat all who come thru Emergency eventho' they can't pay. Perhaps we need to seek a more democratic approach by respecting people's self-selection, that is, if they haven't reasonably tried to take care of themselves thru a responsible lifestyle, they won't be taken care of. It may sound callous but with the increasing medical ability to sustain life, people need to be required to take more responsibility, as do the 'pushers' who pander to them.

22. Fat tax—There's a beginning movement to put "a 'fat tax' on food that could be used to offset the cost of health problems society is likely to incur."—AT&T Worldnet Jan28'03. But the money won in the 1998 tobacco settlement is being used by many states to plug fiscal deficits rather than fund anti-smoking programs—AT&T Worldnet Jan7'03. Even so it might discourage fat-food.

23. Roman slavery—Thomas: 29.

24. Consume what level of Life—Singer: 34–5, 46, 97–100 & thru-out uses sentience—whether animals feel pain—as his criterion for deciding which animals not to consume. It might be argued that we're not eating Life when we consume dairy products or fruit—but we're eating products that nature 'intended' to nurture offspring.

25. Pets—other peoples' pets are like grandchildren—I can enjoy them occasionally without having to take care of them all the time.

26. Complex Life feeds on less complex Life—the converse is also true—bacteria and viruses, lice and mosquitoes feed on us.

27. Eugenics was not unique to Nazi Germany. In 1931 Vermont became the 31st US state to enact a sterilization law for the handicapped or 'the feeble-minded'—per Discovery News Brief Aug9'99 reporting on 'Boston Globe' Aug7'99 article and Nancy L. Gallagher's *Breeding Better Vermonters: The Eugenics Project in the Green Mountain State*. University Press of New England, 1999.

28. Master race—Nazis presumably were instituting Nietzsche's concept of *übermensch* wherein his warrior, a 'hunter' had privileges over the 'herd' of inferior humans, like a hawk over sparrows. But most humans have evolved beyond just the hunter-gatherer stage and besides we're all one species unlike hawks and sparrows. Moreover the 'hawk' can't discern what's best for its species much less for evolution's trajectory. If we interpret Nietzsche's *übermensch* to mean self-actualizing persons, then we should encourage and enable all humans to be the best they can be, so that we optimize.

29. The Enlightenment began with Baruch Spinoza in the late 1600s and led a century later to the foundation to the United States of America—see MS Encarta for an overview of the Enlightenment and on Spinoza, Damasio'03: 8–24, 170–5, 184–7, 209–20 & 223–89 and Israel: thru-out.

30. Religious indoctrination—I sometimes think of my IHM-Jesuit 'religious education' as an oxymoron—'religion' is based on revealed truth whereas 'education' seeks truth with an open mind—if you've already decided what's true your mind's not open to alternatives. I was required to take religion classes every year up thru sophomore in college repeating the same material elaborated some. What a waste—I can think of other stuff I'd rather learned.

31. Ten Commandments—Moses though a Hebrew, was raised and educated in the Pharaoh's palace until he killed an Egyptian who'd murdered a Hebrew. Moses fled Egypt and for years lived among Bedouin nomads where he learned wilderness skills. But a numinous experience with a 'burning bush' inspired him to return to Egypt to lead his people from bondage to the land of Canaan. En route he had another numinous experience on Mt. Sinai which inspired him to set down 'commandments' to discipline his unruly mob. MS Encarta.

32. Holocaust—Jews rightly want the world to know and never forget how the Nazis persecuted European Jews 1933–45 murdering some six-million, half in concentration camps. Slavs, Gypsies, gays and other 'inferiors' also were exterminated in Hitler's holocaust. Unfortunately such 'cleansings' have occurred thruout history. Just in the past century the Ottomans massacred untold Armenians (Warraq'95: 238 and the 2002 film "Ararat" say over a million); Stalin murdered, starved or imprisoned millions; Khmer Rouge killed 1.7–million Cambodians; African tribes massacred each other; and on and on—see MS Encarta. So it seems to me Jews might esteem higher ground by broadening the scope of their Holocaust museums to included not just Jews but all these other victims, as well as American Indians, "lest we forget" "man's inhumanity to man" and vow "never again"—Jews speaking for all mankind.

33. Science vs religion—D.S.Wilson: 220–31 agues that the word 'religion' is from Latin meaning 'to unite or bind together' (MW says 'to restrain') and that its evolutionary function is to adapt its group to their environment. Thus religions in-

terpret revelation to suit their perception of a viable social system, and enforce that system thru sacred symbols and with sanctions both in the here and hereafter. He says the criterion of 'truth' is not its rationality but its adaptive value.

34. Science vs religion—Gould'03: 33 & thru-out argues (at his convoluted erudite best/worst) "... the leaders of the Scientific Revolution did encounter genuine intellectual opponents of no mean force, powerful critics who held all the advantages of incumbency and the weight of tradition. One can scarcely blame science for a little pugnacity in its infancy." But that was then and now science should acknowledge that there are some things that can only be known thru the humanities and abandon the dichotomy, he asserts.

35. Many Germans obeyed Hitler early on for many reasons—they were raised in an authoritarian tradition, Germany had been humiliated and virtually devastated by unreasonable reparations after World War I and they believed Hitler could circumvent the restrictions and restore pride and prosperity, and they didn't fully realize the extent of Hitler's ruthlessness until it was too late to resist (altho' a few did to their peril).

36. Sun-god—Weatherford: 26–7.

37. Zuñi fetishes—see Cushing: 39 & thru-out. As I understand it because the fetish possessor believes in its magical powers, the Zuñi gives his unconscious free rein to use its intuitive powers unimpeded by his conscious mind's judgments.

38. 'Seeds of Simplicity' is a program of Cornell U's Center for Religion, Ethics & Social Policy providing educational material and sponsoring local 'simplicity circles'. Another is The Center for a New American Dream. PBS broadcasted shows dubbed 'Affluenza'. Reported on AT&T Worldnet Oct26'02.

39. Commodity money—Weatherford: 18–21. Cacao beans were ground into paste by the Aztecs to make chocolate. After World War II in the chaos of Europe once again chocolate became a medium of exchange along with cigarettes. Salt was used in China, North Africa and the Mediterranean; hence 'salary' from the Latin *salarius* = 'of salt'.

40. Lydia—Weatherford: 30–3.

41. Greeks—Weatherford: 36–45.

42. Rome—Weatherford: 49–61.

43. Feudalism—Weatherford: 62–3.

44. Templars—Weatherford: 64–71. Knights Templar is also a degree in Freemasonry today.

45. Italians—Weatherford: 72–92.

46. Coins' proliferation—Weatherford: 95–108.

47. Bank of England—Weatherford: 155–67.

48. US money—Weatherford: 169–89.

49. Deflation—Weatherford: 205–6.

50. Currency traders—Weatherford: 251–63.

51. Future money—Weatherford: 264–8. On 'card money' see ~: 237–48 and *Scientific American* Aug'02: 86–7. Also see Kaku: 37–9. My debit card worked as fast

at ATMs on the streets in New Zealand as it does back home at the ATM in the lobby of my credit union. My credit card works as well with amazon.co.uk as it does with amazon.com.

52. Third world—Only in the last century did mortgages become routine in the US. But in the third world and post-communist countries mortgaging property is extremely difficult because of the seemingly simple problem of proving title, a problem that plagued the US into the 1800s. See Soto thru-out. His thesis is that the lack of clear-title-deeds prevents owners from using their property as collateral to obtain capital hence impeding capitalism. For an interview of Soto see *NewScientist* 27Apr'02: 46–9.

53. Earn credit in Heaven—As I write Islamic extremists are convincing young Muslims to turn themselves into bombs and blow themselves up along with 'infidels' in order to collect the rewards awaiting them in their Heaven. A millennium ago it was Christian crusaders who were being promised rewards in the hereafter.

54. Constant instantaneous contact—Fifty years ago Teilhard de Chardin: 180–3 & elsewhere, proposed that our species is evolving toward one organism he called the 'noosphere', toward his 'omega-point'. With our coming ubiquitous communications turning us into a global village, this is becoming more and more feasible. Also see Stock'93 thru-out.

55. Supra-human organisms—Stock'93: 20–6 describes the planetary *super*-organism, "Metaman," as "that part of humanity, its creations, and its activities that is interdependent—[*loosely*] joined together by trade, communications, and travel ... primarily the world's industrialized countries and the urban areas in developing lands ..." The *supra*–human organisms I'm referring to are *tightly* joined humans functioning as entities perhaps in Stock's Metaman. Also see Stock'93: 225–6 & 243–5. D.S.Wilson thru-out presents an analysis of religious &al organizations as organisms (his research was funded by the John Templeton Foundation whose objective is to foster religion, tho' it doesn't appear to have unduly biased his work).

56. Blaise Pascal's *Pensées*, *"Le coeur a ses raisons que la raison ne connaît point."*

57. Population growth—World population went from 2 billion in 1930 to 6 billion by the end of the century but it's thought growth will slow as women worldwide become more educated, per Zero Population Growth reported by the Environmental News Network Jun7'99. It's forecast to peak at 9 billion in 2070 then decline to 8.4 billion in 2100 with 35% then 45% over 60 years old, per *Nature* Science Update 2Aug'01. Also see *NewScientist* 20Jul'02: 38–41. But according to the United Nations by 2050 there will be 9.3 billion threatening the Earth's resources especially water, per AT&T Worldnet Nov7'01. Yet it's not just resources. If the developing world acquires our standard of living and generates as much waste as we do we'll drown in it.

58. Interrupt education—Sydney Harris: see Ch.9's note 180.

59. What you're teaching may not be what they're learning—e.g. maybe they're learning how to deal with an autocratic teacher.

60. Language skills—My older daughter when in fourth-grade wrote a page-and-half narrative of walking up the road thru the woods on a blustery evening to her friend's house. Her story was gripping but her spelling was atrocious (I'd told her to concentrate on creativity, that later in life she could get a stenographer to correct spelling—this was around 1970 before word processors). When her teacher gave back her paper, it was all marked up in red and she had to rewrite it. Her rewrite was only a half-page drained of any drama, but the spelling was correct! Now she's an excellent writer but uses her spelling checker, as do I (good ole F7).

61. Scientific concepts can be taught without math—as I think I've demonstrated thru-out this book—so it needn't be an impediment. Science is feared partly because it's coupled with math. Math is necessary if the student is to become a scientist or engineer but even then concepts should be taught, not just rote procedures. But math frightens some others away so they don't learn the scientific concepts gained in the past two centuries and are left susceptible to myths originating two millennia ago.

62. Obsolete religion—as said earlier (note 30) I was required to take religion classes all thru IHM taught grade-school, and Jesuit taught high-school and sophomore year of college, each year repeating much the same thing embellished some. Consequently there wasn't time to teach subjects like biology and sociology which would have been more propitious.

63. Computer games teaching skills—car driving might be one. Most kids quickly become adept at maneuvering a car but it takes years of driving experience to learn judgment—what might happen, what to expect, how to deal with it—about the thousands of situations encountered in driving. Realistic unpredictable computer simulations could teach and test aspiring drivers. Also see *Nature* Science Update 29May'03.

64. Vicious appetite—I don't know if the virtual violence stimulates viciousness or helps them get it out of their system so they don't have to enact it in reality. A writer for Salon.com in a Jun11'01 editorial claimed there's no "... proof that exposure to images or descriptions of sex and violence does children any harm." A subsequent study found a correlation between television viewing and aggressive behavior—*Science* 29Mar'02: 2377–9 & 2468–71 and ~ 5Jul'02: 49–50. A UofMi study presented in the Mar'03 journal *Developmental Psychology* reported in *The Oakland Press* (Mi) Mar10'03: A-5 also found a correlation. I've attended movies with chase scenes and afterward found myself driving aggressively. It seems to me that seeing graphic violence would stimulate the amygdala with lingering affects which the mature frontal cortex would attempt to counter once it's strong enuf.

65. Teens' brains are more susceptible to addiction—AT&T Worldnet Jun25 '03 citing a study by Andrew Chambers &al in the *American Journal of Psychiatry*.

66. Prefrontal growth spurt—*NewScientist* 19Oct'02: 16.

67. I used to lecture telemarketers: "If I came into your house, interrupted what you were doing and insisted you pay attention to me, that'd be pretty rude wouldn't it?" When they agree I say "But isn't that what you're doing to me!" But I've since given up. Maybe the National Do-Not-Call Registry will minimize it.

68. Quasi-religious functions—see Ninian Smart in Aziz: 5–6. There's a better analysis I read somewhere but I'm damned if I can retrieve it!

69. I recently attended a funeral service for an aunt (-in-law) in Midland Michigan in a Catholic Church we'd attended years ago when visiting my mother's folks. They'd aggiornamento'd the church and service with an additional altar facing the congregation and the monster organ alongside. The priest had white vestments for the Black Mass and they played Bach and Beethoven music. The talks were very loving and personal, but clearly afterlife oriented. That service may be atypical—I've since learned that Bishop Untner of the Saginaw Diocese is quite progressive, indeed was both ordained and promoted by Cardinal Dearden over the Vatican's objections (he's missing a lower leg)—per Harry Cook Jul10'03.

70. Religious affiliations—Church attendance: *Free Inquiry* Summer'02: 39–9. Belief: ~: 28–34 and *Scientific American* Sept'99: 88–93.

71. A *new* understanding of 'faith' and 'spirituality' indeed may be closer to the *old* Greek-Christian understanding before Roman orthodox Christianity was championed by Constantine eclipsing the Greek emphasis on individual independence—Hamilton: 213–6. Also see Ch.3's note 55.

72. Intrepid priests—Duve'02: 306.

73. Longevity—*The Peter Principle* a 1969? book by Laurence J. Peter and Raymond Hull argued, "In a hierarchy every employee tends to rise to his level of incompetence." It seems such people follow an inverted interpretation of F.D. Roosevelt's dictum "The man who never made a mistake never did anything" —they figure if they don't do anything, they won't make any mistakes!

74. Career maneuvering—Shepherd Mead's 1950s book—later made into a musical—*How to Succeed in Business Without Really Trying* satirized unprincipled ladder-climbing. About the same time at Ford the admonishment circulated, "Be careful who you step-on on the way up, you use the same steps coming down."

75. Public utilities are legal monopolies to avoid duplicating expensive networks of delivery systems, like gas or electric lines. Early-on water companies were also private; so were fire-companies operated by fire-insurers to put-out fires of their insureds' property while letting adjacent uninsured property burn. The reverse is also done—privatizing publicly-owned utilities.

76. My incorrigible slice taught a valuable lesson. One summer Sunday in the early 1950s a neighborhood buddy got me to try golf using his dad's old wooden 'sticks'. Before the first tee I tried a few practice swings to get a feel for it, then teed-off. The ball went straight down the middle a good distance as did most of the other drives, and I was told I was a natural. So my buddy arranged a trade to get me an incomplete set of clubs. Being a fledgling autodidact I bought a golf book to study the dynamics of the swing. The more I studied and practiced, the worse I got. It took a few persistent years before I gave up. The lesson: not to let my head mess with my body. (I've since learned how my head can guide my body.)

77. Compulsive play—A running friend (actually years before we'd gone to grade- and high-school together) was constantly concerned about his race finish times. (He damn near killed himself finishing ahead of me—I let him pass—in a

triathlon where he'd had trouble swimming and gotten out of the water long after me.) He'd have his marathon finish times printed on his T-shirt from the race. After our Sunday morning runs we'd meet for breakfast where one day he said he'd gone to a party the night before. I asked if he had a good time and he said Yes. So I asked what his time was. He was confused so I asked again, What was your time? I don't think he got it. He seemed more interested in having a fast time than in having a good time. (The trick is to have a good time while you're pursuing a fast time—in a foot race or in Life.) Even so, he was about to run his 50th+ marathon when cancer caught up with him—after several years he's still 'out running' the cancer, so tenacity does have its benefits.

78. Competitive sports an alternative to war—see Winston: 121 & 146ff. About 1970 when the Kashmir border war was heating up I asked a colleague who was a native of India what it was all about. He said annual ritual border skirmishes had been going on for decades but hadn't gotten serious until the US and Soviets armed each side. I also recall a TV show about the Yanomami along Venezuela's Orinoco River where there just 'happened' to be a border skirmish with neighboring tribes each harvest season so the men had to go fight and couldn't help the women with the harvest.

79. Cooperation vs competition—In some events a worthy adversary can spur improved performance such as in long-distance running. I recall a marathon TV scene of Bill Rodgers and an unknown runner rounding a corner where his then wife handed Rodgers a bottle. He drank some and handed it to his competitor.

80. For those of us in the twilight of our years, take heart from these words of Tennyson's *Ulysses*: "Free hearts, free foreheads,—you and I are old; / Old age hath yet his honor and his toil. / Death closes all: but something ere the end, / Some work of noble note, may yet be done, / Not unbecoming men that strove with Gods. / . . . / Tho' much is taken, much abides; and tho' / We are not now that strength which in old days / Moved earth and heaven; that which we are, we are,— / One equal temper of heroic hearts, / Made weak by time and fate, but strong in will / To strive, to seek, to find, and not to yield." Ulysses had returned from the Trojan War via his long *Odyssey* to his wife, cleaned her suitors out of his house, ensconced his son as head of his kingdom and now restlessly soliloquizes with his old mariners. I printed this excerpt of Tennyson's long poem in verse form in deep red onto parchment-like paper and framed it where it now hangs on my study wall.

81. Age & sage—*NewScientist* 31 Aug '02: 44–7 and *Science* 28 Feb '03: 1300–2.

82. There's a myth abroad that our Founding Fathers were all religious including those who were Deists. "If [Jefferson] had been completely scrupulous, he would have described himself as a deist ... In modern-day parlance, he was a secular humanist."—Ellis: 259. "[Jefferson] can be viewed as a deistic Christian, a thinker who endorsed what he took to be the rational heart of Christianity while jettisoning, in good Enlightenment style, its supernaturalist excesses. Reviled as an infidel during his lifetime, he might just as well, from another perspective, have

been regarded as an advocate of radical theological reform."—Walters'92a: 183. Tom Paine, the man whose *Common Sense* in January 1776 galvanized our nascent republic, was an outspoken Deist—Keane: 107–14, 150, 390 & passim. Ethan Allen, Franklin and Washington also held Deistic views—MS Encarta Encyclopedia on 'Deism'. (Deists "... rejected [or doubted] such traditional Christian doctrines as revealed knowledge, the divinity of Jesus, original sin, miracles, eternal damnation, and the Trinity. Their concept of God was that of a Supreme Architect who served as the original cause of uniform physical laws and whose existence and nature could be inferred from an examination of those laws."—Walters'92b: 26–7. "Elements of the Deists' ideas have been absorbed by Unitarianism ..."—Encarta) In 1776, it would be eighty-three years before Darwin would publish his *Origin of Species*. Virtually everyone acquiesced to the Bible's creation story, so Deists used the euphemism "nature's God" which Jefferson drafted into the *Declaration of Independence* along with "... endowed by their Creator ..." Just as they didn't know about automobiles, airplanes, telephones, radios and a myriad of other ideas that would come later, they didn't know about evolution, so how could they be expected to have applied knowledge that didn't exist back then? Being progressive thinkers, had they known some certainly would have adopted evolution just as they would have adopted cars, phones &c had they been available. To say that we should cling to our Founding Fathers' outdated theistic ideas is like saying we should cling to their outdated technology.

83. On freedom *from* religion, Lamont'90: 216 cites Supreme Court Justice Jackson in a 1952 ruling, "The day that this country ceases to be free for irreligion it will cease to be free for religion—except for the sect that can win political power."

84. "In God We Trust"—in whose God do you trust? The Islamic God that extremist suicide-bombers believe tells them to blow up by-standers? The God of the Old Testament that preached "an eye for an eye"? ("... and soon the whole world's blind!"/Gandhi) The God of the Christian Fundamentalists? All these Gods 'were created in the image and likeness' of their respective believers so they each have their own agendas. I suppose we could put a positive spin on it by realizing they're each misconstruing their own Life Urge but then why not change it to "In Life We Trust"?—unlikely in my lifetime. (Similarly in *America the Beautiful* the line "God shed His grace on thee" could be changed to "Life shed its grace on thee.")

85. On Congress' laws see *The World Book*; for 1954: vol.15, p.508b; and for 1955: vol.13, p.597b. The insertion of "... under God ..." was championed by then President Eisenhower, the KofC &al per AP 6/27/02. Also see Ehrenreich: 220 and Lamont'90: 215. (To justify a new Michigan law authorizing displaying "In God We Trust" in pubic buildings, a legislator wrote that it first appeared during the Civil War on the 1864 two-cent coin, and said it's the national motto; Oakland Press, Feb11'02: A-6.) (I recall in the 1950s some droll short-order restaurants displayed notices: "In God We Trust. All Others Pay Cash.") As I write, Jun26'02 the 9th Federal District Court of Appeals in San Francisco overturned the 1954 Act that added "under God" to the Pledge as unconstitutional which is provoking much 'outrage'

in Washington. (Why are theists so outraged if it has no religious connotation?) Now onto the US Supreme Court which begins its sessions with "God save the United States and this honorable court." If "under God" is to stay in the Pledge then the next word "indivisible" should come out since "under God" is divisive, and the following words "*liberty* ... for *all*" should also come out since, if non-believers are compelled to pledge "under God," they're not at liberty *to not* believe in God. What if believers had to pledge *not to* believe in God? They'd lose some of their liberty, so they can't have it both ways, it's one or the other. Alternatively I suppose they could add "liberty ... for all who believe in God" which would *really* be divisive! But the Pledge is not to God but to a symbol of that nation which was founded on freedom of religion. Diminishing liberty diminishes its ideals.

86. Declaration of Independence quotes—Adler: 165.

87. Internet rôle in politics—some are concerned that the 'Net is being usurped by big-business to control content—for example see the Center for Digital Democracy's www.democraticmedia.org. (Dean is disproving that?)

88. TV campaign expenses—This nation has dominion over our airspace but I understand we gave away our rights to the airways years ago to encourage TV development. Maybe we should take back some so candidates can get some free airtime and thus reduce their dependence on fund-raisers and indebtedness to contributors.

89. Parsonage exemption—"Voice of Reason" 2002, No.2: 10a.

90. Retrogressive Christianity—reviews of Philip Jenkins' *The Next Christendom: The Coming of Global Christianity* at amazon.com.

91. Bypass our technology—Stock'93: 142–5.

92. Some of the impediments to global vision are antiquated parameters such as GNP—see Stock'93: 142.

93. Plurarchy—Bard & Söderqvist: 72, 186 & 220–4. They make thought provoking reading tho' I can't buy all their arguments. As I understand it, they believe as information becomes the dominant parameter in society, money and capitalism will be relegated to a lesser status. Those who can glean knowledge from information will become the elite 'netocracy' while those who can't will be the consumers, the 'consumtariat', manipulated by the netocracy.

94. Science is a work in progress—for a good comparison of science's methods vs religion's see Kurtz'03: 18–20.

95. Constantine II—In modern times a Constantine II was King of Greece until deposed in 1973. MS Encarta

96. *Aggiornamento*—'updating' see Küng: 181–96 and West'96: 125–32.

97. Does God work thru the Life Urge?—If prototheism accepts either belief—that the Life Urge is natural or supernatural—does it lead to an argument like the early Christians with their *homoousios* versus *homoiousios* mentioned in Ch.3's 'Constantine'? Hopefully in this third millennium the 'true believers' won't murder the 'heretics' like they did in the early *Anno Domini* centuries. But if each could accept the other's right to their belief and work together on their shared beliefs— what unites them rather than what separates them—imagine what might be ac-

complished? (I personally don't see how one could straddle such a fence—trying to be open to the unknown but closed to the possibility that it's *not* 'God'—but I suppose such bracketing is quite common.)

98. Novel—A younger novelist might follow in the shoes of Morris West like his 1963 *The Shoes of the Fisherman* about the surprise election of a Pope from behind the Iron Curtain long before Krakow's Cardinal Wojtyla became Pope JohnPaul II in 1978. Some saw West's novel as prescient including West'96: 138 himself. West wrote two other novels of Popes, *The Clowns of God* and *Lazarus*, drawing on his seven years' experience in Rome as an accredited reporter at the Vatican for London's *Daily Mail*—West'96: 136.

99. Crisis to induce change—As I write the Church's pedophile scandal is working its way through the hierarchy and the courts. Whether the abused plaintiffs' lawsuits will bankrupt the American Catholic Church, already contributions are being withheld. To shield parish property dioceses might turn it back to the parishes which could precipitate a democratizing of the US Catholic church—the Church is not the church, the faithful are. See the *Voice of Reason* No.3'02: 15 review of Jay P. Dolan's *In Search of an American Catholicism*, Oxford U.Press, 2002. (I haven't read it yet.)

100. Hitler—As mentioned in above note 35, the German people supported Hitler because they thought he was their savior, *der führer*, who'd free them from the unfair reprisals of World War I and the demonized Jewish merchants and bankers, and lead them as the most advanced (Teutonic) master race to a thousand-year Third-Reich. Hitler tried to purify their race which he argued would advance evolution. Soviets had similar goals which Stalin betrayed.

101. When the Chinese took over Tibet they attempted to destroy the Buddhist theocracy by destroying the monasteries and killing many monks. For centuries the common people had worked to support the monks and lamas in the belief that it would improve their next incarnation when they too might become a lama. I agree with the Chinese's ends but not with their means. Liberal education (not indoctrination) might have been a better tho' slower means.

102. Islamic—The fundamentalist Taliban in Afghanistan imposed strict codes and restricted education to the Koran and males. They also harbored Al Qaeda terrorist camps. While they've been routed in Afghanistan, their sentiments are found thru-out Islam. They hate the US, I suspect, because most of what they see of us is our exploitative exports and franchises, violent and sexual movies and TV, and greed for their oil. The Twin-Towers were seen as a blatant symbol of financial greed. If we hope to change them we must first change ourselves—we mustn't be smug about our democracy without seeing its hazards.

103. Closet atheists—*Free Inquiry* Summer'02: 40–3.

104. Homosexuality—a recent study of gay sheep found that the pre-optic area of their hypothalamus was smaller than normal males', as is females'. A similar pattern is seen in brains of gay men who've died of AIDS but it's uncertain if the abnormality was pre-existing or was caused by the disease and/or by the medication—AT&T Worldnet Nov4'02 citing a presentation at the meeting of the Soci-

ety for Neuroscience in Orlando Florida. *Nature* Science Update 18Feb'03 reported "Female macaques fraternize most with other females."

105. A fagot is a bundle of gathered fallen branches and twigs. It's my understanding that this is the basis of the slang word for a homosexual tho' I don't find it in MW or MS dictionaries. See Clendinen & Nagourney on *Faggots*.

106. Gay Rights Movement—Clendinen & Nagourney thru-out and *free inquiry* Summer'03: 26–7.

107. Demote Life—ABC's Peter Jennings narrated a series "In Search of America" which Saturday evening Sept7'02 profiled Frito-Lay, a PepsiCo company which markets potato-chips globally. He cited George Wills' definition of potato-chips as "a delivery system for fat and salt." Jennings showed how Frito-Lay is penetrating new foreign markets by using US trained native managers. An example he showed is how in China they've industrialized growing Lay's own strain of potatoes, producing standardized chips and marketing them by changing Chinese snacking habits. But they're displacing the locally-produced traditional dry-fruit/sunflower-seed snack, a much healthier food. While I acknowledge the efficiencies of Frito-Lay's operation I was appalled by their rapacious myopia and embarrassed that it's portrayed globally as the 'American way'. It got me thinking, what food could Frito-Lay produce instead that's more nutritious and doesn't pander to people's soft-addiction to salt? Potatoes are basically healthy food and a little salt and unsaturated fat are essential. But Lay's chips use as little potato and as much salt and fat as feasible (plus the empty sacks are trashed). It probably generates a high margin—their management is driven by the shareholders' desire for 7% annual growth. So to change, they need an enlightened cadre of shareholders who'll steer management to healthier products and/or we need less gullible consumers who'll boycott unhealthy products. Making 'the world free for democracy' shouldn't mean free for greed to exploit.

108. Consulting firms—I think of Stanford Research Institute (now SRI International) for which I worked from 1962–7, and their progressive approaches then to corporate planning, diversification and stakeholder 'equity'. They could do some initial research, then lead multiclient studies in compatible industries to help guide firms to viable products and services that enhance Life's evolution.

109. Stepping stone—For example I've known entrepreneurs who renovated a dilapidated building in our resurging downtown using their personal savings and 'sweat', then opened a business which failed. The next entrepreneur had the benefit of the first's work to build on and thus was enabled to succeed.

110. Dreams are made on—Shakespeare's *The Tempest* act 3, sc. 2, l. 156–7. John Gielgud did a marvelous job playing Prospero in Greenaway's 1991 movie of *The Tempest* titled "Prospero's Books."

111. Light one candle—*The Oxford Dictionary of Quotations*'99: 740 credits Adlai Stevenson for a paraphrase of this motto in his 1962 tribute to Eleanor Roosevelt, but it was familiar long before then. Bartlett'68: 981b credits the Motto of the Christopher Society. There's also a perverted version of the motto which some seem to prefer: "Better to curse one candle than forever light the darkness."

Appendix A—Protestant & Eastern Christians

1. Eastern Christians—MSEncarta: see Orthodox Church, Eastern Church, Eastern Rite Churches and Byzantine Empire.

2. A contemporary of Luther's was Erasmus, also a Catholic priest who wrote extensively to reform the Church but who remained Catholic, tho his writings were banned by the Council of Trent.

3. Protestantism, Luther, Erasmus—MSEncarta.

Appendix B—Prototheism for Skeptical Jews

1. Jewish fundamentalists—Armstrong'00: ix-xvi, 3–31, 98–132 and thru-out.

2. Spinoza—Damasio'03: 224–6 & elsewhere, Israel thru-out and Kogel & Katz: 3–8 who survey Jewish skeptics from Spinoza on.

3. Entrenched religious—in Kogel & Katz, Wine: 222.

4. Believing—in Kogel & Katz, Wine: 223–8.

5. Books of the Hebrew Bible—Finkelstein & Silberman: 6.

6. Finkelstein & Silberman: 23, 283–5, 302–5 & 310–3. (Juxtapose 321n23)

7. Finkelstein & Silberman: 37. Also see Schlagel: 79–113.

8. Finkelstein & Silberman: 59–60. Also see Schlagel: 113–25.

9. Finkelstein & Silberman: 64.

10. Finkelstein & Silberman: 75 & 81.

11. Finkelstein & Silberman: 132–4, 141–5 & 169ff. See Salon.com Feb7'01 for a lengthy review of Finkelstein & Silberman's book captioned "King David was a nebbish." However later carbon dating favors the Bible's version in this politically charged debate—*Science* 11Apr'03: 229–31 & 315–8.

12. See Cahill'98 thru-out for a glowing tribute to the Jews—and he's Irish! DSWilson: 133–47 examines Judaism's methods of group cohesiveness. Islamic tradition asserts that it arose independent of both Judaism and Christianity but that's refuted in Appendix C.

13. Joseph Campbell titled his celebrated book thus.

14. Jewish survival—in Kogel & Katz, Katz: 317–23.

15. Kabbalah (aka cabala or cabbala)—Aczel'00: 25–44 describes how, after the second destruction of the Temple in 70AD and Exile from Jerusalem, Rabbi Akiva "... apparently chanced upon ..." meditation practices inducing "... out-of-body experiences, altered mental states and heights of ecstasy ..." Even so he "... exhorted his students not to succumb to hallucinations or lose their grip on reality." However in 11th century Spain it degenerated (in my view) into numerology. But with the Inquisition many fled to Safed in Galilee where a man called the "... Ari introduced a new method of meditation ... a form of deep concentration aimed at binding the world of form to the Absolute." But it again 'degenerated' into intellectualizing—numerology and mathematics—so I'm not much interested in it. On Spinoza and the cabbala, see Israel: 645–50.

16. Traditional Judaism—MSEncarta. Reconstructionism is an addition based on Wine'88: 11 and elsewhere.

17. Jewish history—in Kogel & Katz, Wine: 228–34.

18. Humanistic Judaism—in Kogel & Katz, Cohn: 302–4, Bendor: 325–7, Rapp: 329–33 and Appendix: 365–6. Also Ibry: 53–62 & 130.

19. Ideology—in Kogel & Katz, Wine: 235–41.

20. Celebration of Life—Kushner: 3ff.

21. Bicameral mind—see Jaynes: 297–8 and the Index hereto for earlier notes, eg Ch.2's note 13.

22. Ideology replace theism—Ch.10's 'Propagating ProtoTheism' says that prototheism is a science *of* religion, *not* a new religion. But the distinction gets murky when trying to plumb the depths of the unconscious as explored in Ch.10.

23. Jewish people—Wine'88: 177. If "by birth" Wine means of a Jewish mother, Ibry: 40 & 74 objects since eventho' his mother was Christian, his father was Jewish, he was born in and fought to free Israel, and was stigmatized as a Jew.

24. Polytheism to monotheism to prototheism—Ch.10's sections on 'Poly- to Mono-Theism' and on 'Non-Theistic Religions' 1st ¶.

25. Monotheism—Akhenaton, pharaoh of Egypt from about 1353 to 1335BC, established solar monotheism as a new religion (which some scholars believe influenced Hebrew prophets) but after his death Tutankhamun restored the old polytheistic religion. Zarathustra (aka Zoroaster) preached monotheistic worship of Ahura Mazda in Persia around 630–550BC. (both MSEncarta) However Kriwaczek: 209 says that some (without citing them) put Zarathustra between 1700 and 1500BC "... which would align him ... with Abraham ..." but thru-out maintains Zarathustra was a dualist, that is he attributed equal power to God and Satan.

26. Jews pioneering prototheism—I'd go along with that eventho I'm not Jewish, altho my dad was from Disraeli Québec and he certainly had *chutzpah*.

Appendix C—Prototheism for Skeptical Muslims

1. Muslim fundamentalists—Armstrong'00: ix-xvi, 32–60, 98–132, *passim*.

2. Ibn Warraq "... pseudonym to protect his identity from Islamic religious-political extremists ..." Center for Inquiry report Jul'03: 1.

3. Testimonies—Warraq'03: 135 summary and 115–388 text.

4. Apostasy—Warraq'03: 15–57. On Salman Rushdie, see ~'95: 3–33.

5. Islamic 'conquest'—Nevo & Koren: 134–5.

6. Hijaz—Nevo & Koren: 10n, 11, 13, 67–71, 174, 179 & 185.

7. Ishmael—Nevo & Koren: 187, 193, 195 & 254.

8. Hagarism—Warraq'95: 81.

9. Byzantine fringe—Nevo & Koren: 21–5 & 87.

10. *Foederati*—Nevo & Koren: 17 & 36–50.

11. Monotheism—Nevo & Koren: 186–90, 207, 231 & 243.

12. Jesus' divinity—Nevo & Koren: 190–9 & 337–8.

13. Arab takeover—Nevo & Koren: 89–96.

14. Sassanian defeat—Nevo & Koren: 47–50.

15. Caliph is defined by MW as "a successor of Muhammad as temporal and spiritual head of Islam" from the Arabic *khalī fah* successor. But how could Muawiyah be Muhammad's successor if Muhammad, much less Islam didn't yet exist?

16. Muawiyah—Nevo & Koren: 96–7, 131, 155–6 & 242–5.

17. Abd al-Malik—Nevo & Koren: 65 & 161–3.

18. Dome of the Rock—Nevo & Koren: 255, 274–6 & 279.

19. Walid—Nevo & Koren: 293–4.

20. Arab history—Nevo & Koren: 256 & 339–48.

21. Islamic empire or Commonwealth—Nevo & Koren: 348–50.

22. Muhammad as rôle—Nevo & Koren: 258, 260 & 264–7.

23. Muhammad in Koran—Nevo & Koren: 265.

24. Scholars' invention—Nevo & Koren: 330–1.

25. Muhammad bn al Hanafiyyah—Nevo & Koren: 280–2 & 346.

26. Muslim debt to Judaism—Warraq'95: 49–60.

27. Hijaz—in Warraq'00, al-Rawandi: 93 & 98–101 and Koren & Nevo: 435–8, and Nevo & Koren: 5–6.

28. Isaac/Ishmael—Warraq'95: 41 & 131–3 and in Warraq'00, Warraq: 64 and al-Rawandi: 112–3.

29. Arabs transpose Bible—in Warraq'00, Warraq: 75–8; more over Koren & Nevo: 431–2 and Nevo & Koren: 5 dispute that Mecca had any significance as either a crossroad in trade-routes or as a sanctuary before Islam. Also Edis: 125–33.

30. Long slow concoction of Islam—in Warraq'00, Warraq: 35–6, 65–7, 96–8 & 109–11 and Koren & Nevo: 424; Nevo & Koren: 354 and Hawting: 12–3.

31. Muhammad's birth date—in Warraq'00, al-Rawandi: 103 quotes Lawrence Conrad, "well into the second century A.H. [*anno hegirae* ~ eighth century AD] scholarly opinion on the birth date of the Prophet displayed a range of variance of eighty-five years." ~Conrad: 368–81. His birth place is even more problematic—in Warraq, al-Rawandi: 99 cites Crone that "... if Ptolemy mentions Mecca at all, he calls it Moka, a town in Arabia Petraea" near Petra; see note 29.

32. Jerusalem and Temple site—in Warraq'00, al-Rawandi: 94–5. Note MSEncarta gives 638 as Muslim conquest by Caliph Umar I.

33. Abandoned Byzantine defenses—in Warraq'00, Koren & Nevo: 432–4. See Warraq'95: 44 on Sassanian influence, 219–23 on Islamic conquests and 345–6 on Muhammad uniting the Arab tribes.

34. Arabs small minority—in Warraq'00, al-Rawandi: 103–5 and Hawting: 518–20 on the acceptance of Islam by those 'conquered'.

35. Repression of science—*NewScientist* 26Apr'03: 27.

36. See the Website of the Institute for the Secularisation of Islamic Society (ISIS), www.secularislam.org/

Bibliography

The references listed below are primarily books. Periodicals and websites are referenced in their respective Notes.

Aczel, Amir D. *The Mystery of the Aleph: Mathematics, the Kabbalah, and the Search for Infinity.* NY: Four Walls Eight Windows, 2000.

Aczel, Amir D. *Entanglement: The Greatest Mystery in Physics.* New York: Four Walls Eight Windows, 2001.

Adams, Fred. *Origins of Existence: How Life Emerged in the Universe.* Simon & Schuster/ The Free Press, 2002.

Adams, Fred, and Greg Laughlin. *The Five Ages of the Universe, Inside the Physics of Eternity.* Simon & Schuster/ The Free Press, 1999.

Adler, Mortimer J. *We Hold These Truths: Understanding the Ideas and Ideals of the Constitution.* Macmillan, 1987.

Agosta, William C. *Chemical Communication: The Language of Pheromones.* Scientific American Library, 1992.

Agustí, Jordi, and Mauricio Antón. *Mammoths, Sabertooths, and Hominids: 65 Million Years of Mammalian Evolution in Europe.* Columbia U.Press, 2002.

Alexander, Denis. *Rebuilding the Matrix: Science and Faith in the 21st Century.* Oxford UK: Lion Publishing, 2001.

Allman, John Morgan. *Evolving Brains.* New York: Scientific American Library, 1999.

Alper, Matthew. *The "God" Part of the Brain: A Scientific Interpretation of Human Spirituality and God.* Brooklyn: Rogue Press, 1999.

Andresen, Jensine, ed. *Religion in Mind: Cognitive Perspectives On Religious Belief, Ritual, and Experience.* Cambridge U.Press, 2001.

Armstrong, Karen. *The Battle for God.* Alfred A. Knopf/ Borzoi, 2000.

Armstrong, Karen. *Buddha.* Viking Penguin, 2001.

Astley, Jeff; Timothy Home and Mark Savage, eds. *Creative Chords: Studies in Music, Theology and Christian Formation.* Herefordshire UK: Grace-wing, 2000.

Attenborough, David. *Life of Earth: A Natural History.* Little, Brown, 1979.

Audesirk, Teresa & Gerald. *Biology: Life on Earth.* 5th ed. Simon &Schuster/ Prentice Hall, 1999.

Aunger, Robert. *The Electric Meme: A New Theory of How We Think.* Simon& Schuster/ Free Press, 2002.

Austin, James H. *Zen and the Brain: Toward an Understanding of Meditation and Consciousness.* MIT Press, 1998 & 2000.

Avise, John C. *The Genetic Gods: Evolution and Belief in Human Affairs.* Harvard U.Press, 1998.

Aziz, Robert. *C.G. Jung's Psychology of Religion and Synchronicity.* Albany: State U.of New York Press, 1990.

Bak, Per. *How Nature Works: The Science of Self-Organized Criticality.* New York: Copernicus/ Springer-Verlag, 1996.

Ball, Philip. *Life's Matrix: A Biography of Water.* Farrar,Straus&Giroux, 1999 (originally H_2O. London: Weidenfeld&Nicolson, 1999).

Banville, John. *Doctor Copernicus.* New York: Random House/ Vintage Books, 1976.

Bard, Alexander, and Jan Söderqvist. *Netocracy: The New Power Elite and Life after Capitalism.* Neil Smith trans., London UK: Pearson Education (Reuters?), 2002 [Stockholm: BookHouse, 2000].

Barnes, Timothy D. *Constantine and Eusebius.* Harvard, 1981.

Basbanes, Nicholas A. *Patience & Fortitude: A Roving Chronicle of Book People, Book Places, and Book Culture.* Harper-Collins, 2001.

Benzon, William L. *Beethoven's Anvil: Music in Mind and Culture.* Perseus /Basic, 2001.

Bergmann, Peter G. *The Riddle of Gravitation.* Scribner/Dover, 1968/92

Bergson, Henri. *Creative Evolution.* Arthur Mitchell, trans. Dover, 1998 (Henry Holt, 1911).

Bergson, Henri. *The Two Sources of Morality and Religion.* R. Ashley Audra and Cloudesley Brereton, trans. U.of Notre Dame Press, 1977 [1935].

Berman, Phillip L. *The Journey Home: What Near-Death Experiences and Mysticism Teach Us About the Gift of Life.* Simon&Schuster/ Pocket Books, 1996.

Berne, Eric. *Games People Play: The Psychology of Human Relationships.* New York: Grove Press, 1964.

Blair, David, and Geoff McNamara. *Ripples on the cosmic sea, The Search for Gravitational Waves.* Addison-Wesley/ Helix Books, 1997.

Blech, Benjamin. *The Complete Idiot's Guide to Understanding Judaism.* Pearson/ Alpha, 1999.

Bly, Robert. *Iron John: A Book About Men.* Addison-Wesley, 1990.

Boa, Fraser. *The Way of the Dream: Conversations on Jungian Dream Interpretation with Marie-Louise von Franz.* Shambhala, 1994.

Boaz, Noel T. *Eco Homo: How the Human Being Emerged from the Cataclysmic History of the Earth.* HarperCollins/ Basic, 1997.

Boehm, Christopher. *Hierarchy in the Forest: The Evolution of Egalitarian Behavior.* Harvard U.Press, 1999.

Bokenkotter, Thomas. *A Concise History of the Catholic Church.* Doubleday/ Image, 1977 & 1990.

Bormann, F. Herbert; Diana Balmori and Gordon T. Geballe. *Redesigning the American Lawn: A Search for Environmental Harmony.* Yale U.Press, 2001.

Bosnak, Robert. *Tracks in the Wilderness of Dreaming: Exploring Interior Landscape Through Practical Dreamwork.* Bantam Doubleday Dell/ Delacorte, 1996.

Bronowski, J. *The Ascent of Man.* Little, Brown &Co, 1973.

Brooks, David. *Bobos in Paradise: The New Upper Class and How they Got There.* Simon&Schuster, 2000.

Brown, Peter. *The Making of Late Antiquity.* Harvard U.Press, 1993.

Browne, Janet. *Charles Darwin: The Power of Place - Volume II of a Biography.* Knopf, 2002.

Boyer, Pascal. *Religion Explained: The Evolutionary Origins of Religious Thought.* Perseus /Basic, 2001.

Brasher, Brenda E. *Give Me That Online Religion.* San Francisco: Wiley/ Jossey-Bass, 2001.

Brockman, John, ed. *The Next Fifty Years: Science in the Twenty-first Century.* Random House/ Vintage, 2002.

Buchanan, Allen; Dan W. Brock; Norman Daniels and Daniel Wikler. *From Chance to Choice: Genetics and Justice.* Cambridge U.Press, 2000.

Budiansky, Stephen. *If a Lion Could Talk: Animal Intelligence and the Evolution of Consciousness.* Simon&Schuster/ Free Press, 1998.

Buehrens, John A., and Forrest Church. *A Chosen Faith: In Introduction to Unitarian Universalism.* Beacon Press, 1998 [1989].

Cahill, Thomas. *The Gifts of the Jews: How a Tribe of Desert Nomads Changed the Way Everyone Thinks and Feels.* Doubleday, 1998.

Calvin, William H. *The Cerebral Code: Thinking a Thought in the Mosaics of the Mind.* MIT Press/ Bradford, 1996.

Calvin, William H., and Derek Bickerton. *Lingua ex Machina: Reconciling Darwin and Chomsky with the Human Brain.* MIT Press/ Bradford, 2000.

Camazine, Scott; Jean-Louis Deneubourg; Nigel R. Franks; James Sneyd, Guy Theraulaz and Eric Bonabeau. *Self-Organization in Biological Systems.* Princeton U.Press, 2001.

Campbell, Joseph, with Bill Moyers. *The Power of Myth*. Betty Sue Flowers, ed. Doubleday, 1988.

Caras, Roger A. *A Perfect Harmony: The Intertwining Lives of Animals and Humans Throughout History*. Simon&Schuster, 1996.

Cardeña, Etzel; Steven Jay Lynn and Stanley Krippner, eds. *Varieties of Anomalous Experience: Examining the Scientific Evidence*. American Psychological Assoc., 2000.

Casti, John L. *Complexification: Explaining a Paradoxical World Through the Science of Surprise*. HarperCollins/ HarperPerennial, 1994.

Casti, John L. *Paradigms Regained: A Further Exploration of the Mysteries of Modern Science*. Harper Collins/ William Morrow, 2000.

Cavalli-Sforza, Luigi Luca. *Genes, Peoples, and Languages*. Mark Seielstad, trans. Farrar, Straus and Giroux/ North Point, 2000.

Ceccarelli, Leah. *Shaping Science with Rhetoric: The Cases of Dobzhansky, Schrödinger, and Wilson*. U.of Chicago Press, 2001.

Chaisson, Eric J. *Cosmic Evolution: The Rise of Complexity in Nature*. Harvard U.Press, 2001.

Chalmers, David J. *The Conscious Mind: In Search of a Fundamental Theory*. Oxford U.Press, 1996.

Chardin, Pierre Teilhard de. *The Phenomenon of Man*. Bernard Wall, trans. New York: Harper &Bros., 1959 [1955].

Chardin, Pierre Teilhard de. *The Divine Milieu: An Essay on the Interior Life*. Harper & Row, 1960 [1957].

Chardin, Pierre Teilhard de. *The Appearance of Man*. J.M. Francoeur, trans. Harper & Row, 1965 [1956].

Chardin, Pierre Teilhard de. *Hymn of the Universe*. Harper & Row, 1965 [1961].

Chown, Marcus. *Afterglow of Creation: From the Fireball to the Discovery of Cosmic Ripples*. Sausalito Calif.: University Science Books, 1996.

Cimino, Richard, and Don Lattin. *Shopping for Faith: American Religion in the New Millennium*. San Francisco: Jossey-Bass, 1998.

Clayman, Charles B. editor-in-chief, *The Human Body: An Illustrated Guide to its Structure, Function, and Disorders*. New York: Dorling Kindersley, 1995.

Clendinen, Dudley, and Adam Nagourney. *Out for Good: The Struggle to Build a Gay Rights Movement in America*. Simon&Schuster, 1999.

Clottes, Jean, and David Lewis-Williams. *The Shamans of Prehistory: Trance and Magic in the Painted Caves*. Sophie Hawkes, trans. New York: Harry N. Abrams, 1998 [1996].

Coen, Enrico. *The Art of Genes: How Organisms Make Themselves*. Oxford U.Press, 1999.

Cole, Jonathan. *About Face*. MIT Press/ Bradford, 1998.

Coleman, James A. *Relativity for the Layman: A Simplified Account of the History, Theory, and Proofs of Relativity*. New York: Signet Science Books, 1958.

Conway Morris, Simon. *The Crucible of Creation: The Burgess Shale and the Rise of Animals*. Oxford U.Press, 1998.

Coppinger, Raymond & Lorna. *Dogs: A Startling New Understanding of Canine Origin, Behavior, and Evolution*. Scribner, 2001.

Coren, Richard L. *The Evolutionary Trajectory: The Growth of Information in the History and Future of Earth*. Amsterdam, The Netherlands: Gordon and Breach, 1998.

Coren, Stanley. *How to Speak Dog: Mastering the Art of Dog-Human Communication*. Free Press, 2000.

Corning, Peter A. *The Synergism Hypothesis: A Theory of Progressive Evolution*. McGraw-Hill, 1983.

Corning, Peter. *Nature's Magic: Synergy in Evolution and the Fate of Humankind*. Cambridge U.Press, 2003.

Crick, Francis. *The Astonishing Hypothesis: The Scientific Search for the Soul*. Simon&Schuster/ Touchstone, 1994. (Scribner, 1994)

Cronk, Lee. *That Complex Whole: Culture and the Evolution of Human Behavior*. Perseus/ Westview Press, 1999.

Cronk, Lee; Napoleon Chagnon and William Irons (eds.) *Adaptation and Human Behavior: An Anthropological Perspective*. Hawthorne, New York: Aldine de Gruyter, 2000.

Crossan, John Dominic, and Jonathan L. Reed. *Excavating Jesus: Beneath the Stones, Behind the Texts*. HarperCollins, 2001.

Crow, Tim J., ed. *The Speciation of Modern Homo Sapiens*. Proceedings of the British Academy-106, Oxford U.Press, 2002.

Cushing, Frank Hamilton. *Zuñi Fetishes*. Las Vegas: KC Publications, 1990 [Smithsonian Inst. 1880–1].

Damasio, Antonio R. *The Feeling of What Happens: Body and Emotion in the Making of Consciousness*. Harcourt Brace, 1999.

Damasio, Antonio. *Looking for Spinoza: Joy, Sorrow and the Feeling Brain*. Harcourt, 2003.

Dante Alighieri. *Inferno*. Robert & Jean Hollander, trans. Doubleday, 2000.

Davies, Paul. *About Time: Einstein's Unfinished Revolution*. Simon&Schuster, 1995.

Davies, Paul. *The Fifth Miracle: The Search for the Origin and Meaning of Life*. Simon&Schuster, 1999.

Dawkins, Richard. *The Extended Phenotype: The Long Reach of the Gene*. Oxford U.Press: 1982 & 1999.

Dawkins, Richard. *The Blind Watchmaker: Why the Evidence of Evolution Reveals a Universe Without Design*. Norton, 1987 & 1996.

Dawkins, Richard. *Climbing Mount Improbable*. Norton, 1996.

Deacon, Terrence W. *The Symbolic Species: The Co-Evolution of Language and the Brain*. Norton, 1997.

Deleuze, Gilles. *Bergsonism*. Hugh Tomlinson & Barbara Habberjam, trans., New York: Zone Books, 1991 [1966 U. France].

Delsemme, Armand. *Our Cosmic Origins: From the Big Bang to the Emergence of Life and Intelligence*. Cambridge Univ.Press, 1998.

Dennett, Daniel C. *Darwin's Dangerous Idea: Evolution and the Meanings of Life*. Simon&Schuster/ Touchstone, 1995.

Denton, Michael J. *Nature's Destiny: How the Laws of Biology Reveal Purpose in the Universe*. Simon&Schuster/ The Free Press, 1998.

Dertouzos, Michael L. *What Will Be: How the New World of Information Will Change Our Lives*. HarperCollins/ HarperEdge, 1997.

Deutsch, David. *The Fabric of Reality: The Science of Parallel Universes—and Its Implications*. New York: Penguin Books, 1997.

Dever, William G. *What Did the Biblical Writers Know and When did They Know it?: What Archaeology Can Tell Us about the Reality of Ancient Israel*. Grand Rapids, Mi: Eerdmans, 2001.

Diamond, Jared. *The Third Chimpanzee: The Evolution and Future of the Human Animal*. HarperCollins, 1992 [HarperPerennial, 1993].

Diamond, Jared. *Why is Sex Fun?: The Evolution of Human Sexuality*. HarperCollins/ Basic Books, 1997.

Diamond, Jared. *Guns, Germs, and Steel: The Fates of Human Societies*. Norton, 1999 [1997].

Dixon, Dougal; Ian Jenkins; Richard Moody and Andrey Zhuravlev. *Cassell's Atlas of Evolution*. London: Cassell/ Andromeda Oxford, 2001.

Dolan, Jay P. *In Search of an American Catholicism: A History of Religion and Culture in Tension*. Oxford U.Press, 2002.

Donald, Merlin. *Origins of the Modern Mind: Three Stages in the Evolution of Culture and Cognition*. Harvard, 1991.

Donald, Merlin. *A Mind So Rare: The Evolution of Human Consciousness*. Norton, 2001.

Douglas, Lloyd C. *The Robe*. Boston: Houghton Mifflin Co., 1942, 1986.

Drury, Stephen. *Stepping Stones: The Making of Our Home World*. Oxford U.Press, 1999.

Dunbar, Robin; Chris Knight and Camilla Power (eds.) *The Evolution of Culture: An Interdisciplinary View*. Rutgers U.Press, 1999.

Duve, Christian de. *Vital Dust: Life as a Cosmic Imperative*. Perseus /Basic, 1995.

Duve, Christian de. *Life Evolving: Molecules, Mind, and Meaning.* Oxford U.Press, 2002.

Dyson, Freeman. *Origins of Life.* Cambridge U.Press, 1999.

Dzielska, Maria. *Hypatia of Alexandria.* F. Lyra, trans. Harvard U.Press, 1995.

Eerdmans' Handbook to The World's Religions. Grand Rapids, MI: 1994.

Edelman, Gerald M., and Giulio Tononi. *A Universe of Consciousness: How Matter Becomes Imagination.* Perseus /Basic, 2000.

Edis, Taner. *The Ghost in the Universe: God in Light of Modern Science.* Prometheus, 2002.

Ehrenreich, Barbara. *Blood Rites: Origins and History of the Passions of War.* New York: Henry Holt/ Metropolitan Books, 1997.

Eigen, Manfred, with Ruthild Winkler-Oswatitsch. *Steps Toward Life: A Perspective on Evolution.* Paul Woolley, trans. Oxford U.Press, 1992.

Einstein, Albert. *The Meaning of Relativity.* Princeton U. Press, 1950.

Einstein, Albert. *Relativity: The Special and the General Theory, A Popular Exposition by Albert Einstein.* Robert W. Lawson, trans. New York: Bonanza Books, 1961.

Einstein, Albert, and Leopold Infeld. *The Evolution of Physics from Early Concepts to Relativity and Quanta.* Simon&Schuster/ Touchstone Book, 1938 & 1966.

Ellis, Joseph J. *American Sphinx: The Character of Thomas Jefferson.* Alfred A. Knopf, 1997.

Ehrlich, Paul R. *Human Natures: Genes, Cultures, and Human Prospect.* Washington, D.C.: Island Press, 2000.

Emsley, John. *Nature's Building Blocks: An A-Z Guide to the Elements.* Oxford U.Press, 2001.

Fauconnier, Gilles. *Mappings in Thought and Language.* Cambridge U.Press, 1997.

Feinberg, Todd E. *Altered Egos: How the Brain Creates the Self.* Oxford U.Press, 2001.

Ferris, Timothy. *The Whole Shebang: A State-of-the-Universe(s) Report.* Simon&Schuster/ Touchstone Book, 1998.

Feynman, Richard P. *The Meaning of It All: Thoughts of a Citizen Scientist.* Perseus/ Helix, 1998.

Finkelstein, Israel, and Neil Asher Silberman. *The Bible Unearthed: Archaeology's New Vision of Ancient Israel and the Origin of Its Sacred Texts.* Simon&Schuster/ Free Press, 2001.

FitzGerald, Edward, trans. *The Rubáiyát of Omar Khayyám.* Mount Vernon: The Peter Pauper Press, >1859, 4th ed.

Fletcher, Richard. *The Barbarian Conversion: From Paganism to Christianity.* Henry Holt, 1997.

Foltz, Richard C. *Religions of the Silk Road: Overland Trade and Cultural Exchange from Antiquity to the Fifteenth Century.* St.Martin's Press, 1999.

Fortey, Richard. *Life: A Natural History of the First Four Billion Years of Life on Earth.* Alfred A. Knopf, 1997.

Fox, Robin Lane. *Pagans and Christians.* San Francisco: Harper, 1986.

Frankl, Viktor E. *Man's Search for Ultimate Meaning.* New York: Plenum Press/ Insight Books, 1997.

Franz, Marie-Louise von. *Alchemy: An Introduction to the Symbolism and the Psychology.* Toronto: Inner City Books, 1980a [1959].

Franz, Marie-Louise von. *Projection and Re-Collection in Jungian Psychology.* Wm. H. Kennedy, trans. La Salle, Ill.: Open Court, 1980b [1978].

Frattaroli, Elio. *Healing the Soul in the Age of the Brain: Becoming Conscious in an Unconscious World.* Viking, 2001.

Freeman, Walter J. *How Brains Make Up Their Minds.* Columbia, 2000.

Frend, W.H.C. *The Rise of Christianity.* Philadelphia: Fortress Press, 1984.

Friedman, Norman. *The Hidden Domain: Home of the Quantum Wave Function, Nature's Creative Source.* Eugene, OR: Woodbridge Group, 1997.

Fry, Iris. *The Emergence of Life on Earth: A Historical and Scientific Overview.* Rutgers U.Press, 2000 [Originally in Hebrew as *The Origin of Life—Mystery or Scientific Problem?* Israel: Broadcast U. Library of the Ministry of Defense Press, 1997].

Gardner, Martin. *The Relativity Explosion.* Random House/ Vintage Books, 1976.

Gazzaniga, Michael S. *The Mind's Past.* U.of California Press, 1998.

Gee, Henry. *In Search of Deep Time: Beyond the Fossil Record to a New History of Life.* Simon&Schuster/ Free Press, 1999.

Geiser, Kenneth. *Materials Matter: Toward a Sustainable Materials Policy.* MIT Press, 2001.

Gell-Mann, Murray. *The Quark and the Jaguar: Adventures in the Simple and the Complex.* New York: W.H.Freeman & Co., 1994.

Genz, Henning. *Nothingness: The Science of Empty Space.* Karin Heusch, trans. Perseus/Helix Books, 1994, 1999.

Gies, Frances & Joseph. *Cathedral, Forge, and Waterwheel: Technology and Invention in the Middle Ages.* Harper Perennial, 1995 [1994].

Giovannoli, Joseph. *The Biology of Belief: How Our Biology Biases Our Beliefs and Perceptions.* Rosetta Press, 1999.

Glynn, Ian. *An Anatomy of Thought: The Origin and Machinery of the Mind.* Oxford U.Press, 1999.

Godwin, Malcolm. *The Lucid Dreamer: A Waking Guide for the Traveler Between Worlds.* Simon&Schuster, 1994.

Gold, Thomas. *The Deep Hot Biosphere.* Copernicus/ Springer-Verlag, 1999.

Goldberg, Elkhonon. *The Executive Brain: Frontal Lobes and the Civilized Mind.* Oxford U.Press, 2001.

Goldsmith, Donald. *Einstein's Greatest Blunder?: The Cosmological Constant and Other Fudge Factors in the Physics of the Universe.* Harvard U.Press, 1995.

Goodenough, Ursula. *The Sacred Depths of Nature.* Oxford U.Press, 1998.

Goodwin, Brian. *How the Leopard Changed Its Spots: The Evolution of Complexity.* Charles Scribner's Sons, 1994.

Goonatilake, Susantha. *Merged Evolution: Long-Term Implications of Biotechnology and Information Technology.* Amsterdam: Gordon and Breach, 1999.

Gould, Stephen Jay. *Ever Since Darwin: Reflections in Natural History.* Norton, 1977a [1973–7].

Gould, Stephen Jay. *Ontogeny and Phylogeny.* Harvard U.Press/ Belknap Press, 1977b.

Gould, Stephen Jay. *The Panda's Thumb: More Reflections in Natural History.* Norton, 1980.

Gould, Stephen Jay. *Full House: The Spread of Excellence from Plato to Darwin.* Harmony Books, 1996.

Gould, Stephen Jay, *Questioning the Millennium: A Rationalist's Guide to a Precisely Arbitrary Countdown.* Harmony Books /Crown, 1997.

Gould, Stephen Jay, *The Hedgehog, the Fox, and the Magister's Pox.* Random House/ Harmony 2003.

Granfield, Linda. *Amazing Grace: The Story of the Hymn.* Toronto: Tundra Books, 1997.

Greene, Brian. *The Elegant Universe.* Norton, 1999.

Greenfield, Susan. *The Private Life of the Brain: Emotions, Consciousness, and the Secret of the Self.* John Wiley, 2000.

Gribbin, John. *Schrödinger's Kittens and the Search for Reality: Solving the Quantum Mysteries.* Little, Brown/ Back Bay Books, 1995.

Griffin, Donald R. *Animal Minds: Beyond Cognition to Consciousness.* U.of Chicago Press, 1992, 2001.

Hamilton, Edith. *The Echo of Greece.* Norton, 1957.

Harris, Paul L. *The Work of the Imagination.* Malden, Ma: Blackwell, 2000.

Hartmann, Ernest. *Dreams and Nightmares: The New Theory on the Origin and Meaning of Dreams.* New York: Plenum, 1998.

Harwit, Martin. *Astrophysical Concepts.* Springer-Verlag, 1998.

Hauser, Marc D. *Wild Minds: What Animals Really Think.* Henry Holt, 2000.

Hawking, Stephen W. *A Brief History of Time: From the Big Bang to Black Holes.* Bantam Books, 1988.

Hawking, Stephen. *The Illustrated A Brief History of Time.* Bantam Books, 1996.

Hawkins, Michael. *Hunting Down the Universe: The Missing Mass, Primordial Black Holes, and Other Dark Matters.* Addison-Wesley: Helix Books, 1997.

Hawting, G.R. *The Idea of Idolatry and the Emergence of Islam: From Polemic to History.* Cambridge U.Press, 1999.

Hayles, N. Katherine. *How We Became Posthuman: Virtual Bodies in Cybernetics, Literature, and Informatics.* U.of Chicago Press, 1999.

Henig, Robin Marantz. *The Monk in the Garden: The Lost and Found Genius of Gregor Mendel, the Father of Genetics.* Houghton Mifflin, 2000.

Hirsch, Martin C. *Dictionary of Human Neuroanatomy.* Springer-Verlag, 2000.

Hobson, J. Allan. *The Dream Drugstore: Chemically Altered States of Consciousness.* MIT Press/ Bradford, 2001.

Hobson, J. Allan, and Jonathan A. Leonard. *Out of Its Mind: Psychiatry in Crisis, A Call for Reform.* Perseus, 2001.

Hobson, Peter. *The Cradle of Thought.* Macmillan, 2002.

Hoeller, Stephan A. *Jung and the Lost Gospels, Insights into The Dead Sea Scrolls and the Nag Hammadi Library.* Wheaton, IL: Quest, 1994.

Hoffmann, Banesh. *Relativity and its Roots.* New York: Scientific American Books, 1983.

Hogan, Craig J. *The Little Book of the Big Bang: A Cosmic Primer.* Copernicus, 1998.

Holland, John H. *Hidden Order: How Adaptation Builds Complexity.* Perseus/ Helix, 1995.

Holland, John H. *Emergence: From Chaos to Order.* Allison-Wesley/ Helix Books, 1998.

Horgan, John. *The Undiscovered Mind: How the Human Brain Defies Replication, Medication, and Explanation.* Simon&Schuster/ Free Press, 1999.

Horgan, John. *Rational Mysticism: Dispatches from the Border Between Science and Spirituality.* Houghton Mifflin, 2003.

Hornblower, Simon, and Antony Spawforth, eds. *The Oxford Companion to Classical Civilization.* Oxford U.Press, 1998.

Horrobin, David. *The Madness of Adam and Eve: How Schizophrenia Shaped Humanity.* London: Bantam Press/Random House, 2001.

Howland, John L. *The Surprising Archaea: Discovering Another Domain of Life.* Oxford U.Press, 2000.

Hrdy, Sarah Blaffer. *Mother Nature: A History of Mothers, Infants, and Natural Selection.* Pantheon, 1999.

Hurford, James R.; Michael Studdert-Kennedy and Chris Knight (eds.) *Approaches to the Evolution of Language: Social and Cognitive Bases.* Cambridge U.Press, 1998.

Huxley, Aldous. *The Doors of Perception* and *Heaven and Hell*. Harper & Row/ Perennial Library, 1954–6 & 1990.

Ibry, David. *Exodus to Humanism: Jewish Identity Without Religion*. Prometheus, 1999.

Israel, Jonathan I. *Radical Enlightenment: Philosophy and the Making of Modernity 1650–1750*. Oxford U.Press, 2001.

Jablonski, Nina G., and Leslie C. Aiello. *The Origin and Diversification of Language*. San Francisco: U.of California Press, 1998.

Jaynes, Julian. *The Origin of Consciousness in the Breakdown of the Bicameral Mind*. Houghton Mifflin, 1976 & 1990.

Johanson, Donald C., and Maitland A. Edey. *Lucy: The Beginnings of Humankind*. Simon&Schuster, 1981.

Johanson, Donald, and James Shreeve. *Lucy's Child: The Discovery of a Human Ancestor*. New York: Wm. Morrow &Co, 1989.

Johnson, Steven. *Emergence: The Connected Lives of Ants, Brains, Cities, and Software*. Scribner, 2001.

Johnston, Victor S. *Why We Feel: The Science of Human Emotions*. Helix/ Perseus, 1999.

Jourdain, Robert. *Music, the Brain, and Ecstasy: How Music Captures Our Imagination*. New York: Avon/ Hearst, 1997.

Jung, C. G. *Memories, Dreams, Reflections*. Aniela Jaffé, ed., Richard & Clara Winston, trans. Random House/ Vintage, 1965 [1961].

Jung, C. G. *The Basic Writings of C.G. Jung*. Violet de Laszlo, ed., R.F.C. Hull, trans. Princeton U.Press/ Bollingen, 1990 [1953–71].

Juslin, Patrik N., and John A. Sloboda, eds. *Music and Emotion: Theory and Research*. Oxford U.Press, 2001.

Kaku, Michio. *Visions: How Science Will Revolutionize the 21st Century*. Doubleday/ Anchor Books, 1997.

Kauffman, Stuart. *At Home in the Universe: The Search for Laws of Self-Organization and Complexity*. Oxford U.Press, 1995.

Kayzer, Wim. *'A Glorious Accident': Understanding Our Place in the Cosmic Puzzle*. Freeman, 1997.

Keane, John. *Tom Paine: A Political Life*. Little, Brown & Co. 1995.

Kellert, Stephen R. *Kinship to Mastery: Biophilia in Human Evolution and Development*. Washington DC: Island Press/ Shearwater, 1997.

Kellert, Stephen R., and Timothy J. Farnham. *The Good in Nature and Humanity: Connecting Science, Religion, and Spirituality with the Natural World*. Washington DC: Island Press, 2002.

Kellert, Stephen R., and Edward O. Wilson, eds. *The Biophilia Hypothesis*. Inland Press/ Shearwater, 1993.

Keys, David. *Catastrophe: An Investigation into the Origins of the Modern World*. New York: Ballantine Books, 1999.

Kirshner, Robert P. *Cosmic Questions: Astronomy from Quark to Quasar.* The Teaching Company, 1996. (audio cassette)

Kirshner, Robert P. *The Extravagant Universe: Exploding Stars, Dark Energy and the Accelerating Cosmos.* Princeton U.Press, 2002.

Klein, Richard G. *The Human Career: Human Biological and Cultural Origins.* U.of Chicago Press, 1989, 1999.

Klein, Richard G., with Blake Edgar. *The Dawn of Human Culture.* John Wiley & Sons, 2002.

Knight, Chris. *Blood Relations: Menstruation and the Origins of Culture.* Yale U.Press, 1991.

Kogel, Renee, and Zev Katz, eds. *Judaism in a Secular Age: An Anthology of Secular Humanistic Jewish Thought.* Farmington Hills, Mi: International Institute for Secular Humanistic Judaism, 1995.

Kohn, Marek. *As We Know It: Coming to Terms with an Evolved Mind.* London: Granta Books, 1999.

Kors, Alan Charles. *The Origin of the Modern Mind.* Springfield VA: The Teaching Company, 1996. (audio cassette and printed outline)

Kriwaczek, Paul. *In Search of Zarathustra: The First Prophet and the Ideas That Changed the World.* Knopf, 2003.

Kuhn, Thomas S. *The Copernican Revolution.* New York: MJF Books, 1957 (1985).

Kuhn, Thomas S. *The Road Since Structure: Philosophical Essays, 1970 — 1993, with an Autobiographical Interview.* James Conant and John Haugeland, eds. U.of Chicago Press, 2000.

Küng, Hans. *The Catholic Church: A Short History.* John Bowden, trans. Random House/Modern Library, 2001.

Kuper, Adam. *The Chosen Primate: Human Nature and Cultural Diversity.* Harvard U.Press, 1994.

Kurtz, Paul, ed. *Science and Religion: Are They Compatible?* Prometheus, 2003.

Kushner, Harold S. *To Life!: A Celebration of Jewish Being and Thinking.* New York: Time Warner/ Warner Books, 1993.

La Cerra, Peggy, and Roger Bingham. *The Origin of Minds: Evolution, Uniqueness, and the New Science of the Self.* Harmony Books, 2002.

Lakoff, George, and Mark Johnson. *Philosophy in the Flesh: The Embodied Mind and Its Challenge to Western Thought.* Perseus /Basic, 1999.

Lakoff, George, and Rafael E. Núñez. *Where Mathematics Comes From: How the Embodied Mind Brings Mathematics into Being.* Perseus / Basic, 2000.

Lamont, Corliss. *Freedom is as Freedom Does: Civil Liberties in America.* New York: Continuum, 1990 [1956–90].

Lamont, Corliss. *The Philosophy of Humanism*. Amherst NY: Humanist Press, 1997 [1949–92]

Lane, Nick. *Oxygen: The Molecule that Made the World*. Oxford U.Press, 2002.

Leakey, Richard, and Roger Lewin. *The Sixth Extinction: Patterns of Life and the Future of Humankind*. Doubleday, 1995.

LeDoux, Joseph. *The Emotional Brain: The Mysterious Underpinnings of Emotional Life*. Simon&Schuster, 1996.

LeDoux, Joseph. *Synaptic Self, How Our Brains Become Who We Are*. Viking/Penguin, 2002.

Lewin, Roger. *Complexity: Life on the Edge of Chaos*. U.of Chicago Press, 1992 & 1999.

Lewis-Williams, David. *The Mind in the Cave: Consciousness and the Origins of Art*. London: Thames & Hudson, 2002.

Lewontin, Richard. *The Triple Helix: Gene, Organism, and Environment*. Harvard U.Press, 2000.

Lieberman, Philip. *Uniquely Human: The Evolution of Speech, Thought, and Selfless Behavior*. Harvard U.Press, 1991.

Lieberman, Philip. *Eve Spoke: Human Language and Human Evolution*. Norton, 1998.

Lieberman, Philip. *Human Language and Our Reptilian Brain*. Harvard U.Press 2000.

Lindley, David. *Where Does the Weirdness Go?: Why Quantum Mechanics is Strange, but not as Strange as you Think*. HarperCollins/ BasicBooks, 1996.

Llinás, Rodolfo R. *I of the Vortex: From Neurons to Self*. MIT Press/ Bradford, 2001

Loewenstein, Werner R. *The Touchstone of Life: Molecular Information, Cell Communication, and the Foundations of Life*. Oxford U.Press, 1999.

Lowen, Alexander. *The Language of the Body*. Collier/Macmillan, 1971. (Originally published as *Physical Dynamics of Character Structure*. Grune & Stratton, 1958.)

Lunine, Jonathan I. *Earth: Evolution of a Habitable World*. Cambridge U. Press, 1999.

MacDonald, Dennis R. *The Homeric Epics and the Gospel of Mark*. Yale U.Press, 2000.

Mack, Burton L. *The Lost Gospel: The Book of Q & Christian Origins*. San Francisco: Harper, 1993.

MacMullen, Ramsay. *Christianizing the Roman Empire*, A.D. *100–400*. Yale U.Press, 1984.

Macphail, Euan M. *The Evolution of Consciousness*. Oxford U.Press, 1998.

Maddox, John. *What Remains To Be Discovered: Mapping the Secrets of the Universe, the Origins of Life, and the Future of the Human Race.* Simon& Schuster/ Free Press/ Martin Kessler Books, 1998.

Maharishi Mahesh Yogi. *Science of Being and Art of Living: Transcendental Meditation.*® Penguin/ Meridian, 1995.

Margulis, Lynn. *Symbiotic Planet: A New Look at Evolution.* Perseus /Basic, 1998.

Margulis, Lynn, and Dorion Sagan. *Microcosmos: Four Billion Years of Evolution from Our Microbial Ancestors.* U.of California Press, 1986 &1997.

Margulis, Lynn, and Dorion Sagan. *Acquiring Genomes: A Theory of the Origins of Species.* Perseus /Basic, 2002.

Margulis, Lynn, and Karlene V. Schwartz. *Five Kingdoms: An Illustrated Guide to the Phyla of Life on Earth.* New York: W.H. Freeman &Co. 3rd ed. 1998.

Maslow, Abraham H. *Religions, Values, and Peak-Experiences.* Penguin/ Arkana, 1994 [1964].

Maslow, Abraham H. *Farther Reaches of Human Nature.* Penguin/ Arkana, 1993 [Viking, 1971].

Matre, Steve Van, and Bill Weiler, eds. *The Earth Speaks: An Acclimatization Journal.* Warrenville IL: Institute for Earth Education, 1990 [1983].

Matthiessen, Peter. *The Snow Leopard.* Penguin, 1996 [Viking 1978].

Maturana, Humberto R., and Francisco J. Valera. *The Tree of Knowledge: The Biological Roots of Human Understanding.* Robert Paolucci, trans. Boston: Shambhala, 1998 (1987).

Maynard Smith, John, and Eörs Szathmáry. *The Origins of Life: From the Birth of Life to the Origin of Language.* Oxford U.Press, 1999.

Mayr, Ernst. *This is Biology: The Science of the Living World.* Harvard U.Press: Belknap, 1997.

McCrone, John. *Going Inside: A Tour Round a Single Moment of Consciousness.* (UK: Faber&Faber, 1999) New York: Fromm International, 2001.

McFadden, Johnjoe. *Quantum Evolution.* Norton, 2000.

McLuhan, Marshall. *Understanding Media: The Extension of Man.* McGraw-Hill, 1964 & 1965.

McLuhan. *Essential McLuhan.* Eric McLuhan and Frank Zingrone, eds. Perseus /Basic, 1995.

McLuhan. *Forward Through the Rearview Mirror: Reflections On and By Marshall McLuhan.* Paul Benedetti and Nancy DeHart, eds. Prentice-Hall Canada, 1997.

McNamara, Kenneth J. *Shapes of Time: The Evolution of Growth and Development.* Johns Hopkins U.Press, 1997.

McNeill, William H. *Plagues and Peoples*. Doubleday, 1976 (updated edition: Peter Smith Pub. 1992).

McSween, Harry Y., Jr. *Fanfare for Earth: The Origin of Our Planet and Life*. New York: St. Martin's Press, 1997.

McWhorter, John H. *The Power of Babel: A Natural History of Language*. Henry Holt/ Freeman, 2001.

Miller, Geoffrey F. *The Mating Mind: How Sexual Choice Shaped the Evolution of Human Nature*. Doubleday, 2000.

Mindell, Arnold. *Quantum Mind: The Edge Between Physics and Psychology*. Portland, OR: Lao Tse Press, 2000.

Mitchell, Stephen. *Genesis: A New Translation of the Classic Biblical Stories*. HarperCollins, 1996.

Mithen, Steven. *The Prehistory of the Mind: The Cognitive Origin of Art, Religion and Science*. London: Thames and Hudson, 1996.

Morgan, Elaine. *The Scars of Evolution: What Our Bodies Tell Us About Human Origins*. Oxford U.Press, 1990.

Morgan, Elaine. *The Aquatic Ape Hypothesis*. London: Souvenir Press, 1997.

Morowitz, Harold J. *The Emergence of Everything: How the World Became Complex*. Oxford U.Press, 2002.

Morris, Charles R. *American Catholic: The Saints and Sinners Who Built America's Most Powerful Church*. Random House/ Vintage, 1997.

Nabhan, Gary Paul, and Stephen Trimble. *The Geography of Childhood: Why Children Need Wild Places*. Boston: Beacon Press, 1994.

Narlikar, Jayant V. *The Lighter Side of Gravity*. San Francisco: W.H.Freeman & Co., 1982.

Nevo, Yehuda D., and Judith Koren. *Crossroads to Islam: The Origins of the Arab Religion and the Arab State*. Prometheus, 2003.

Newberg, Andrew; Eugene d'Aquili and Vince Rause. *Why God Won't Go Away: Brain Science and the Biology of Belief*. Ballantine, 2001.

Nichols, Johanna. *Linguistic Diversity in Space and Time*. U.of Chicago Press, 1992.

Noble, William, and Iain Davidson. *Human Evolution, Language and Mind: A Psychological and Archaeological Inquiry*. Cambridge U.Press, 1996.

Noll, Richard. *The Jung Cult: Origins of a Charismatic Movement*. Princeton U.Press, 1994.

Nolte, John, and Jay B. Angevine, Jr. *The Human Brain in Photographs and Diagrams*. St. Louis: Mosby, 2000.

Norman, Donald A. *The Invisible Computer: Why Good Products Can Fail, the Personal Computer is So Complex, and Information Applications Are the Solution*. MIT Press, 1998.

Nugent, S. Georgia. *Heroes, Heroines and the Wisdom of Myth.* Springfield, VA: The Teaching Company, 1994. (audio cassette)

Ofek, Haim. *Second Nature: Economic Origins of Human Evolution.* Cambridge U.Press, 2001.

Olson, Sigurd F. *Listening Point.* Alfred A. Knopf, 1989.

Omnès, Roland. *Quantum Philosophy: Understanding and Interpreting Contemporary Science.* Trans. Arturo Sangalli. Princeton U.Press, (1994) 1999a.

Omnès, Roland. *Understanding Quantum Mechanics.* Princeton U.Press, 1999b.

Oubré, Alondra Yvette. *Instinct and Revelation: Reflections on the Origins of Numinous Perception.* Amsterdam: Gordon and Breach, 1997.

Pagels, Elaine. *The Gnostic Gospels.* New York: Vintage, 1989.

Pais, Abraham. *'Subtle is the Lord ...': The Science and the Life of Albert Einstein.* Oxford U.Press, 1982.

Parker, Sue Taylor, and Michael L. McKinney. *Origins of Intelligence: The Evolution of Cognitive Development in Monkeys, Apes, and Humans.* Johns Hopkins U.Press, 1999.

Passingham, Richard. *The Frontal Lobes and Voluntary Action.* Oxford U.Press, 1993/7.

Peacocke, Arthur. *Paths from Science toward God: The End of All Our Exploring.* Oxford UK: Oneworld, 2001.

Penrose, Roger. *Shadows of the Mind: A Search for the Missing Science of Consciousness.* Oxford U.Press, 1994.

Penrose, Roger, et al. *The Large, the Small and the Human Mind.* Cambridge U.Press, 1997.

Perkins, David. *Archimedes' Bathtub: The Art and Logic of Breakthrough Thinking.* Norton, 2000.

Perls, Frederick; Ralph E. Hefferline and Paul Goodman. *Gestalt Therapy: Excitement and Growth in the Human Personality.* Dell/ Delta, 1951.

Pert, Candace B. *Molecules of Emotion: Why You Feel the Way You Feel.* Scribner, 1997.

Pfenninger, Karl H., and Valerie R. Shubik, eds. *The Origins of Creativity.* Oxford U.Press, 2001.

Pico, Richard M. *Consciousness in Four Dimensions: Biological Relativity and the Origins of Thought.* McGraw-Hill, 2002.

Pirsig, Robert M. *Zen and the Art of Motorcycle Maintenance: An Inquiry into Values.* Morrow/ Quill, 1974 & 1999.

Poag, C. Wylie. *Chesapeake Invader: Discovering America's Giant Meteorite Crater.* Princeton U.Press, 1999.

Pockett, Susan. *The Nature of Consciousness: A Hypothesis.* Lincoln NE: iUniverse/ Writers Club Press, 2000.

Porter, Eliot. *"In Wildness Is the Preservation of the World."* Ballantine, 1974 [1962].

Porter, J.R. *The Lost Bible: Forgotten Scriptures Revealed.* U.of Chicago Press, 2001.

Potts, Rick. *Humanity's Descent: The Consequences of Ecological Instability.* Morrow, 1996.

Prigogine, Ilya. *The End of Certainty: Time, Chaos, and the New Laws of Nature.* Simon&Schuster/ The Free Press, 1996.

Pyne, Stephen J. *Fire: A Brief History.* U.of Washington Press, 2001.

Quartz, Steven R., and Terrence J. Sejnowski. *Liars, Lovers, and Heroes: What the New Brain Science Reveals About How We Become Who We Are.* HarperCollins/ William Morrow, 2002.

Radin, Dean I. *The Conscious Universe: The Scientific Truth of Psychic Phenomena.* HarperCollins, 1997.

Ramachandran, V.S., and Sandra Blakeslee. *Phantoms in the Brain: Probing the Mysteries of the Human Mind.* New York: Wm. Morrow, 1998.

Rees, Martin. *Before the Beginning: Our Universe and Others.* Perseus/ Helix, 1997.

Rees, Martin. *Just Six Numbers: The Deep Forces That Shape the Universe.* Perseus /Basic, 2000. (London: Weidenfeld&Nicolson, 1999)

Regan, Ciaran. *Intoxicating Minds.* London: Weidenfeld&Nicolson, 2000.

Rensberger, Boyce. *Life Itself: Exploring the Realm of the Living Cell.* Oxford U.Press, 1996.

Restak, Richard. *The Secret Life of the Brain.* The Dana Press and Joseph Henry Press, 2001.

Reston, James, Jr. *Galileo, A Life.* HarperCollins, 1994.

Richard, Carl J. *The Founders and the Classics: Greece, Rome, and the American Enlightenment.* Harvard U.Press, 1994.

Ridley, Matt. *The Origins of Virtue: Human Instincts and the Evolution of Cooperation.* Viking, 1997.

Ridley, Matt. *Genome: The Autobiography of a Species in 23 Chapters.* HarperCollins, 1999.

Roberts, J. M. *A History of Europe.* Penguin/ Allen Lane, 1997.

Rogers, Carl R. *On Becoming a Person: A Therapist's View of Psychotherapy.* Houghton Mifflin, 1961.

Rogers, Carl R. *Carl Rogers on Encounter Groups.* Harper & Row, 1970.

Rolston III, Holmes, ed. *Biology, Ethics, and the Origins of Life.* Boston: Jones and Bartlett Publishers, 1995.

Rose, Steven. *Lifelines: Biology Beyond Determinism.* Oxford U.Press, 1998.

Rowland, Wade. *Galileo's Mistake: A New Look at the Epic Confrontation between Galileo and the Church.* New York: Arcade, 2001.

Rowlands, Mark. *The Nature of Consciousness.* Cambridge U.Press, 2001.

Rucker, Rudolf v.B. *Geometry, Relativity and the Fourth Dimension.* New York: Dover Publications, 1977.

Ruse, Michael. *Can a Darwinian be a Christian? The Relationship between Science and Religion.* Cambridge U.Press, 2001.

Ryan, William, and Walter Pitman. *Noah's Flood: The New Scientific Discoveries About the Events That Changed History.* Simon&Schuster, 1998.

Sagan, Carl. *Cosmos.* Random House, 1980.

Sagan, Carl. *Pale Blue Dot: A Vision of the Human Future in Space.* Random House, 1994.

Sartori, Leo. *Understanding Relativity: A Simplified Approach to Einstein's Theories.* U.of California Press, 1996.

Schacter, Daniel L. *The Seven Sins of Memory: How the Mind Forgets and Remembers.* Houghton Mifflin, 2001.

Schlagel, Richard H. *The Vanquished Gods: Science, Religion, and the Nature of Belief.* Amherst NY: Prometheus, 2001.

Schonfield, Hugh. *The Passover Plot.* Rockport: Element, 1965.

Schonfield, Hugh J. *The Jesus Party.* Macmillan, 1974.

Schopf, J. William. *Cradle of Life: The Discovery of Earth's Earliest Fossils.* Princeton U.Press, 1999.

Schwartz, Jeffrey H. *Sudden Origins: Fossils, Genes, and the Emergence of Species.* John Wiley &Sons, 1999.

Schwartz, Jeffrey M., and Sharon Begley. *The Mind and the Brain: Neuroplasticity and the Power of Mental Force.* HarperCollins/ Regan Books, 2002.

Seife, Charles. *Zero: The Biography of a Dangerous Idea.* Penguin Putnam/ Viking, 2000.

Sellers, David. *The Transit of Venus: The Quest to Find the True Distance of the Sun.* Leeds UK: MagaVelda, 2001.

Sheldrake, Rupert. *A New Science of Life: The Hypothesis of Formative Causation.* Los Angeles: Houghton Mifflin/ Tarcher, 1981.

Sheldrake, Rupert. *The Presence of the Past: Morphic Resonance & the Habits of Nature.* Rochester Vt: Park Street Press, 1988, 1995a.

Sheldrake, Rupert. *Seven Experiments That Could Change the World: A Do-It-Yourself Guide to Revolutionary Science.* New York: Berkley/Riverhead Books, 1995b.

Sheldrake, Rupert. *Dogs that Know When their Owners are Coming Home: and Other Unexplained Powers of Animals.* New York: Three Rivers Press, 1999.

Sheldrake, Rupert. *The Sense of Being Stared At and Other Aspects of The Extended Mind.* New York: Crown, 2003.

Shermer, Michael. *How We Believe: The Search for God in an Age of Science.* W.H. Freeman, 1999.

Shlain, Leonard. *Art & Physics: Parallel Visions in Space, Time, and Light.* New York: Morrow, 1991.

Shlain, Leonard. *The Alphabet versus the Goddess: The Conflict Between Word and Image.* Viking, 1998.

Shorto, Russell. *Gospel Truth: The New Image of Jesus Emerging from Science and History, and Why It Matters.* New York: Riverhead Books, 1997.

Shreeve, James. *The Neandertal Enigma: Solving the Mystery of Modern Human Origins.* New York: Hearst/ Avon, 1995.

Singer, Peter. *Writings on an Ethical Life.* HarperCollins/ Ecco, 2000.

Spong, John Shelby. *Why Christianity Must Change or Die: A Bishop Speaks to Believers in Exile.* HarperCollins/ HarperSanFrancisco, 1998.

Spudis, Paul D. *The Once and Future Moon.* Smithsonian Institution Press, 1996.

Sober, Elliott, and David Sloan Wilson. *Unto Others: The Evolution and Psychology of Unselfish Behavior.* Harvard U.Press, 1998.

Solé, Ricard, and Brian Goodwin. *Signs of Life: How Complexity Pervades Biology.* Perseus /Basic, 2000.

Soto, Hernando de. *The Mystery of Capital: Why Capitalism Triumphs in the West and Fails Everywhere Else.* Perseus /Basic, 2000.

Staikos, Konstantinos Sp. *The Great Libraries: From Antiquity to the Renaissance (3000 B.C. to A.D. 1600).* Timothy Cullen, trans. New Castle, Del.: Oak Knoll Books, 2000 (in Greek 1996).

Stanley, Steven M. *Children of the Ice Age: How a Global Catastrophe Allowed Humans to Evolve.* New York: Harmony Books, 1996.

Steel, Duncan. *Marking Time: The Epic Quest to Invent the Perfect Calendar.* John Wiley, 2000.

Steele, Edward J.; Robyn A. Lindley and Robert V. Blanden. *Lamarck's Signature: How Retrogenes Are Changing Darwin's Natural Selection Paradigm.* Perseus, 1998.

Stenger, Victor J. *The Unconscious Quantum: Metaphysics in Modern Physics and Cosmology.* Amherst, NY: Prometheus, 1995.

Steriade, Mircea. *The Intact and Sliced Brain.* MIT Press/ Bradford, 2001.

Stevens, Anthony. *Archetypes: A Natural History of the Self.* New York: Quill, 1983.

Stevens, Anthony, and John Price. *Prophets, Cults and Madness.* London: Duckworth, 2000.

Stewart, Ian, and Jack Cohen. *Figments of Reality: The Evolution of the Curious Mind.* Cambridge U.Press, 1997.

Stock, Gregory. *Metaman: The Merging of Humans and Machines in a Global Superorganism.* Simon&Schuster, 1993.

Stock, Gregory. *Redesigning Humans: Our Inevitable Genetic Future.* Houghton Mifflin, 2002.

Stringer, Christopher, and Robin McKie. *African Exodus: The Origin of Modern Humanity.* Henry Holt/ John Macrae, 1996.

Swisher III, Carl C.; Garniss H. Curtis and Roger Lewin. *Java Man: How Two Geologists' Dramatic Discoveries Changed Our Understanding of the Evolutionary Path to Modern Humans.* Scribner, 2000.

Sykes, Bryan. *The Seven Daughters of Eve.* Norton, 2001.

Tattersall, Ian. *The Last Neanderthal: The Rise, Success, and Mysterious Extinction of Our Closest Human Relatives.* Macmillan, 1995.

Taylor, John G. *The Race for Consciousness.* Bradford/MIT Press, 1999.

Taylor, Mark C. *The Moment of Complexity: Emerging Network Culture.* U.of Chicago, 2001.

Taylor, Michael Ray. *Dark Life: Martian Nanobacteria, Rock-Eating Cave Bugs, and Other Extreme Organisms of Inner Earth and Outer Space.* Scribner, 1999.

Taylor, Shelley E. *The Tending Instinct: How Nurturing Is Essential for Who We Are and How We Live.* Henry Holt/ Times Books, 2002.

Tennyson, Alfred. *The Complete Works of* .... New York: Hurst & Co., <1886.

Thomas, Hugh. *The Slave Trade: The Story of the Atlantic Slave Trade: 1440–1870.* Simon&Schuster, 1997.

Thorne, Kip S. *Black Holes and Time Warps: Einstein's Outrageous Legacy.* Norton, 1994.

Turkle, Sherry. *Life on the Screen: Identity in the Age of the Internet.* Simon &Schuster, 1995.

Velmans, Max. *Understanding Consciousness.* Routledge/ Taylor & Francis, 2000.

Virgil. *The Aeneid.* Robert Fitzgerald, trans. Random House, 1983. (audio cassette: HighBridge Company, 1995)

Viroli, Maurizio. *Niccolo's Smile: A Biography of Machiavelli.* Anthony Shugaar, trans., Farrar, Straus and Giroux, 1998 & 2000.

Waal, Frans de. *Bonobo: The Forgotten Ape.* U.of California Press, 1997.

Walker, Evan Harris. *The Physics of Consciousness: Quantum Minds and the Meaning of Life.* Perseus, 2000.

Wallin, Nils L.; Björn Merker and Steven Brown, eds. *The Origins of Music.* MIT Press/ Bradford, 2001 [2000].

Walsh, Denis M. ed. *Naturalism, Evolution and Mind.* Cambridge U.Press, 2001.

Walters, Kerry S. *Rational Infidels: The American Deists.* Durango, Colorado: Longwood Academic, 1992a.

Walters, Kerry S. *The American Deists: Voices of Reason and Dissent in the Early Republic.* U.Press of Kansas, 1992b.

Walters, Kerry S. *Benjamin Franklin and His Gods.* U.of Illinois, 1999.

Ward, Peter D., and Donald Brownlee. *Rare Earth: Why Complex Life Is Uncommon in the Universe.* Copernicus/ Springer-Verlag, 2000.

Ward, Peter D., and Donald Brownlee. *The Life and Death of Planet Earth: How the New Science of Astrobiology Charts the Ultimate Fate of Our World.* Henry Holt/ Times Books, 2002.

Warraq, Ibn. *Why I Am Not a Muslim.* Amherst, NY: Prometheus, 1995.

Warraq, Ibn, ed.& trans. *The Quest for the Historical Muhammad.* Amherst, NY: Prometheus, 2000.

Warraq, Ibn, ed. *Leaving Islam: Apostates Speak Out.* Prometheus, 2003.

Watson, Lyall. *Jacobson's Organ and the Remarkable Nature of Smell.* Norton, 2000.

Weatherford, Jack. *The History of Money: From Sandstone to Cyberspace.* Random House/ Three Rivers, 1997.

Weinberg, Steven. *Dreams of a Final Theory.* New York: Pantheon Books, 1992.

Weiner, Jonathan. *The Beak of the Finch: A Story of Evolution in Our Time.* Random House/ Vintage, 1994.

West, Morris. *The Shoes of the Fisherman.* St. Martin's Press, 1991 [1963].

West, Morris. *A View from the Ridge: The Testimony of a Twentieth-Century Christian.* HarperCollins/ HarperSanFrancisco, 1996.

Wheeler, John Archibald. *A Journey into Gravity and Spacetime.* New York: Scientific American Library, 1990.

Wheeler, John Archibald, with Kenneth Ford. *Geons, Black Holes, and Quantum Foam: A Life in Physics.* Norton, 1998.

Whitfield, Philip. *From So Simple a Beginning: The Book of Evolution.* Macmillan, 1993.

Wills, Christopher, and Jeffrey Bada. *The Spark of Life: Darwin and the Primeval Soup.* Perseus, 2000.

Wilson, David Sloan. *Darwin's Cathedral: Evolution, Religion, and the Nature of Society.* U.of Chicago Press, 2002.

Wilson, Edward O. *On Human Nature.* Harvard U.Press, 1978.

Wilson, Edward O. *Biophilia.* Harvard U.Press, 1984.

Wilson, Edward O. *Naturalist.* Washington DC: Island Press/ Shearwater, 1994.

Wilson, Edward O. *Consilience: The Unity of Knowledge.* Knopf, 1998.

Wilson, Edward O. *The Future of Life.* Knopf, 2002.

Wilson, Frank R. *The Hand: How Its Use Shapes the Brain, Language, and Human Culture.* Random House/ Pantheon, 1998.

Wine, Sherwin T. *Celebration: A Ceremonial and Philosophic Guide for Humanists and Humanistic Jews.* Prometheus, 1988.

Wine, Sherwin T. *Staying Sane in a Crazy World.* Birmingham, Mi: Center for New Thinking, 1995.

Winston, Robert. *Human Instinct.* Bantam, 2002.

World Book Encyclopedia, The. Field Enterprises Education Corp. 1966.

Wright, N.T. *The Challenge of Jesus: Rediscovering Who Jesus Was and Is.* Downers Grove, IL: InterVarsity Press, 1999.

Wright, Robert. *Nonzero: The Logic of Human Destiny.* Pantheon, 2000.

Yanow, Morton Leonard. *The Nolan: Prisoner of the Inquisition.* New York: Crossroad Publishing, 1998.

Zahavi, Amotz & Avishag. *The Handicap Principle: A Missing Piece of Darwin's Puzzle.* Naama Zahavi-Ely and Melvin Patrick Ely, trans. Oxford U.Press, 1997.

Zeki, Semir. *Inner Vision: An Exploration of Art and the Brain.* Oxford U.Press, 1999.

Zirker, Jack B. *Journey to the Center of the Sun.* Princeton U.Press, 2002.

Acknowledgments

First I must acknowledge my debt to all the authors cited in the References and Bibliography who went before giving us the benefit of their research, thinking and work. On their shoulders we've stood for a better view and hopefully seen a little further (to paraphrase Newton). Yet I realize my perspective is also limited and perhaps distorted, though I know not how else I'd correct it. Hopefully in bequeathing my views to those who'll come after, you'll stand even higher, see further still, and refine and extend this perspective—or maybe use it as a window to a whole different perspective. Whatever, I hope your quest is as exhilarating as mine's been.

However in addition to these live and 'dead poets', I've sought help along my way from 'fellow travelers' who might be willing to struggle with my drafts. Early on, a brother-in-law took a look at a draft of the first five chapters and politely declined further involvement with a subtle hint that I was going off the deep end (again?). A year-or-so later a niece seemed intrigued and I sent her a draft of the first nine chapters but heard nothing back. Accordingly I resolved to put off further reviews until I'd completed a working draft of the entire book.

Having accomplished that, I again risked exposing myself to sardonic comments, giving out copies to one-and-a-half dozen friends and relatives including the above two once more, as well as to ten scholars and scientists. Not all read enough to give me feedback but to those who did I give sincere thanks for helping me see things I'd missed or was blind to. They include Sue Allum and friends, Mariette Carleton, Jerry Cavanaugh SJ, Jo Faul, Jack Fuller, Laurent Gosselin, Sid Halsor, Al Menendez, Frank Moelich, Gary Pfund and Rabbi Sherwin Wine. Sharon Shulick provided encouragement throughout. In addition Richard Burke, Charles Mabee and Michael Sevilla at nearby Oakland University provided valuable scrutiny and needed encouragement. Marcia Garland flyspecked the final draft.

I owe Kendrick Frazier thanks who unbeknownst suggested the term 'science-minded skeptics' used in the revised subtitle of this book. He used the term first in his "Are Science and Religion Conflicting or Complementary? Some Thoughts About Boundaries" reprinted from the *Skeptical Inquirer* Jul/Aug'99 in Kurtz'03: 25.

After mailing inquires and follow-ups to over a half-dozen prospective major publishers with barely a response—much less a request to see the manuscript—I confirmed what I'd read, namely that unless you're an established author or a celebrity, publishers ignore you. So I resolved to self-publish, studied a few books on it and began exploring prospective printers. The folks at Sheridan Books were not only very professional in designing and printing the book, but supportive in both the pre-publication and distribution phases.

Permissions to use the quotes herein were diligently sought for most all but the shortest quotes. Some responded that the quotes are within the 'fair use doctrine' so formal permission is not required. A few asked, in addition to the citation in the References and Bibliography, that the following statements be included in the Acknowledgements:

Quote from page 88 of Leo Sartori's *Understanding Relativity: A Simplified Approach to Einstein's Theories* is copyright © 1995 by The Regents of the University of California, who gave permission.

Quotes from Armand H. Delsemme's *From the Big Bang to the Emergence of Life and Intelligence* pages 253–4, from Mark Rowlands' *The Nature of Consciousness* page 25 and from Ian Stewart's and Jack Cohen's *Figments of Reality: The Evolution of the Curious Mind* page 202 were reprinted with the permission of Cambridge University Press.

Quote from page 214 of David Sloan Wilson's *Darwin's Cathedral: Evolution, Religion, and the Nature of Society* is copyright © 2002 by The University of Chicago. All rights reserved.

Quote from page 389 of Michael J. Denton's *Nature's Destiny: How the Laws of Biology Reveal Purpose in the Universe* is copyright © 1998 by Michael J. Denton. The quote from page 259 of John Horgan's *The Undiscovered Mind: How the Human Brain Defies Replication, Medication and Explanation* is copyright © 1999 by John Horgan. The quotes from pages 23, 37, 64, 75, 81 & 132 of Israel Finkelstein's and Neil Asher Silberman's *The Bible Unearthed: Archaeology's New Vision of Ancient Israel and The Origin of Its Sacred Texts* is copyright © 2001 by Israel Finkelstein and Neil Asher Silberman. All reprinted with the permission of The Free Press, a Division of Simon & Schuster Adult Publishing Group. All rights reserved.

Quote from pages 204–205 & 209 of John C. Avise's *The Genetic Gods: Evolution and Belief in Human Affairs* is copyright © 1998 by the President and Fellows of Harvard College. Reprinted by permission of Harvard University Press, Cambridge, Mass.

Quote from pages 280–3 of *The Robe* by Lloyd C. Douglas was Copyright, 1942 by Lloyd C. Douglas. Copyright © renewed 1969 by Virginia Douglas Dawson and Betty Douglas Wilson. Reprinted by permission of Houghton Mifflin Company. All rights reserved.

Quote from page 17 of Gregory Stock's *Redesigning Humans: Our Inevitable Genetic Future* is Copyright © 2002 by Gregory Stock. Reproduced by permission of Houghton Mifflin Company. All rights reserved.

Quote from page 2 of Euan M. Macphail's *The Evolution of Conciousness*, © Copyright 1998 by Euan M. Macphail, is reprinted by permission of Oxford University Press.

Index

To reduce clutter this Index doesn't reference endnotes that are already referenced in that subject's text. **Bold** page references are to subjects' definitions in the text or endnotes (in lieu of a glossary).

Paul Dehn Carleton

The author had a Jesuit education receiving a bachelor's in engineering and a master's in business. His career covered product, corporate, organization, community and economic development, and innovation. Upon retirement he embarked on an extensive research project of his own initiative. This book is the product of that research. (For more detail see the Index under 'author'.)

Compositor, Printer, Binder:	Sheridan Books, Inc.
Text:	10/13 Palatino
Display:	Tekton
Paper:	50# House Natural Smooth

Dust-jacket design by Susan Miller

Dust-jacket cover and title-page photo of Edale Valley, Peak District, Derbyshire, England, UK; by Digital Vision/Getty Images

Author's photos by William E. Dwyer

Ways I the reader might advance Life's trajectory:

Ways I the reader might advance Life's trajectory:

Ways I the reader might advance Life's trajectory:

Ways I the reader might advance Life's trajectory: